CONTENTS

Name

Manager

Planned date for NAAS

Notes about initial plan

MEET THE AUTHORS

SIOBHAN MACLEAN

I've been a social worker for almost thirty years. When I first qualified, we worked generically but during my career I have worked in a variety of specialist settings. For many years now I have worked independently, writing and training on a variety of generic social work topics – my passion lies around the use of theory and reflection in practice.

I spent eight years working with the International Federation of Social Workers and the learning from that role permeates all of my current work. I have recently been appointed a Visiting Professor at the University of Chester.

Six years ago, I had a stroke which had a significant impact on my physical health. As a result, I did not return to direct practice although I maintain my links with practice by acting as a practice educator. My experiences of receiving health and social care services during the recovery process has reinforced for me the vital need for services and professionals to listen carefully to the voices of people with lived experiences and in recent years I have enjoyed working with some amazing people to support them in sharing their voice.

I am also a mother to two amazing young women and I have been a foster carer.

ANNIE (SURVIVING SAFEGUARDING)

I am a care-experienced birth mother with many years of experience of the child protection system in England. I have experienced several sets of legal proceedings in respect of my children, including two sets of concurrent care proceedings and a new-born removal with an ultimate plan of adoption. I recognised the local authority's concerns and worked hard to overcome issues of poor relationship choices, domestic abuse and mental health difficulties arising out of my own abusive childhood, turning my life around and succeeding in bringing my new-born home. I then went on to write Surviving Safeguarding: a parent's guide to the child protection process where I aim to support parents to navigate the system, and also turn their own lives around. I now act as Consultant for many local authorities in England and I train social workers, students, family lawyers, the judiciary, the police and health and education professionals to support them to engage better with families who are experiencing their own difficulties. I sit on the Family Justice Council as the Parent and Relative Representative and am part of several working groups. I am also a member of the Transparency Project, a legal education charity which aims to make family justice clearer. I live in the North East with my children, my husband and a menagerie of pets. Annie is a pseudonym to protect my identity and that of my children.

PAUL YUSUF (MCCORMACK)

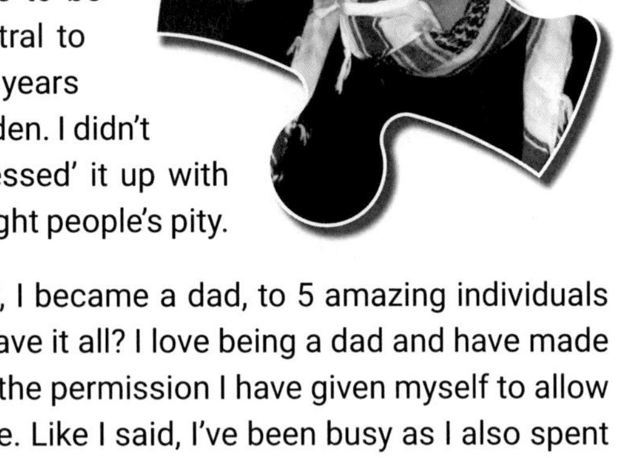

I grew up in institutional care during the 1960s and 1970s at a time when society wasn't so accepting of illegitimacy or children of colour, so I, along with thousands of others, were left to languish in the care system. Care, back in the day, was quite a different experience than the one experienced today. Some things have moved on, yet we can all agree that more still needs to be done. None of us must forget, that the 'child' is central to what we do! After I left the institution, and for many years later, I continued to keep this significant part of me hidden. I didn't discuss my childhood in any detail and if I did, I 'dressed' it up with humour (my way of protecting me) as I have never sought people's pity.

I've been kept fairly busy since I left the 'care system', I became a dad, to 5 amazing individuals (4 birth and 1 through adoption), who says you can't have it all? I love being a dad and have made my 'dad role' up as I go along. A plus of being a dad is the permission I have given myself to allow the 'child' within me, a place to venture out and explore. Like I said, I've been busy as I also spent 30 plus years, working for the civil service where I held a variety of positions, working with many communities and people until I decided to opt out and follow my instinct.

Currently, as a family, we foster, and I get to help children regain a sense of themselves again, allowing them space, to laugh, play and be a child, knowing that they belong and are loved. All the children who join my family become 'ours' immediately and are afforded the same love and advocacy as our own. I'm mindful that the children who arrive here never chose to.

I love this part of my life knowing sometimes 'I' can be the difference.

More recently I found my way to start talking about my beginnings using written word. I developed a form of poetry (spoken word) that articulates my childhood journey, both physically and, probably more importantly for me, emotionally, where I can explore and attempt to verbalise pictures of me in the form of verse for those who care to listen. These 'verbal' pictures have developed further, and I have moved my words onto canvas. I use my own style to give an honest, yet shocking view of the world I grew up in. I hope that a combination of my voice and the roles I have lived and still live will give you a picture that you can take forward.

So, who'd have thought that after all this time I would be collaborating with social workers? My childhood experience saw me throw stones at most of those that came near me, how times have changed! I am now fortunate to have met some of the most inspiring individuals who work in this profession and who passionately care.

I will gladly and willingly work with anyone who has passion.

HOW TO USE THIS RESOURCE TO MOVE TOWARDS A REFLEXIVE APPROACH

This resource has been designed to support you to work towards National Accreditation as a child and family practitioner, completing the NAAS. The first, introductory, chapter will help you to reflect on your own professional development and then each numbered chapter will support you in considering how you meet the individual aspects of the knowledge and skills statement (KSS). This will help you to work towards the NAAS. The title of the resource suggests that there are a number of pieces to be put together as you work towards accreditation and this resource can be used in exactly that way. Each chapter begins with the specific statement that needs to be addressed in the KSS, inviting you to think about what the statement means to you and how you might both develop, and evidence, your practice in that area. You might then want to work through that whole chapter, which will contain some theory, some ideas from practice and some advice from others. You may choose not to work through the whole of every chapter, but you will want to discuss this in supervision, seeking advice on your route towards accreditation.

As social workers develop, they should progress from simple reflection to critical reflection and onto reflexivity in practice. I have found that often social workers lack confidence in articulating the differences between reflection, critical reflection and reflexivity and ultimately this can impede progression.

Reflection is a core aspect of social work qualifying training and reflective abilities are widely acknowledged in research as essential for social work practice. Most social workers are confident with reflection and reflective practice, although this can always be revisited and further developed.

Introducing the word critical to the concept of reflection often leads to social workers thinking that this is about self-critique, exploring the negatives of practice and thinking about what can be done differently. However, in social work the word critical could be replaced with the word power. Critical theory is basically about power, critiquing society and cultural contexts, whilst critical race theory is about understanding power in relation to race and society. So, in this context the word critical isn't about criticism or critique, rather critical reflection should always involve a consideration of power. The Post-Qualifying Standards for Social Work Practice Supervisors in Adult Social Care are very clear about the difference between reflection and critical reflection, stating that:

> **"Reflection becomes critical when it involves two aspects:**
> **• When it is fundamental enough (goes deep enough) to effect transformative change**
> **• When it is based on an analysis of power dynamics and strives to equalize power imbalances and maximize democratic relations"**
> **(Department of Health and Social Care 2018:13)**

Reflexivity has been on the academic agenda in social work for many years, however it is now regularly raised in relation to social work practice. In many ways working towards the development of reflexive practice is what accreditation as a children and families professional is about.

There is no universally agreed definition of reflexivity, meaning it can be understood in a range of ways in both research and practice (D'Cruz, Gillingham and Melendez 2007, Brown, Sawyer and Norris 2016). So, the very concept of reflexivity in social work is contested, but drilling down into what reflexivity means in practice will be particularly helpful in working towards the NAAS.

The easiest way to think about what reflexivity means is to look in depth at the word.

Breaking down the word into its components and looking at what they mean can be helpful:

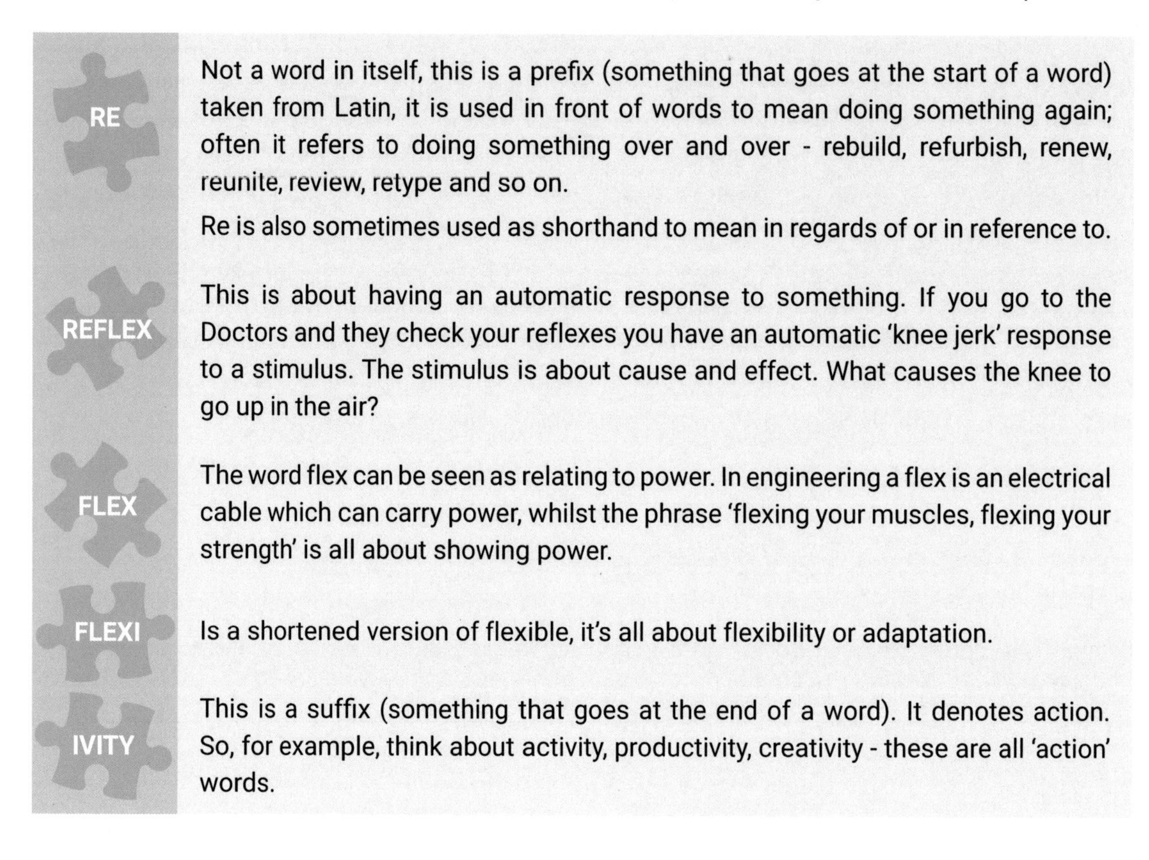

RE

Not a word in itself, this is a prefix (something that goes at the start of a word) taken from Latin, it is used in front of words to mean doing something again; often it refers to doing something over and over - rebuild, refurbish, renew, reunite, review, retype and so on.

Re is also sometimes used as shorthand to mean in regards of or in reference to.

REFLEX

This is about having an automatic response to something. If you go to the Doctors and they check your reflexes you have an automatic 'knee jerk' response to a stimulus. The stimulus is about cause and effect. What causes the knee to go up in the air?

FLEX

The word flex can be seen as relating to power. In engineering a flex is an electrical cable which can carry power, whilst the phrase 'flexing your muscles, flexing your strength' is all about showing power.

FLEXI

Is a shortened version of flexible, it's all about flexibility or adaptation.

IVITY

This is a suffix (something that goes at the end of a word). It denotes action. So, for example, think about activity, productivity, creativity - these are all 'action' words.

Connecting the different parts of the word helps to build an understanding of what reflexivity is about.

Reflexivity is:

- Something that should be constant and ongoing.
- Understanding cause and effect.
- Recognising power and working effectively with the flow of power.
- Being flexible and adapting to new information and changing situations.
- All about action.

To further build understanding it can be helpful to think about a word which is similar to reflexivity, that many people are familiar with, **reflexology**.

Reflexology, sometimes known as zone therapy is basically a holistic therapy which builds on how the feet connect to the rest of the body. If you went to a reflexologist with a headache they would touch a certain part of your foot, if you had a pain in your shoulder then they would touch a different part of your foot. Reflexologists develop maps of the feet and connectivity. If you had a headache you couldn't fiddle with your own big toe to fix it, it takes a professional to see the interconnections. Drawing on this can help us to deepen our understanding about reflexivity in social work, it is all about the interconnectivity of practice and the way a professional should be able to see those interconnections. In many ways it is a systemic way of reflecting, combining systems thinking with reflection. Reflexologists map your feet and thinking about maps can be helpful in making the journey towards reflexivity as the following illustrates.

MAPPING THE JOURNEY TOWARDS REFLEXIVITY

It is perhaps in thinking about the journey towards reflexivity that the fullest understanding of what it actually means in social work practice can be gained. Think about mapping the journey.

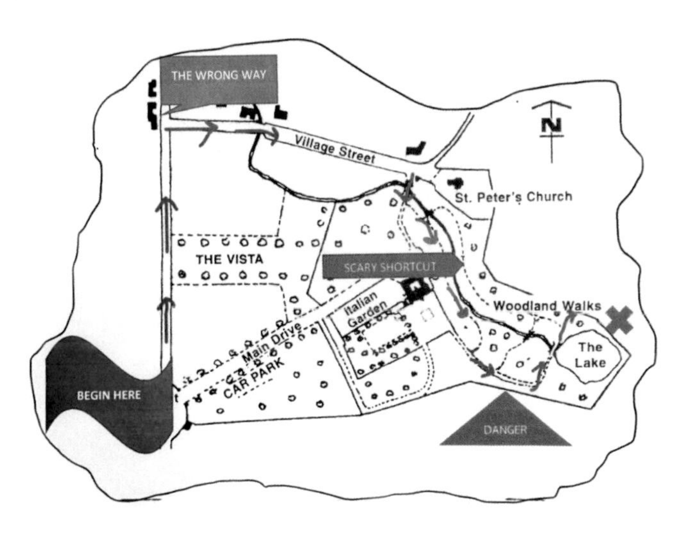

On treasure maps X is seen as marking the spot where the treasure lies. So, take another look at the X in reflexivity, sometimes you will hear reference to reflexive practice or taking a reflexive approach, you may come across the word reflexion. Whichever of these words you look at, the X lies in the same spot; between the 'e' and the 'i':

RefleXivity

RefleXive

RefleXion

So, the X lies within EI. EI of course is short for Emotional Intelligence. So, the treasure of reflexivity in social work practice is about connecting emotional intelligence with reflection. The letters could also be used to represent the following:

- **E** → Environmental or external factors.
- **I** → Individual or internal factors.

Look at the word complexity and how this is formed around the x.

CompleXity

The X sits in exactly the same spot between the 'e' and the 'i'.

Connecting emotional intelligence and looking at the individual in the environment or the relationship between internal and external factors is where the treasure of social work lies. These connections help to address the complexity of social work practice.

SELF AWARENESS

An X on a map can also help to indicate where you are. Seeing the 'I' after the X in both complexity and reflexivity is an important way of thinking about "I am here". What impact do I have in the situation and what impact does it have on me? Self-awareness is a vital aspect of reflexive social work and understanding the use of self is key in the journey towards reflexivity in practice.

Whilst the 'use of self' may sound strange, in fact it is vital for social workers. At times it feels as though you have nothing but yourself to use in your work. You are the main tool of your practice.

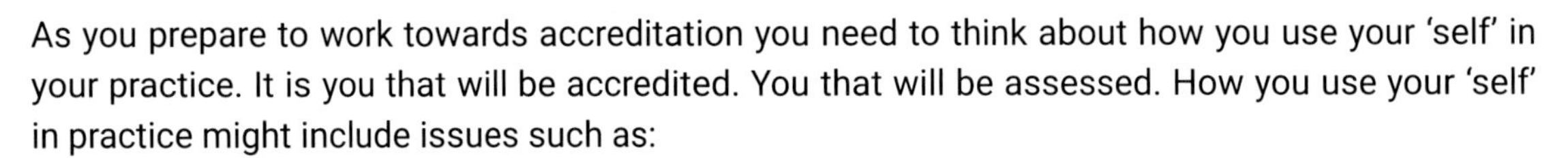

As you prepare to work towards accreditation you need to think about how you use your 'self' in your practice. It is you that will be accredited. You that will be assessed. How you use your 'self' in practice might include issues such as:

- Using your personality to create relationships.
- Communicating effectively.
- Developing empathic listening.
- Understanding your knowledge base.
- Being clear about your decision making practice.
- Knowing your own limitations.
- Recognising your own bias and knowing what to do to mitigate the impact of this.
- Self-management skills.
- Building on your place in the organisation.
- Connecting with a community of practice.
- Demonstrating professional leadership on a range of levels.

This resource will help you to develop your professional sense of self. It will encourage you to think about key points which will enable you to work towards accreditation. You may, at times feel as though you have lost some of your sense of self as a practitioner in the busy world of social work. You might, for example, wonder why you are being asked to work towards accreditation.

Value this time as you prepare for the NAAS. If you use this time well it will allow you to reconnect with your professional self. This is about you. Valuing the knowledge that you have and skills that you use is a key part of looking after your professional self. Accreditation will enable you to do that. Don't take a surface approach or see this as ticking a box. If you do you, you will lose out.

People who have gone through the process see it as a positive experience. The very final page of this resource is from a social worker who has been through the NAAS themselves. They valued the experience. Try to do so yourself.

A NOTE ABOUT THE BASICS: WHAT? WHY? HOW?

The basic framework for good social work practice is What? Why? How?

When we start to work with children and their families, a good social worker should be looking at:

- What is happening for this child and their family?
- Why has this situation come about?
- How can I work with them to bring about improved outcomes and positive change?

The danger is that in contemporary practice, social workers are so busy, bureaucracy can be so significant and timescales so tight that the 'why' question falls off the agenda. The approach can become:

- What's happening?
- How am I going to deal with it?

This is dangerous on a range of levels. It creates essentially proceduralised, managerial practice. More dangerously it creates a medical model to practice – what's the diagnosis? How do we treat it? The medical model rarely involves a consideration of *why*.

Keeping the WHY question on the agenda is vital. For many reasons:

- Good social work starts with *why*. Why am I working with this child? Why am I involved in this family's life? Clarity of involvement certainly improves practice.
- Hypotheses are developed from an initial starting point of asking *why*. Thinking through a range of answers to the question 'Why is this happening?' can aid analysis and decision making.
- Professional curiosity, which is seen as so important in social work practice and yet has been found lacking in a number of high-profile cases, is all about the *why* question.
- Understanding why something needs to happen has been widely evidenced to improve motivation and therefore starting with *why* can assist with using motivational techniques with children and their families.
- Being clear about why we are doing things improves confidence and job satisfaction (Sinek 2009) which can offer a great deal to social workers in the current climate of practice.

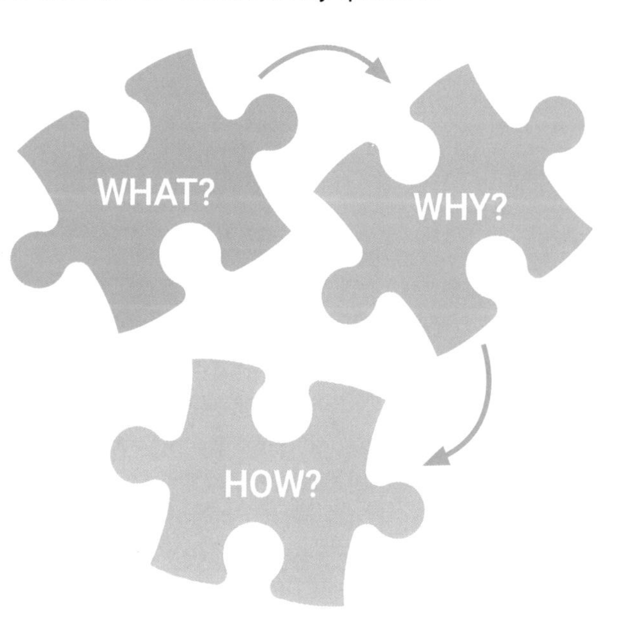

Since this is such an important framework, it is used regularly throughout the resource, so that the what? why? and how? of the subject matter in each chapter is covered.

As you work through this resource take the time to revisit some basics. It is always useful and can sometimes help you to see things in a new way. Whilst the situations that we see and work with in our practice are incredibly complex, to me a good social worker can always see the simplicity in the complexity. The basic fact that the child or young person must always be at the centre of the practice is in many ways the simplest of everything in social work. Yet how many times have social workers lost sight of a child?

The What? Why? How? framework whilst simple in itself, provides a great all-round tool and in many ways can be reflexive, since the different questions are often connected (for example, sometimes you need to explore 'how', before you can really understand 'why') If you put yourself at the centre, then you are also clarifying the use of self. So, for example, ask yourself:

- What am I currently feeling about working towards accreditation?
- Why do I feel like that?
- How might these feelings impact on my approach to, and my experience of, accreditation?

Do you need to change the way that you feel? How will you do that?

This resource provides a range of models and frameworks to encourage you to have a dialogue with yourself as you work towards accreditation. How often do we stop and think about the distance we have travelled on our development journey? There are often bumps in the road and sometimes poor signposting as we make the journey. This resource will encourage you to pause and reflect, to think about where you have been and where you are going. Take some of the material to supervision, share your reflections. All of this will enable you to be more prepared for the assessment day. It will also help you make the most of the accreditation process. Don't just survive but thrive!

The main idea is that you use this workbook to support you to work towards reflexivity in practice. The different aspects of the KSS are inter-connected such that the knowledge and skills referred to in one area will be relevant in another. The content of this workbook has been tried and tested with people who have undertaken the NAAS in a number of geographical areas. The material contained and the reflective questions are drawn from what they have found particularly helpful in evidencing the KSS, gaining employer endorsement and on the day.

As you work through the resource you should see that it has been designed as a reflexive resource. For example, will see that there are a range of connections between the material in each chapter. The way that the material progresses (if you work through the chapters in numerical order) should also reflect the journey of a practitioner. For example, messages from research are included at the end of Chapters 1 and 2, but in subsequent chapters the research base is more incorporated into the material. This mirrors the way in which practice develops as a social worker. In the early career stage, a social worker will look to research and theory, they may not always be able to make the clear connections with practice, but as they progress their use of knowledge becomes more intuitive and their knowledge and skills become more connected. A range of people have contributed to this resource, but I have tried to keep the voice of the child at the centre of every chapter – making clear connections with the importance of this in practice. Look out for the other ways in which this is a reflexive resource and enjoy the journey!

DEVELOPMENT AS A CHILD AND FAMILY PRACTITIONER

his chapter explores professional development in social work, starting with the standards of actice used in England. The chapter introduces some of the main theories and models of adult arning and professional development. Understanding these can help you to think about your own evelopment and how you might begin to put the pieces together as you work towards accreditation. aving an understanding of adult learning can also help you when you are working with families – pporting people to develop their parenting skills and to reflect on their family circumstances, is rtainly enhanced by a basic level of knowledge in this area.

THE RELATIONSHIP BETWEEN THE KSS AND PCF

Social workers who have trained in England, especially those who have qualified in recent years are generally very familiar with the Professional Capabilities Framework (PCF), having been assessed on the capabilities included in this during their qualifying programme. Although increasingly many students are also being introduced to the Knowledge and Skills Statement (KSS) during their training, there are still times where they lack awareness of this when starting their Assessed and Supported Year in Employment (ASYE). When the PCF was refreshed in 2018, the British Association of Social Workers and the two Chief Social Workers in England released a Joint Statement on the relationship between the Professional Capabilities Framework (PCF) for Social Work and the Knowledge and Skills Statements for Children and Families and Adults, demonstrating the important role that each framework has to play. The statement explains that whilst the PCF is about the purpose, practice and impact of social work, **"the KSS set out what a social worker should know, and be able to do, in specific practice settings, in specific roles and at different levels of seniority."** (Department for Education and Department of Health and Social Care 2017)

HORIZONTAL AND VERTICAL DEVELOPMENT

When thinking about the difference between the standards, and indeed the need for two sets of standards it can be helpful to consider horizontal and vertical development. Initially this concept comes from the field of information technology where computer professionals focus on either the software or hardware, but it is now widely used in thinking about professional development at a range of levels.

In relation to social work it can be helpful to think about this in the following way:

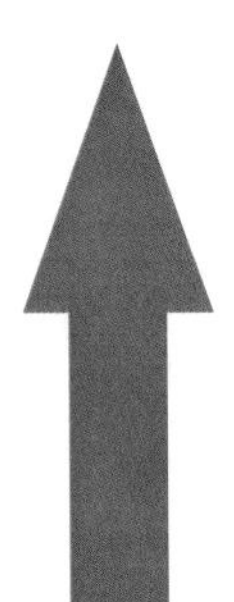

Vertical development is about the skills and knowledge that all social workers share. This is the generic learning which we undertake through our qualifying training. As we progress during our career, we develop those skills and the knowledge we have, such that we can work in more complex, systematic and independent ways. Vertical development is also about increasing levels of responsibility (potentially progress up some kind of career ladder). In social work, vertical development is represented in the PCF which considers the growth and progress of our skills and knowledge within generic domains as we move up through the different levels of experience.

Horizontal development is about context specific learning and development. Does a practitioner have the skills and knowledge to work in a particular sector? Horizontal development helps a practitioner to demonstrate that they can be a social worker in a particular setting or sector (as laid out in the KSS).

On a number of occasions, I have heard social workers talking about the PCF and KSS with a lack of clarity about why we have two separate frameworks. Advice that is often given to "cross reference" suggests in many ways that we have two sets of professional standards in England as some kind of mistake. However, this is no mistake, we have two sets of standards because:

- **The PCF helps us to look at our development as a social work professional.**
- **The KSS helps us to look at our capability and development in the specific context of children and families.**

The two sets of standards help us to ensure that we are developing both vertically and horizontally. Social work is widely recognised as a leadership profession and in leadership the idea of horizontal and vertical development with standards which address both is nothing new. Creativity in complex leadership is increasingly recognising the need to work on both horizontal and vertical skill development. The following quotation, taken from an international white paper exploring the future of leadership development, could just as easily be applied to considering the future of social work development:

"Let me be clear—traditional, horizontal competencies still matter. No executive is going to be effective without being able to think strategically or lead change. But the real opportunity lies in looking at competencies through the horizontal AND vertical lenses at the same time. As leaders advance vertically, the way they think about and enact those competencies expands." (Petrie 2014: 10).

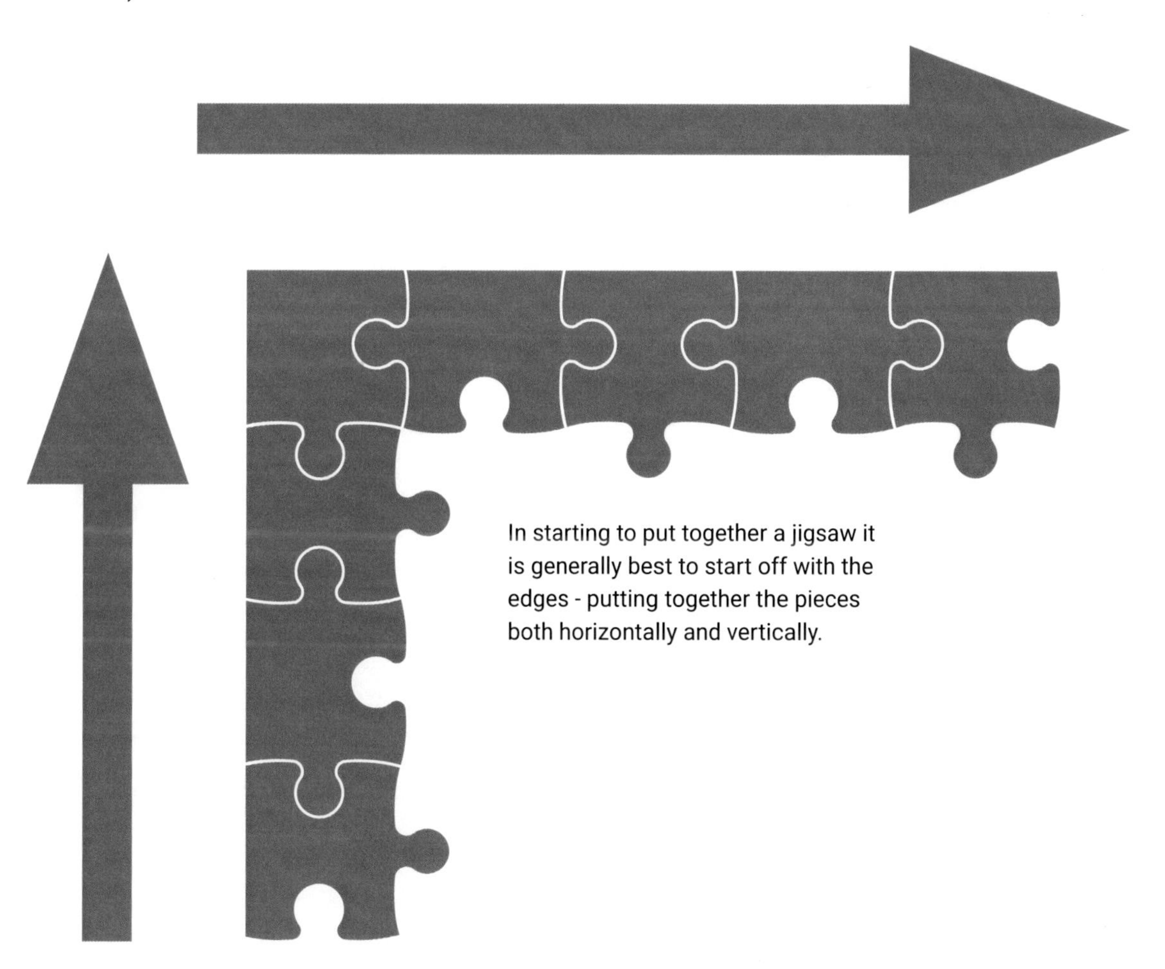

KNOWLEDGE SKILLS AND VALUES: THE INTERCONNECTIONS

Our Knowledge, skills and values interact in a range of ways. As a framework often attributed to social pedagogy, the idea of head, heart, hands can be helpful in considering the interconnections.

Head

The knowledge that you need to work as a children and families practitioner is all about your head – intellectually what can you draw on? This relates not just to what knowledge you have collected, but also to the wider issues of how you use your intellectual skills.

Heart

The heart represents the values and ethics of practice, it also represents the emotional intelligence which connects the knowledge you have and the skills you use.

Hands

The skills that you need to work as a social worker are all about the hands – what can you actually do? What can be left in your hands?

Discussing social work supervision Ingram (2013) added feet to this framework.

Feet

These 'ground' the practitioner. Ingram discussed the way that this grounding of practice (the feet) is about the values of social work and the way that the value base of social work can be used by the practitioner to help them persevere in challenging situations.

PAUSE TO REFLECT

HEAD

What knowledge do you draw on the most in your practice?	*What knowledge do you need to develop more?*

HEART

What lies at the heart of your practice?	*What challenges do you face in keeping the heart of your practice central?*

HANDS

Where do your strengths lie in terms of skills?	*Which skills would you like to further develop?*

FEET

What grounds you in your practice?	*Where might you be losing your footing?* *What could you do to address that?*

COGNITIVE DISSONANCE

Cognitive dissonance comes from psychology, originally developed by Festinger (1957). It is basically about a mental (cognitive) discomfort (dissonance) created when a person has a range of ideas, values or beliefs which contradict each other. Cognitive dissonance can be very painful and difficult for people and may create a fight or flight type response. The parents that we work with as social workers (and indeed many of the professionals we work with) may experience cognitive dissonance and this can impact on how they respond to a given situation. Cognitive dissonance can be seen as linking closely to the ladder of learning.

THE LADDER OF LEARNING

It is difficult to attribute the ladder of learning to any particular author. It has been around the field of adult learning for many years. The idea is that when someone is called upon to learn something new, to develop their knowledge or skills, then they climb up a ladder of learning.

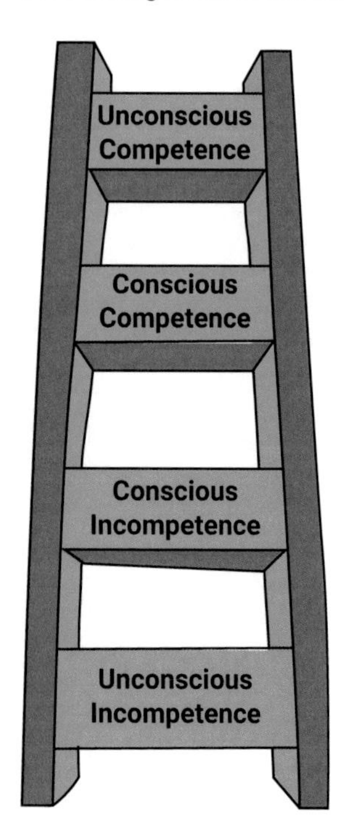

The first rung of the ladder, so the starting point for the climb, is **unconscious incompetence**. That is a kind of blissful ignorance. If the skill or knowledge is entirely new to you, you may well have no idea what you don't know, what you can't do. Do you remember being a student and being asked "what are your learning needs?". That could often be really difficult to answer.

When learning, you quickly move off the first rung of the ladder, stepping onto **conscious incompetence**. This is the stage at which you become aware of what you don't know or what you can't do. Given that we are often socialised to believe "there is no such word as can't" this can be a very painful stage. We thought we could, now we learn we can't – this is where cognitive dissonance can come in. We may well avoid the task and pretend that we can do it, rather than really working at the new knowledge or skill until we can climb to the next stage of the ladder - conscious competence.

At the start of new learning it is common to feel conscious of what we can't do.

Conscious competence is where the skill is so newly acquired that we are very conscious of it, we are thoughtful and focused on the task and plan and prepare effectively when we are undertaking it. We put thought into how we can use the new knowledge. We are very careful about our new skills. After a while we relax more – the skill isn't so new now, we climb to what is seen as the final rung of the ladder of learning - unconscious competence.

When we have a newly acquired skill, we are often very aware of this.

Unconscious competence is where the skill is so embedded in what we do everyday that we no longer need to really think about it. We do it on an automatic pilot. Whilst this is generally seen as the final rung of the ladder it is important to recognise that it can be a dangerous rung to be on – if we are not conscious about the task, how do we know that we are still competent? If I am honest, if there was a driving instructor sitting in the car with me and I didn't know they were there assessing me, I may well fail the test. I have slipped into bad habits, I take short cuts. If you drive the same journey home every day, how many times have you come to a certain point on the journey and thought "I don't remember going under the bridge / over the roundabout..."? You are driving on automatic pilot! This is why professionals need to regularly revisit their practice through continuous professional development – being consciously aware of our competence is important in practice. Working towards accreditation can be very helpful in maintaining a consciousness to competence.

Automatic pilot may not be very safe!

MODELS OF PROFESSIONAL DEVELOPMENT

One of the most well known models of professional development is the Dreyfus and Dreyfus developmental model. Developed by two brothers in 1980 the model draws on research to consider skill acquisition and the best ways to instruct new staff. The model is now often used to consider professional career progress (Benner 2004). Dreyfus and Dreyfus identified five stages of professional development, from novice to expert. The following table summarises the model with some specific reference to the development of social workers.

	Knowledge	Skills	Autonomy	Working with Complexity	Contextual Understanding
1. Novice	'Textbook' type knowledge not connected to practice	Developing skills	Needs to work in close contact with others, work needs constant overseeing	Little or no understanding of complexity and how to recognise this in practice	Sees action in isolation
2. Beginner	Working knowledge of key aspects of practice	Straightforward tasks likely to be completed to an acceptable standard	Able to achieve some steps using own judgement, but supervision needed for decision making and anything out of the ordinary	Recognises complex situations but seeks clear direction from others in dealing with this	Sees actions as a series of steps, not recognising the impact of environment and context
3. Competent	Good background professional knowledge and clear working knowledge. Able to apply this and use it in practice	Good skill level. Some skills will be very well developed, others will need refinement	Able to achieve most tasks using own judgement. Beginning to advise others	Works with complex situations through deliberate analysis and planning	Recognises that actions are influenced by both internal and external factors
4. Proficient	Breadth and depth of different types of knowledge. For example, "I know that.", "I know how to...", "I know where...", and ability to use this in practice	Very good standard of work drawing on a range of skills routinely	Able to take full responsibility for own work (and that of others)	Deals with complex situations holistically. Confident decision making	Understands holistic context of practice. Can challenge wider external factors and work with the range of dilemmas which can occur in context
5. Expert	Authoritative knowledge and practice wisdom. Able to confidently share this with others to influence wider practice	Excellence achieved with relative ease	Able to take responsibility for going beyond existing standards and innovation in practice	Holistic grasp of complex situations, moves between intuitive and analytical approaches with ease	Develops vision and supports others to work towards this

PAUSE TO REFLECT

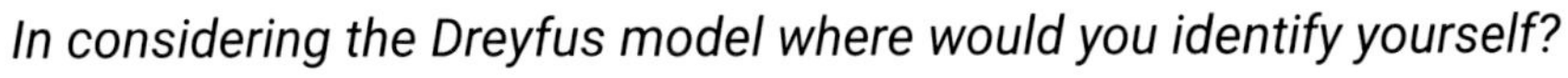

In considering the Dreyfus model where would you identify yourself?

What has had the most significant impact on your professional development to date:

Positively (so what has helped?)	*Negatively (so what has hindered you?)*

On a scale of 1-10 how good are you at planning and taking control of your own professional development?

What could you do to move up the scale?

In Stockport we love recruiting newly qualified and experienced social workers and have developed a sophisticated matrix approach to employing the right people for our Stockport Family programme. We have adopted a value driven, assessment centre approach with value-based interview questions (we don't want to know whether you know how to carry out a Section 47 investigation, we want to know all about your thinking that would lead to the s47, your style with children and families and what you take into account and what your learning is after the event). Skills and knowledge are tested in a written exercise and a group activity to test those all-important 'thinking on your feet and working in a team' skills. We believe that this approach has been very successful and we have appointed some superb social workers....no need to worry about succession planning!!

When thinking about what we are looking for in a social worker, it is helpful to think about what we would want a social worker to be like if they were to walk through our doors. We would like that social worker to be able to build and maintain helpful relationships and have a strong value base, care about us as people, see our strengths, vulnerabilities and challenges Skills such as empathy and compassion help build positive and respectful relationships in which change is more likely to happen. We are also looking for social workers who have the ability to recognise and respond to risk whilst also noticing and building on the strengths and skills that families have to manage that risk.

The reality is that relationships are not always easy, there are challenges. Sometimes change doesn't happen, or support might not be accepted (or indeed offered in the best way for that family). We are looking for social workers who are able to rise to this challenge. A reflective social worker will recognise what they might have done differently and that we are all learning all the time. Learning and development is essential for all social workers if we are to continue to rise to the challenges and conundrums that the families we work with and social workers and colleagues face on a daily basis.

One of the challenges we have been considering is the role of parents in our development. A key restorative principle is that we aim to work with families. The question we are asking ourselves is how can we truly understand what will help families if we don't involve them in the development of services? We are in the process of developing a parents' panel and have high hopes for the members providing the challenge for all of us to continue to develop to be the best possible social workers.

We are currently part of NAAS in its early phases and have colleagues who have volunteered for phase 1 and 2 of the programme. We believed it was important to be part of this if we are to really help shape the profession, highlighting, as experts by experience, what is great about the programme and what just doesn't hit the mark. As Principal Social Worker I felt it was important that I put myself up for the first round of assessment. I have strong views about NAAS but felt it was only right that I properly immerse myself in the programme, even doing a mock test at a local University (thank you Salford it was so helpful), to support my colleagues and teams and to contribute from an informed base to the national debate. The formal assessment is now a week away....see you on the other side!

Chapter 1

RELATIONSHIPS AND EFFECTIVE DIRECT WORK

It is very fitting that the first statement of the Knowledge and Skills Statement, and therefore the first main chapter of this resource is about relationships and direct work. Relationships are the very cornerstone of social work practice. They very much represent the first piece of the puzzle in working towards accreditation.

This chapter explores the importance of relationships and revisits some of the basics, including theory and practice frameworks which can help practitioners to develop meaningful relationships with children and families. Ideas for direct work and examples from practice are shared. As you work through the chapter you should be able to reflect on your strengths and the areas of practice you would like to develop.

THE KSS REQUIRES PRACTITIONERS TO:

Build effective relationships with children, young people and families, which form the bedrock of all support and child protection responses. Be both authoritative and empathic and work in partnership with children, families and professionals enabling full participation in assessment, planning, review and decision making. Ensure child protection is always privileged.

Provide support based on best evidence, which is tailored to meet individual child and family needs, and which addresses relevant and significant risks. Secure access to services, negotiating and challenging other professionals and organisations to provide the help required. Ensure children and families, including children in public care, receive the support to which they are entitled.

Support children and families in transition, including children and young people moving to and between placements, those returning home, those being adopted or moving through to independence. Help children to separate from, and sustain, multiple relationships recognising the impact of loss and change.

Take a look at the standard above in detail. Highlight key phrases and anything that jumps out at you. Then take some time to reflect on the statement.

- *What are your immediate thoughts?*
- *What might you want to discuss and clarify?*
- *How will you clarify meanings?*
- *Who will you discuss it with?*

GETTING FEEDBACK ON PRACTICE

Who can give me feedback on my practice in this area?	*How will I get the feedback?*

Make sure to keep a record of any feedback you receive.

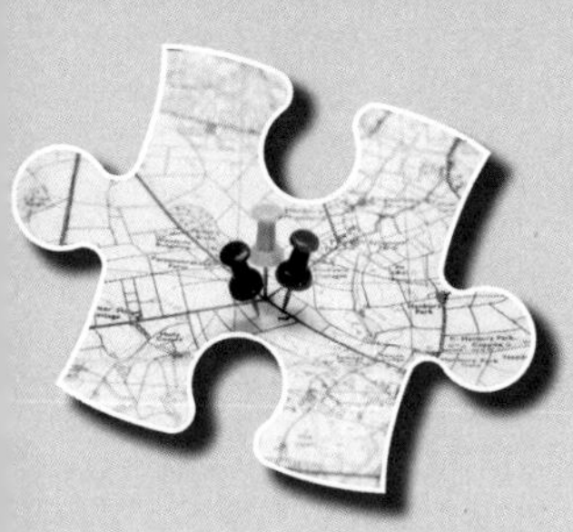

INITIAL SELF-ASSESSMENT

What do I already do well?

How do I know? (What's my evidence?)

What do I need to work on?

How will I work on this?

RELATIONSHIP BASED PRACTICE

The standard that this chapter addresses describes relationships as the "bedrock of all support and child protection responses". The importance of social work practice being based on a clear foundation of good relationships is widely recognised within the profession, although social workers often report feeling that they face challenges in taking a relationship based approach to practice. The Global Agenda for Social Work developed by social work practitioners and academics working across the world (IFSW, ICSW, IASSW 2012) details one of the current priorities for the social work profession as "strengthening the recognition of the importance of human relationships." In the push towards relationship based practice it is essential to recognise that whilst creating and developing relationships is a key part of social work those relationships must have purpose. Why are we creating this relationship? This chapter begins with Claudia Megele who is the Chair of the Principal Children and Families Social Worker Network explaining the importance of relationship based practice and outlining a model which can be used in social work practice.

Claudia Megele is the Head of Service for Quality Assurance and Practice and the Principal Social Worker at Hertfordshire County Council. She is also a Fellow of National Institute for Health Research (NIHR) and a member of the Advisory Council of What Works Centre for Children's Social Care and the Advisory Board at Social Work England.

Early in my career as a social worker, I worked with a 13 year old boy who often ran away from school after lunch. His teachers felt that he was a disruptive boy who didn't like school boundaries and labelled him as a 'trouble maker'. He found school work hard and didn't have many friends; he found it difficult to connect with others. It was only after he was able to build a relationship with his teaching assistant and felt safe that he was able to tell her that he ran away from school because he wanted to be home to protect his mother. He explained that his father worked shifts and would return home in a foul mood wanting to beat his mother. He tried to be home before his father in order to redirect his father's anger toward himself and his truancy. This was his way of protecting the only person he felt ever loved him. Therefore, this boy was communicating with us through his behaviour although he was misunderstood, he and his lived experience were made invisible.

Some years later I worked for a very wealthy family in an affluent local authority and was assessing the couple for a private fostering arrangement. Therefore, I tried to understand the family dynamics and their motivation for private fostering and the appropriateness of this arrangement. As the assessment progressed, I realised that the little boy had known the man since he was born and spent many summers in London living with him and that the man had also paid for his private schooling in Switzerland. I suspected that the man was actually the biological father of the boy that he wanted to privately foster. Therefore, I asked the man whether this was the case. He was enraged with me for asking such a question and I promptly received a formal letter from his lawyer advising that he would take legal action if this was ever suggested again. I continued to work with the couple and about a month later, the man phoned me to tell me that the little boy was indeed his son.

Although these two experiences may seem worlds apart the people involved in both cases were driven by fear and their desire to protect the people they loved. Indeed, fear and the desire to protect loved ones are often part of everyday practice and are represented in so many ways. Fear of failure or negative outcomes; fear of risks; fear of social workers; fear of losing professionals, and so on. Therefore, containing these fears and building on people's desire to protect their loved ones through empathy is the first step to relationship based practice (RBP) and building connection with others.

RBP takes place at the intersection between the individual's psychological/internal world and subjective states (e.g. happiness, sadness, depression, etc.) and their social/external world and objective statuses (e.g. age, race, poverty, unemployment, etc). Therefore, RBP is interdisciplinary by nature, systemic in thinking and integrative in approach and practice (Megele, 2015:3; 2017). However, as Nigel Elliot (2017) says such 'eclecticism can be misapplied amounting to no more than a random magpie way of doing things.' Instead what is needed is a disciplined and flexible eclecticism, based on a reflective understanding and assessment of the context and matching the method to the situation and desired outcomes (Elliott, 2017: 2).

Therefore, in consultation with over 180 practitioners we co-created the EMPOWER model as a systematic and holistic approach to what is needed for effective RBP. EMPOWER stands for Empathy, Motivation, Person-centred and Purposeful, Observation, Whole-System, Empower, and Restorative approach. This cultivates meaningful relationships and supports young people and their families to achieve positive change while promoting practitioners' creativity and systemic thinking within a disciplined approach to ensure that direct work with children and families remains purposeful.

Empathy: Empathy sets the foundation for healthy and effective relationships. It creates a non-judgemental space that promotes self-expression and acceptance.

The experience of the 13 year old boy mentioned earlier demonstrates the importance of empathy and how our own professional anxiety can result in labelling which can make children invisible and their lives and experiences misunderstood in practice. In contrast, empathy and practitioner's non-judgemental acceptance offers the experience of being understood and these in turn foster self-acceptance and trust in others.

Motivation: Although empathy and positive regard lay the foundation for relationships, without motivation we can't achieve positive change. In fact, cognition (i.e. knowledge of something) alone does not lead to action. For example, often people who smoke know that smoking is bad for their health and every packet of cigarette has explicit warning about the dangers of smoking. However, the risk associated with smoking does not stop smokers from smoking. We need motivation to move from cognition (e.g. knowledge of cigarettes being bad for one's health) to action (e.g. stop smoking). Therefore, to initiate and maintain positive change practitioners should harness motivation.

Motivation is a complex and multifaceted phenomenon and although our understanding of motivation continues to evolve (Kanfer et al, 2008), it is evident that people are motivated by a wide range of factors. Understanding people's motivation offers better understanding of their actions, aspirations and intentions and enables practitioners to co-produce better and more sustainable change. It is by tapping into and harnessing people's motivations and the motivation to change that we can induce and achieve positive change.

Person-centred and purposeful: Person-centred is about putting the person at the centre of the service and all we do and ensuring their best interests by allowing them to take the lead in practice and tailoring solutions and interventions to their circumstances, identity, culture and preferences.

Being purposeful is about being outcome-focused and clear about the purpose of all we do; e.g. the purpose of a home visit, assessment, communication or initiating statutory intervention. Therefore, a purposeful person-centred approach provides a balance for achieving positive change within the framework for social care services.

Observation: When I lead master classes on observation for social workers, managers or senior managers, I often start with a simple exercise asking people to close their eyes and identify details about the person next to them or objects in the room. On average about 70% of people find it difficult to recall such details (e.g. colour of the next person's shoes). This exercise raises participants' awareness of others and their surroundings and highlights the observational gap between what we see and what we recall; this is also the difference between being mindful (i.e. fully focused on the present moment) and mind-full (i.e. with our mind full of different thoughts and with little space for absorbing additional elements). As demonstrated in the earlier example, the same gaps can apply in practice and therefore, it is important to practice good observational skills. This includes having the awareness to distinguish between our own emotions, fears and anxieties and the projected emotions and anxieties from the people we work with.

Whole-system: A whole-system approach is about applying systemic thinking in practice and thinking about the family as a system in interaction with, and within, other systems such as the school system, the parents employment and workplace, the community, as well as cultural and social influences and systems, and so on.

Systemic theories provide an enriching approach to appreciating and thinking about the experiences of the people we work with and the complexities of everyday practice. Therefore, as systemic practitioners we enter the world of the family through attentive observation of verbal and non-verbal behaviours to understand the language, beliefs, motivations and values of the people we work with. Furthermore, while prioritising the needs and interest of children, as systemic practitioners we work with the whole family and aim to empower the parents and carers to provide good enough care for their children.

Empower: When I ask social workers why they chose this profession, 95% say because they want to help people. Although this is a noble cause we should not confuse helping others with wanting to rescue other people. Providing professional help and support is a privilege that entails great responsibility and that can only be 'helpful' when it is carried out within professional boundaries and led by the people we are trying to support. In this process respecting and honouring the views, preferences and motivations of the people we work with and their expertise in their own lives within the professional boundaries together with an outcome-based focus are essential prerequisites for positive and sustainable change. Furthermore, we can only empower people through a balanced, person-centred and purposeful relationship.

Restorative and reflective approach: In contrast to deficit-based approaches, the restorative approach is about building on positives and enhancing people's social capital. This is a relationship based approach that can be adopted flexibly from a more informal to a more structured manner. This can include tapping into and developing people's connections and support networks in a safe and purposeful manner in a series of more or less structured meetings and activities.

Finally, reflection is at the heart of RBP and is the prerequisite to empathy. The ability to see one's self and critically examine our own actions, emotions, thoughts and motivation and their outcomes within the context of practice is foundational to professional development and good and effective RBP.

Life and relationships are multi layered and complex. By the same token social work and RBP are complex and require an integrative and creative approach. The EMPOWER model offers a practical roadmap to ensure our practice is purposeful and benefits from a 'disciplined eclecticism'.

Jodie Atkins-White is a newly qualified social worker.

Siobhan asked me to contribute towards this book in response to a photo of practice that I'd shared on Twitter. Being newly qualified, with a small social media following, I was surprised by both the response online and Siobhan's message. I recently qualified as a Social Worker through the Step Up to Social Work program. Prior to this I'd worked in a young person's homeless hostel and a drug and alcohol rehab service. Whilst Step Up is a 'fast track' option, the teaching was rooted in traditional social work practice. The course emphasised empowering those we work with, advocating for social justice and the importance of relationships and humanistic social work practice. Once on placement I struggled with the realities of implementing these ideas outside of a classroom. Many social workers I met were dealing with high case loads, lots of paperwork and stress. I wondered if it would be possible for me to be the kind of social worker I had envisioned over the years in this difficult climate.

Conversations with social workers in practice, university staff and other students, led me to conclude something really simple. Even with those challenges I am responsible for how I practice. I can control the way I communicate, how I act and the things I do on a micro level day to day. I had come to witness this first hand when on my final placement in a Children in Care team. I saw reports that bore unwanted outcomes hand delivered, in the hope that carefully thought out words would ease some anguish. Birthday cards sent. Christmas presents given. I saw kindness towards children and families. This is what continues to inspire me in my own practice. I was pleased to accept a post in the team and upon having children allocated to me I set about thinking how to introduce myself.

I had been reminded of the joy of receiving something personalised and handwritten when I finished my course, each of my cohort was given a handwritten congratulatory message on a postcard. With this in mind, I decided to send the children that I would be working with a card, with a photo of me and some stickers. I thought this might make me turning up on their doorstep a bit less daunting. I decorated and hand stamped the envelopes, wrote in the cards and took awkward selfies in the office to print and include. I sent them off once I'd introduced myself to foster carers and families. I didn't imagine anyone would think much of this when I posted the photo online, but I think other social workers appreciated the sentiment and simplicity of what I did. I have started as I mean to go on in this incredible, life changing profession. Kind words and acts alone won't overhaul the current systems and environments that we are working in, but I think that empathetic, relationship-based, humanistic practice is essential to reclaiming social work and owning my practice as a Social Worker.

How do you introduce yourself to children?

THE 3 Ps

The 3 Ps is a concept originating in social pedagogy. Social pedagogy can offer a great deal to social workers, particularly in terms of developing a relationship based approach to practice. Bengtsson et al (2008) identify that pedagogues need to be aware of three different aspects of the self in developing relationships, which have become known as the 3 Ps. These can be summarised as follows:

P ***The private pedagogue:*** The person who is known to friends and family. The private pedagogue should not be in any familial / kin relationship with a service user. The private pedagogue is the pedagogue outside of work.

P ***The personal pedagogue:*** The person within the professional setting. The personal pedagogue offers aspects of their own self to the person they are working with. Social pedagogues need to put aspects of their personal selves into relationships so service users can relate to them.

P ***The professional pedagogue:*** The professional pedagogue is that aspect of practice which enables the social pedagogue to keep on offering contact even if this is being refused. A professional reflection on practice enables social pedagogues to evaluate the progress they have seen with people.

I have found the 3 P framework helpful in practice, although I do see it slightly differently and have added a fourth P, as follows:

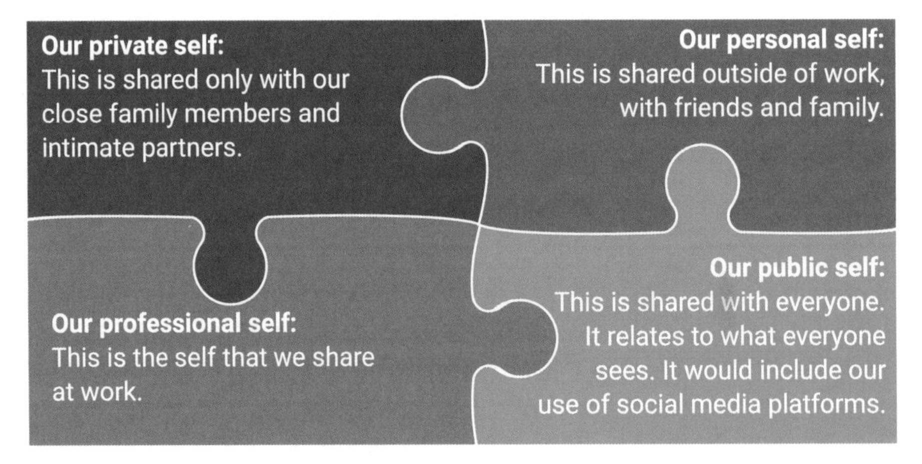

The 3 or 4 Ps can be adapted and used in a wide range of ways in social work practice. For example, we all know that our professional P can be incredibly busy, but we can manage that effectively when everything is going well in our private and personal P. As soon as we have a problem arise in one of the other Ps it will impact on our professional P. So, the 4 P framework can be used to think about work life balance. The Ps can also be used to think about the way that aspects of our Ps may be in conflict with each other, so personal and professional values may at times be in conflict.

One useful way to think about the Ps is around the boundaries to relationships and what we might share with the children and families we work with. The following account from a service user (Maclean, Finch and Tedam 2018) highlights the importance of professionals considering aspects of the boundaries to their relationships using the 3 Ps.

I was invited to attend a family group with my daughters. I say invited, because that's how it was described to me. I didn't feel able to say no, so it wasn't really an invitation. I reckon if I'd said no that I would have been judged as lacking commitment or something similar. So, we went. The group sessions were actually OK. We generally had a bit of time together with other families at the start then we would separate out into a kids' group and a parents' group. We'd talk about things and then we would all come back together to eat a meal and do something together like play a game or do some making stuff. Actually, we got quite a bit from it as a family.

There were three staff at the sessions. One would be with the kids and one with the adults and one would get stuff ready and then all three of them would be involved at the end when we all came together. Different ones did different things each week so we pretty much got to know the three of them. They were really different. One was really cold, you know, she never said anything about herself at all. If we asked her if she had kids she would refuse to answer and say stuff like 'this isn't about me...', another one was more friendly like and would say a bit of stuff about himself and he said he had found being a parent to teenagers difficult, you know that kind of stuff. Not a lot but I felt like we could relate. The other one, well she talked all the time about herself. What she was going through with a divorce, where she had been on her holidays, how her kids were going away with their dad, you know everything. To be honest I got a bit fed up hearing about her problems. I was thinking 'hang on a minute I thought this was about helping me with my girls.'

PAUSE TO REFLECT

It is very common for children and family practitioners to be asked "Do you have children?"

How do you answer this question?

Why?

DEEPENING THE USE OF THE 4 Ps IN CREATING RELATIONSHIPS

A few years ago, I had a stroke. I spent a considerable length of time in hospital. One aspect of the stroke was that I lost the ability to read and write. I was determined to relearn this skill so that I could return to work and as a result I was given a series of appointments to explore why I wasn't able to read. One of the professionals that I went to see regularly was an ophthalmologist. She would greet me by telling me her name and pointing to her badge. Whilst I couldn't read the badge, what I could see was two logos - the NHS and the HCPC. Social workers had recently become registered by the HCPC and I said hello by explaining "I'm registered with HCPC too". I regularly told the ophthalmologist that I too was registered with HCPC (repeating this many times on lots of occasions!) Sometime later on reading my rehab file I noted that this was given as an example of a supposed communication problem. On reflection I realised that what I was trying to do was reclaim my professional P. When you are in hospital you are stripped of every element of your identity and simply become another P – patient. I wanted to be seen as an equal, I wanted to be able to build a relationship based on more than being a 'stroke victim'.

The time that I spent in hospital taught me a great deal about developing effective relationships. Most people will be able to identify with the situation of lying in a hospital bed when someone comes to the end of the bed. They are wearing a uniform, but you don't really know who they are. They pick up a folder from the edge of the bed, look at it (often not at you) and ask "Have you opened your bowels today?" This is one of the most personal and intimate questions you can ask. It is not something we discuss in our usual communication with people, but the person is in their professional P and they think it's fine to go straight to the most private of questions. This is what we do in social work, we ask incredibly private questions of people. The way that we go about asking these questions is vitally important.

In many ways a hospital is a public space and, on most occasions, social workers are asking questions in the person's own home (a very private space). If a person doesn't reply straight away or seems reluctant, social workers might label this as 'disguised compliance' or 'failure to engage'. Think about it. Should we go straight to those most intimate of questions? The questions must be asked, of course. They must be asked authoritatively but also empathically. It may be better to begin the conversation with some personal P discussion, some brief opening communication around a subject where everyone party to the conversation can share something. I'm not suggesting that the nurse should start with "Good afternoon. I've opened my bowels today. Have you?" but starting with something safe which can be used to open private intimate discussions in social work is important. Acknowledging how private some matters are, as well as understanding need to share and explore these is vital.

How do you go about opening up discussions about very private topics?

In my experience, the relationship between a social worker and a family is unlike any other. It's not a friendship, though some children, young people and families may perceive it as such. It's not a practitioner-client relationship, though some social workers may feel more comfortable framing it as such.

What both families and social workers should be striving for is a humane, respectful working partnership with a mutual interest in supporting and protecting children and young people.

Sounds easy, doesn't it? (Spoiler: It isn't).

Think of the personal relationships and connections you have around you. Your children, your partner, your wider family, close friends, your peers, your colleagues; these relationships take time to cultivate, and it takes time to learn how to interact with another person. Sometimes all will be well in the relationship and everyone gets along. Sometimes it doesn't go so well; you, or the other person may feel there has been a breakdown in communication, or a misunderstanding. Sometimes you, or they may say something hurtful, or unkind, or point out flaws and failings. Sometimes you might have expectations of the other person which are not met – or vice versa – and so you feel let down. The trust ebbs away, and you don't feel you have the same relationship you once had. We've all experienced it; it's just life.

The same happens in relationships between social workers and families – with some differences. As a social worker, you are there because you need to be, and this need may be voluntary on the family's part, or involuntary. There is a power dynamic which is either not present in our personal relationships or is different.

As a social worker, you have power. We, as families, know it – and if at first we don't, we learn pretty quickly.

We learn you have the power to come into our homes, to look in our fridges and cupboards and make judgements on our cleanliness. We learn you have the power to talk to our children without us being present. We learn you have the power to talk to our children's schools, nurseries, doctors, health visitors without us. And, ultimately, we know you have the power to take our children away. We've seen the television programmes, the soaps and the news reports. And we're scared.

■

Our relationships with you sometimes begin at times of crisis. Not many personal relationships start this way and if they do, they are often toxic. Your relationship with our family will be a transient one. The ideal is to get our family back on their feet and go away. Essentially, to us you should be Nanny McPhee... " When you need me but do not want me, then I must stay. When you want me but no longer need me, then I have to go."

Think about the first time you meet a family; the first time you sit down on their sofa and the first questions you ask. If you come into my home, sit down on my sofa and start by asking me what I think is not going well; I'm going to get defensive. If you start by asking me what is going well, I'm going to feel proud to share with you all of the things I feel I'm doing "right". If you then respond to me in a positive way, reflecting back to me all of these things, I'm going to be far more inclined to talk about what's not going well.

Our working relationship needs to feel like a partnership. As a mum, I need to feel that you are interested in, and care about my children, my family – and me. I need to be able to feel safe enough to share my own concerns – and listen to yours. I need to feel that you're there to help, that I have your support, and you are a member of the team around my child.

From my perspective, here are a few ideas on how to achieve that:

- Your starting point should be about working with us. You'll probably know this as the "Restorative" practice model. We don't, we've never heard of it. But working with us from the beginning means that we feel like a partnership from the beginning. And when there are difficult conversations to be had, you've already formed that bedrock; that solid foundation.

- At the centre of everything should be the child. We love our kids, they might get on our nerves at times, we might not be the most patient and we might not be the best parents. But, in the main, we want what's best for them. We are not the enemy. Try not to slip into the "them and us" dynamic. It helps no one and only serves to isolate parents and make it less likely to want to work with you.

- Strength-based practice (again, we've never heard of this) is another "must" for working in partnership with us. Let's face it, it's a good base for any relationship in our lives. Celebrating our strengths and telling us how well we're doing matters. Sometimes, no one has ever told us that before. Sometimes, our self-esteem and self-worth are low, and no one has ever taken the time to challenge that. If we haven't had good relationships with our own parents or carers growing up, we might not know which parts of our parenting are good enough, and we might need that pointing out. Conversely, we might not know which parts of our parenting aren't quite good enough, and that leads me on to my next point.

- It's easier to take concerns on board if we don't feel blamed. It's never that straightforward anyway. Not many parents set out to consciously neglect or abuse their child; those that do are in the minority. But if your, or other professionals' concerns are highlighted to us in a condemnatory way, we revert to feeling like a naughty child. On the surface, we will likely become defensive and angry; deeper down we may know you're right and feel guilt which only serves to fuel more feelings of anger. None of this is helpful. A better way is to probe and ask us what we think might be concerning professionals, making links with our own pasts to explain why we may be behaving in this way. If we feel you understand us, we're more likely to feel safe enough to take it on board. This is not about "excusing" our behaviours; it's about understanding what's at the root of them and showing us that you can see how we have ended up where we have, and then helping us to find the tools to change. Empathy helps. It really does.

- In this, and every interaction you have - straight talking works best. Every "service user", family member and child or young person I've ever met who have had social work involvement have all said the same thing. Don't tiptoe around us and don't sugar-coat what's happening. Be honest and upfront with us; we are much more likely to respect you for it.
- Acknowledge our losses. When a child is removed into care, regardless of whether it is over-archingly the best thing to do for that child, it is still a loss for both child and parent. When children are moved from placement to placement; these are all losses. The end of contact sessions are losses to parents, and to children. Loss needs to be talked about so that we can learn to manage it in a healthy way.
- Treat us with dignity at all times. Yes, we've messed up – and we probably secretly feel utterly wretched about it. But we're still human beings, and if you treat us with dignity it breeds respect on our part towards you.
- Don't say things like "we're only here for the child". Yes, I've had that said to me. No, it doesn't help. And I was fully aware that this was my children's social worker, not my family's. However, children are part of a family, or a network of carers. If you form a good relationship with us, you make it feel safe for a child to do the same, and – once again – you make us feel like we're part of the team.
- When we ask you challenging questions, answer them. Even if you know that answer will cause distress. Someone recently asked me: "Do you really think I'm part of the problem?". "Yes", I answered, without pausing. I then explained why I had come to that conclusion and what we could do together to change that. If we ask you something and you don't know the answer, tell us you don't and will go away and find out. Then make good on that promise. These small things build our confidence in you.
- Be aware of the power you hold, and how that dynamic will affect our working relationship. Be upfront about it; don't shy away from discussing it with us. Similarly, don't be afraid to have those difficult conversations. We are having a tough enough time, we need you to be bold and honest with us.
- Finally, remember that parents are, in the main, experts in their family's lives, and children are the experts in their own. During meetings and conferences, we should be given the same respect as a health visitor, or a paediatrician, or a psychologist. We know our family best, and we can be of great use if we are made to feel as such.

I hope this helps. Ultimately, remember why you got into social work. It wasn't for the flash car, long lunches and clothing allowance (yes, I can hear you laughing). You got into social work because you wanted to build human relationships. You got into children's social work because you wanted to support and protect families. We need you, and we appreciate you. We might not always say it, but we do.

RESTORATIVE APPROACH

Restorative practice is described as a specific social science which explores how social capital can be developed. It seeks to achieve social discipline through participatory learning and decision making (Wachtel 2016). Restorative practice is having a significant impact in education, criminal justice, organisational management and, increasingly, social work. The increasing popularity of restorative practice in social work has become clear in the UK in recent years, with a number of local authorities now adopting the approach across all local authority services or all services for children and young people.

A restorative approach is based on the importance of relationships and working directly with people. It is built on a continuum of methods which range from formal methods such as circles and restorative meetings, to informal practice which focuses on the vital importance of relationships in creating change.

RESTORATIVE QUESTIONS

Restorative questions are based around Borton's (1970) model of reflection and analysis (What? So what? Now what?) They are designed to support a person to reflect on a situation and analyse what might have happened. These questions can be useful to social workers both in terms of gathering information from people they work with and enabling and encouraging change in families, as well as in terms of reflecting on an incident they have been involved with.

What happened? What were you thinking? What were you feeling?

These questions help to explore each individual's perspective.

Who has been affected? What is the impact on them and on you? How do you feel now?

These questions help to identify the way that thoughts and feelings influence behaviours.

What needs to happen? What does that look like? What and who can help you?

These questions help to identify solutions from different perspectives, concluding with action.

Restorative questions draw on What? How? Who? When? and Where? but do not include a consideration of Why?. It is important to recognise that social workers need to maintain the why dimension to questioning, particularly in terms of reflexivity. However, restorative questions can be helpful in exploring situations with people in a non-threatening way. They also enable movement and change by focusing on the what next?

One key aspect of the restorative approach is the social discipline window (Wachtel 2016). This has wide application across a range of settings.

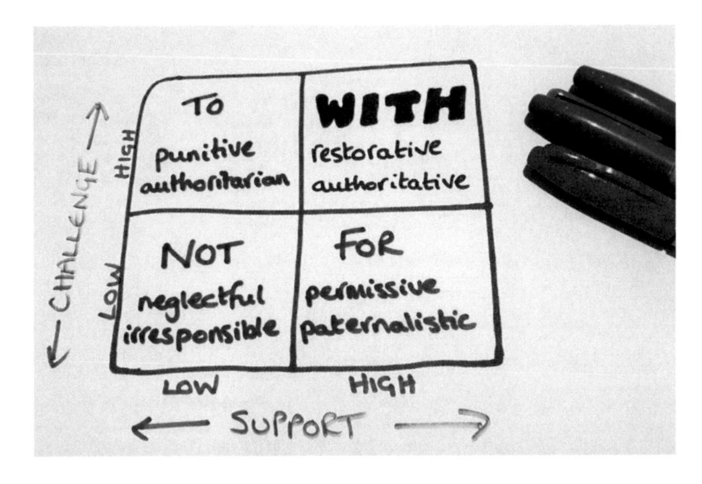

The social discipline window is based around the two aspects of challenge and support, creating four domains. The restorative domain draws on high support along with high challenge to work with people collaboratively. Doing things <u>to</u> people is authoritarian, falling into the punitive domain, whilst doing things <u>for</u> people (without involving the person fully) is paternalistic, falling into the permissive domain.

'With' is the most important aspect of a restorative approach. This is about working with people in a way which offers high levels of support but also high challenge. Working with people involves creating, developing, sustaining and repairing relationships. According to Lloyd (2016) working with people is not a tool, or model but a way of being.

PAUSE TO REFLECT

What do I do to ensure that I am working with the children and families I support?

Are there times when I need to operate in other parts of the social discipline window? Why? How?

New Beginnings is a project which specialises in working 'with' families who are involved in the child protection process. It is part of the not-for-profit Stobbe Social Care Community Interest Company. For more information: www.newbeginningsgm.com

Jadwiga Leigh is a Senior Lecturer in Social Work at Lancaster University. She is also the Director and Programme Leader of New Beginnings Greater Manchester.

Stobbe

A few years ago, when I was in practice, I noticed that in the area where I worked, we had lots of different services providing different kinds of support to families but there wasn't one service which tried to meet the holistic needs of families who were on child protection plans. This seemed to pose a problem as parents whose children were on child protection plans, or who were on the edge of proceedings, appeared reluctant to engage with individual services because it not only meant they would have to repeat themselves but also keep building relationships with different people in different places. I felt we were missing a service that brought everything together to provide coherence and consistency for those who needed that form of intensive support.

In 2012, when I went to Belgium as part of my doctoral research, I was introduced to an agency called 'Stobbe' which in English means 'tree stump' and symbolises new beginnings. I still remember the first day I walked into the centre- I felt like I had entered another world. Hidden behind a garage door, lived a community of families who with the support of professionals had come to this residential centre to try and turn their lives around. I soon learned that the main ethos of the Stobbe team was that if parents who had experienced significant trauma in earlier life were to engage with services, and those services were to be effective, then families needed to remain together. In addition, the team recognised that the majority of families they worked with also needed their service to be flexible and able to adapt to the individuals who were involved with it. Although Stobbe was a residential service, I recognised that there were elements of it that could be translated into a community programme. Following my visits to Belgium, I started to wonder if a similar service in England would work.

New Beginnings

A number of years passed before I turned that 'wonder' into a reality. It was in February 2018 that I approached Stockport Local Authority to ask them if they would consider collaborating with me to see if a version of Stobbe could work. The pilot programme would be called New Beginnings, and although intensive and therapeutically informed like that of Stobbe, it would be based in the community with the intention of working with families who lived close to one another. Stockport agreed to give it a go and with a little bit of impact funding, the pilot project launched in May 2018 with 6 families and two workers (me and Leanne Boylan).

The main objective of New Beginnings was to create a service that could be tailor made to meet the needs of the families it worked with. The primary aim of the project was, like that of Stobbe, to keep families together by working 'with' parents while children remained in their care. I wanted to work predominantly with families whose children are on child protection plans or on the edge of care proceedings because I recognised that this was a group that needed coherence and consistency more than anyone. However, I was also prepared to work with families whose children were on supervision, interim or full care order, providing the children were at home or there was an intention to return them home so regular contact arrangements were in place.

The First Group of Families

The main criteria for the first group was that it was for women and their children who had been victims of domestic abuse and that they came from one particular area in Stockport. The reason being, I wanted the group to develop into a network that could be supportive and understanding of each other's backgrounds and needs. Living close to one another would, I hoped, provide the women with the opportunity of creating new friendships.

As it so happened, of the six families referred, all of the women had not only experienced physical and emotional abuse but also prolonged episodes of trauma, often as a child within their own home, and at more than one point in their lives. I soon learned from the women that the traumatic events they encountered, have led to them experiencing issues with their mental and physical health and this has in turn affected the relationships they have had with their children, their friends and other family members. In addition, when children's services became involved in their lives, they were often left feeling angry, frightened, ashamed, defensive, vulnerable, lonely and isolated.

Unexpectedly, the partner of one of the women joined the New Beginnings project as he felt he might benefit from the 1:1 sessions I carried out with the mother of his child. His addition brought a new dimension to the project and reminded me that flexibility is always important if we were to remain true to our vision of being inclusive.

Many of the parents we were working with found 'being a parent' difficult because of the issues they had experienced in their own childhood. This tended to stem from the fact that they had grown up in a situation where they'd had to face a number of different social, emotional, environmental and health related challenges. Collectively, these factors affected the parents' ability to provide, what children's social care services often refer to as, 'good enough care'.

The Programme

I knew that if the New Beginnings programme was to be effective it needed to be intensive and run for a period of six months. I designed it so that it would include: group work where parents could learn with others, 1:1 work in which they could focus on their own lives and advocacy which would involve their keyworker supporting them in professional meetings. Twice a week, therefore, the parents would attend a group sessions. One was designed to be therapeutically informed so that using a range of different approaches we could work towards exploring the past, the present and the future. The other was created to as a self care session which offered holistic therapy, yoga and meditation and art therapy. Once a week, parents would attend 1:1 counselling and also meet with their key worker to discuss what they had learned in the group sessions, receive support with homework and work towards their identified short and long term goals.

When the families first joined the project they were all assigned a key worker (either me or Leanne) and our primary role was to provide them with support throughout the duration of the programme so that both parents and their children could feel part of a safe and supportive, learning environment. If the family wanted, we would also attend and support them in professional meetings such as child protection conferences and core groups. Not surprisingly all of the families took us up on this offer. Professional meetings can be very daunting activities to take part in when you already feel overwhelmed by the child protection process.

In addition to the support they received from their key worker and the other therapists/ practitioners on the team, parents also had the opportunity to develop connections with other families on the programme. This was probably the most worrying part for the parents - meeting other people who might judge them and expose their secrets to others. With appropriate support, guidance around confidentiality and reassurance that everyone was in the same position, the parents overcame this initial concern but it still took some time before I noticed them properly start to bond. But it was once they did start to bond that I observed the positive changes begin to occur. Most likely because they were now part of a peer support network, and therefore less likely to feel isolated and stigmatised. Once they felt comfortable with one another, and with us the team, they started to grow in confidence and were able to assert themselves with other professionals.

It is during the school breaks that we run family activities. This is where all the families go out together and have some fun! We have done all sorts of things during this holiday period from growing and eating fruit and vegetables at the allotment; going bowling or to an indoor play gym. We have found that this time has been beneficial for families in a number of ways either through having support and maintaining connection during the holidays; stepping in and helping a peer who may be struggling that day for whatever reason; practising skills with their children that they have learned in group sessions or watching the children developing their own new networks.

Although the programme may sound intense, and it is, it has been designed with the goal of helping parents explore aspects of their life that are buried deep within them. A mantra the group developed was "You've got to feel it to heal it" as they started to recognise that the past would not go away. They realised they needed to return to their childhoods to understand who they were, why they felt the way they did and why they parented in the way they did, so that they could develop new skills to help them move forwards. Something which I did not expect, was the learning I would gain from the parents. As a result of the constant feedback I asked for and received, and being part of their new journey, I feel I have changed as a person, a practitioner and a parent. Their experiences and views have and will shape the way in which sessions for future groups are held.

It was in December 2018 that the pilot programme came to end. Of the 6 families we worked with, 5 completed. The 6th stepped off halfway through because the programme was too intense for her and there was already too much going on in her life. She will however be returning for the next group we run (we hope). The five families who completed have been stepped down from child protection or child in need plans with some ending their involvement with children's social care altogether. The feedback we have received has been incredibly positive and we are pleased that two of the women who were part of the first group have completed the peer mentoring training. This means that when we start the next stage, they will be with us, using their newly acquired knowledge to be peers and mentors to the next group of newcomers who join the project.

Changes

By building relationships and working closely with families, we have learned that parents feel appropriately supported and, as a result, are more likely to turn their lives around. We have learned that parents value the new networks they make because they make connections with others who are in a similar situation and so they feel less ashamed, less isolated and less vulnerable. Many of the parents we worked with said at the start that the programme was "too intense" but after 10 weeks they changed. They told us they liked the fact that they had established a routine and also that everything they needed was provided "under one roof". In fact, what we found was that when the programme was drawing to a close many of the parents were worried about what they were going to do because they didn't want to leave. The benefit of having the peer mentoring training attached to the end of the programme is that parents don't feel they have to leave - they can stay with us for as long as they want to.

However, when creating the programme, something I didn't properly anticipate was that some parents might not want to go onto be peer mentors and yet they might not want to leave New Beginnings either. These parents have taught me that being flexible and adaptable is an aspect of our practice that needs to continue even at the end of the programme because not everyone wants the same thing. By listening to them, I have learned that families often want to stay connected because either they want to keep the project going by helping with fundraising or because we have become a part of their life that they now value and cherish. They don't want to lose the connection they have with us.

As I write this it is January 2019 and me and the team are getting ready to start New Beginnings again with new families, peer mentors and volunteers. This time we will be working with 15 families all of whom we have already met and started to build a relationship with. I know New Beginnings is still in its early stages but it is a project that both the parents and the team feel incredibly passionate about. It is a project which is constantly evolving and developing in partnership with the families we work with. It is a form of co-production that feels right. Our parents are at the heart of the progress we have all made and we feel immensely proud of everything we have, so far, collectively achieved. This journey that began with me wondering if doing things differently could be a reality is nowhere near the end- it is just at the beginning.

What's your immediate response to reading about New Beginnings?

SOCIAL GGRRAAACCEEESSS

The social GGRRAAACCEEESSS framework was developed by John Burnham working with Alison Roper-Hall. It was a mnemonic developed around looking at how to consider social difference in therapeutic interactions. Burnham describes how the framework "has, in its various forms, been making a practical contribution ... in the systemic field since 1990" (Burnham 2012: 139)

The framework can provide a really useful way for social workers to consider similarities and differences between them and the children and families they work with. The basic idea is that everyone can think about their identity in relation to the following:

Gender

Geography

Race

Religion

Age

Ability

Appearance

Class

Culture

Ethnicity

Education

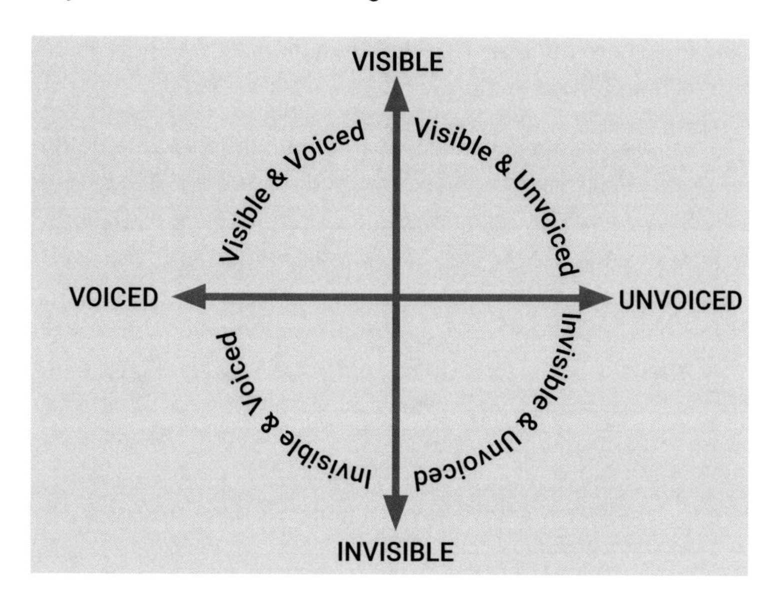

Employment (I add economics, to ensure that aspects of poverty are included in the consideration. I also add experience, to ensure that peoples experiences are considered in terms of similarities and differences)

Sexuality

Sexual orientation

Spirituality

This list type presentation of the GGRRAAACCEEESSS can be helpful to clarify them, but of course they are connected in a range of ways. One aspect of identity included on the list will impact on others. Sometimes the connections are complex and they are always ever evolving. There may be difference or similarity in each of these areas between the practitioner and the people they are working with. This can impact on relationships and practice in a range of ways. A helpful starting point is for the practitioner to be clear about their own social GGRRAAACCEEESSS. Developing a sense of self awareness can certainly enhance the ability to use the self effectively in creating relationships. Burnham has produced a helpful framework for considering what he calls "differences among the differences" (2012: 146). Some differences are visible, and some are not, some differences are voiced (discussed) and some are not. This creates four quadrants as summarised in the illustration.

It may or may not be helpful to voice difference when working with families in order to encourage deeper partnership and to explore aspects of power and identity.

PAUSE TO REFLECT

Reflect on your identity in terms of the social GGRRAAACCEEESSS. What strikes you?

Think of a child or young person you are working with. What is their identity in terms of the social GGRRAAACCEEESSS?

How might this impact on the creation of an effective relationship?

How might you be able to draw on the social GGRRAAACCEEESSS to develop the relationship further?

PAUL'S PERSPECTIVE

As an adult I've had plenty of time to reflect and look at the relationships I had as a child. The sad thing is I don't have many positive memories.

Growing up in care taught me 'mistrust' when it came to adults. I very quickly became suspicious of their intentions and their motives. I developed a sixth sense or radar when it came to meeting people. I learnt to weed out and immediately dismiss adults who I believed held no interest or that I couldn't gain anything from (cynical at such a young age!) but life had already taught me a few things, relationships aren't permanent, there are too many changes and I'll only find out after the change! I learnt that professionals aren't consistent in word or deed, as promises are made and often not fulfilled, so that words spoken became meaningless, telling me that I'm not important enough to matter and so the 'mistrust' begins.

As each of these layers are embedded, it becomes even more difficult from both sides to be able to make headway.

I recall my very first social worker who in the initial stages I was happy to see. I associated her with cake (I was only 4½!) When she visited, I would be allowed to join her in the parlour room in the children's home and she always let me have her slice of cake (the sisters in charge never left a slice purposely for me!) At first, I believed that I could trust her as she seemed to want to help me. She told me all the things she would be doing for me, taking me out, playing with me, even finding me a 'real' home, so I disclosed the violence and abuse that I was being subjected to. I remember becoming very tearful and I asked her to stop all the things that were happening to me and pleaded with her to find a family who I could live with forever. She repeatedly told me that I had to be good and then these things wouldn't happen (by that very token I believed my being hurt was my own fault), she even told me that she had been looking but couldn't find anyone who wanted me! (sometimes a little honesty causes devastation and damages self-worth as these words broke my heart).

I realised after several meetings with her that all her visits coincided with some of my most severe and prolonged beatings at the hands of 'my' carers. This awareness brought about a significant change in me and I gradually became silent and offered the expression "I'm fine." (My files note that I never engaged with social workers and even when I did, I refused to discuss anything of significance to do with me, using the phrase "I'm fine" as a stock response. No one tried to get beneath it.) I was taught from such an early age that 'big people' lie and pretend, and never mean things. It also highlighted my difference to 'regular' kids and I understood that I wasn't the same as them and therefore mustn't deserve or warrant the things they had, because 'children like me can't.

Unfortunately, this initial experience set the scene for my future dealings with social workers and relationships with adults. I no longer trusted their intentions.

It always felt a one-sided relationship and I had no intention of changing that by taking part. Reading the notes in my file, it seems and feels that no one cared enough!

On reflection, I do see how some of the relationships I experienced impacted in a positive manner for me. Sometimes to the rest of the world these would be of little significance but at the time to me they were such a magnitude, for example aged 7, I was presented with a book (Robinson Crusoe) for my excellent needlework (I know, but yes boys were taught to sew). As awards were being presented parents of other children clapped loudly, their applause reflected in the smiles of their sons and daughters. I was called out (I dreaded the silence that would follow) barely able to look up until I heard someone clapping loudly and enthusiastically. It was my teacher, not only was she clapping, but she was standing and smiling at me and I recognised 'pride' on her face...just for me! It is such a clear memory for me that I can still feel the confused emotions I felt then. I knew that day, I mattered.

Sometimes an incident like that can be the difference. I know because it made me feel that I could do as well as the 'day' kids who I schooled with, and sometimes a little self-belief is all you need to stop you from completely sinking.

My experiences as a child were formed in the brutal institutional systems of the 1960s and 1970s, it really wasn't a safe place for a child to grow up in. Thank goodness some things have changed, but some things haven't and what I now see and perhaps am more aware of since we as a family adopted and continue to foster, is the relationship that exists between the social worker, the child and carer.

I never knew which social worker would turn up until they arrived, that privileged information was on a needs to know basis, just not mine! Besides their names, I knew very little if anything about them, they never personalised my experience, yet I was expected to talk about me and how I feel etc., how does that one work?

Hopefully you'll have picked out the references to how all of this made me 'feel', it's a key element of relationships and children, regardless of age need to know their feelings will be heard and respected. So fast forward to today, do I see improvement in the way relationships are developed both with children and the people who are caring for them. I think 'could do better' would be a fair comment overall; however, I'm aware of some exceptional individuals who go that extra step, who forge personal relationships and only wish these individuals had been part of my life.

So, here's a few things I'd have wanted from a social worker when I was a child and they still apply today:

- I'd like to know some things about you, what you like, fun things, not the standard, rank, name and number
- I want you to play with me, especially games I like, allow me to be in charge, making the decisions or rules. It makes me think you're listening to me and I might believe that you genuinely want to be with me!
- When you talk about me or my family or background, say something nice. I already feel bad that I can't live with them, otherwise I may continue to worry about what I'd done.
- Never be afraid to acknowledge how I may feel. It's important for me to feel that you really care

- Don't promise what you can't deliver otherwise I'll stop believing you and won't engage
- Stop visiting me in school, you make me feel different to others. Arrange to see me in a normal' setting.
- Ask my permission to read my file, to learn about me, when you meet me for the first time. I might also have questions. It'll make me feel you respect me, I may even begin to start trusting you!
- Don't be afraid to explain why I'm in care. I can understand far more than you think. Not knowing eats away inside me.
- I don't want to see you 'scribbling' when you're supposed to be seeing me. If you must, explain why and what you're doing and let me read it and agree it, so that I understand. Don't forget when I'm big, I may read my file, let it reflect the truth
- Only use words that you would use for your own family. Professional jargon tells me I'm less than others. I'm a child and want to be the same as all my friends really! Don't make me feel different. I'm not a service user, a placement or other. I'm a child and I never chose to be here.
- Never forget to say goodbye in person, I need to know I mattered to you, I've already lost enough people in my life who just disappeared, don't be another. I don't want to believe I was responsible in anyway.

This list isn't exhaustive, it's about putting yourself in the shoes of a child. What would you want and need?

As an adopter and someone who fosters, the relationship needs to be equal and isn't that dissimilar to the relationship between the child and social worker. Respect and being heard is probably my biggest gripe. There have been occasions when it feels like a battle. Surely if the child is central to us both, then that's where the focus needs to be. On one occasion, the social worker for the children we were looking after insisted she tell them they were getting adopted. I spoke at length as to why this wasn't the best way forward, highlighting the child's understanding of the world, their mistrust of the social worker ("she took me away", was a phrase they often stated!) I offered to approach the news in a much gentler way and feed the idea in over a period of time based on the child's pace. On this occasion, I was completely overruled. I very much felt like the line that, "I'm the social worker and therefore know best" was taken. The upshot was a child who became emotionally distraught and eventually had to be told it wasn't happening. I asked if I could approach things again a week or so after the initial telling using books, stories, my knowledge of the child and my relationship with them. Approval was given and within a short period of time the child themselves thought this was a good idea. Five years on, this child is happy, secure and has a wonderful attachment with their new family.

Sometimes it's okay to admit that the skills and knowledge one side has is better suited for the situation.

Equally I've experienced social workers who have listened to us and supported us in finding out information or championing the needs of a child. Our own son who joined us through adoption struggled initially to form any attachment with my wife. His social worker 'battled' with their own authority to secure a course of 'filial therapy' with a psychologist who worked over a three-month period with both my wife and son. If they hadn't intervened and gone that extra step, the impact for our son and our family could have become very different, even raising the possibilities of the adoption failing.

I hope that a combination of my voice and the roles I have lived and still live will give you a picture that you can take forward. Again, I'm reminded (as per my file!) that I was once asked by my social worker, "What would you like most?"...I didn't ask for anything grand or big! I asked, 'if I could be allowed to be a bit happy, maybe to be told something good about me sometimes, would be nice ...Quite small, not big asks, but it tells you that it's the little things that meant more to me as a child..... and that's my ask, use what you read, as a tool, to enable you to make those small changes that mean you become the difference.

.....and finally I want you to know that I look back, and I recall the amazing talented kids who I grew up with. Hard kids, tough kids, smart kids, some who have gone on to do brilliant stuff. A generation, not of 'Lost children', instead, these were children of potential, fuelled and filled with possibilities and so much passion....and all they needed was someone to believe them and believe in them. LET IT BE YOU.

What changes might you make to your practice based on Paul's perspectives?

DIRECT WORK: THE WHAT? WHY? AND HOW?

WHAT?

In many ways, direct work is exactly what it says it is - directly working with children, young people and families. Generally the phrase direct work refers to more than just working with people on a day to day basis, with direct work having a particular purpose, going beyond simply creating relationships, although it often begins with this. Direct work might include:

- Playing games
- Craft activities
- Conversations
- Reading together
- Watching something together
- Using technology
- Creative activities
- Developing resources for the child to use in the present and or future

WHY?

The starting point for good quality direct work is why?

- Why am I involved in this child's life?
- Why am I going to do direct work?

The why? question will influence every other question in relation to direct work. For example, why the work is being undertaken will impact on how it is done and where it takes place. The reasons why a practitioner might undertake direct work include:

- Supporting children to express their wishes and feelings
- Supporting transitions
- Helping children and young people to further develop their relationships
- Promoting change
- Helping children and young people to understand their life circumstances and their current living situation
- Helping children to process trauma and life events
- Addressing issues of behaviour which are limiting the child's opportunities
- Helping keep children and young people safe
- Raising awareness and understanding in families

HOW?

Too many times practitioners use the same direct work methods over and over again. Worksheets and standardised tools are used too often. Some children and young people will tell you that they have done the same activity five or more times during their experiences of working with social workers. Worksheets can be useful in direct work, but sometimes it feels as though a practitioner lacks skills and is simply looking for something that can be scanned onto a file.

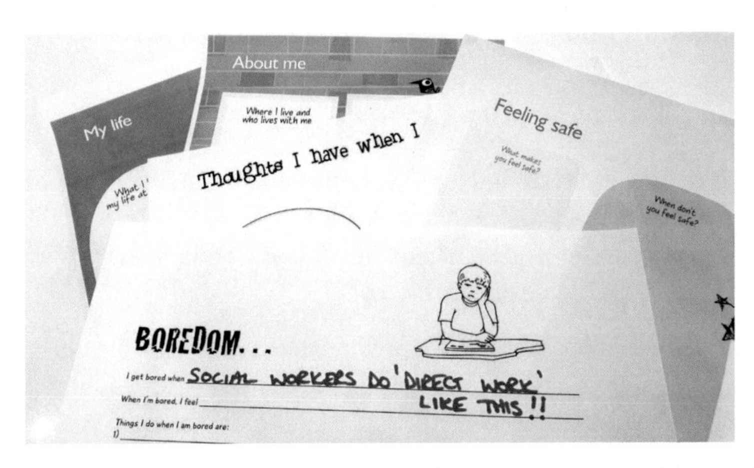

The how of direct work must be individual to the child and the purpose of the work. The following questions should all be considered when planning the how:

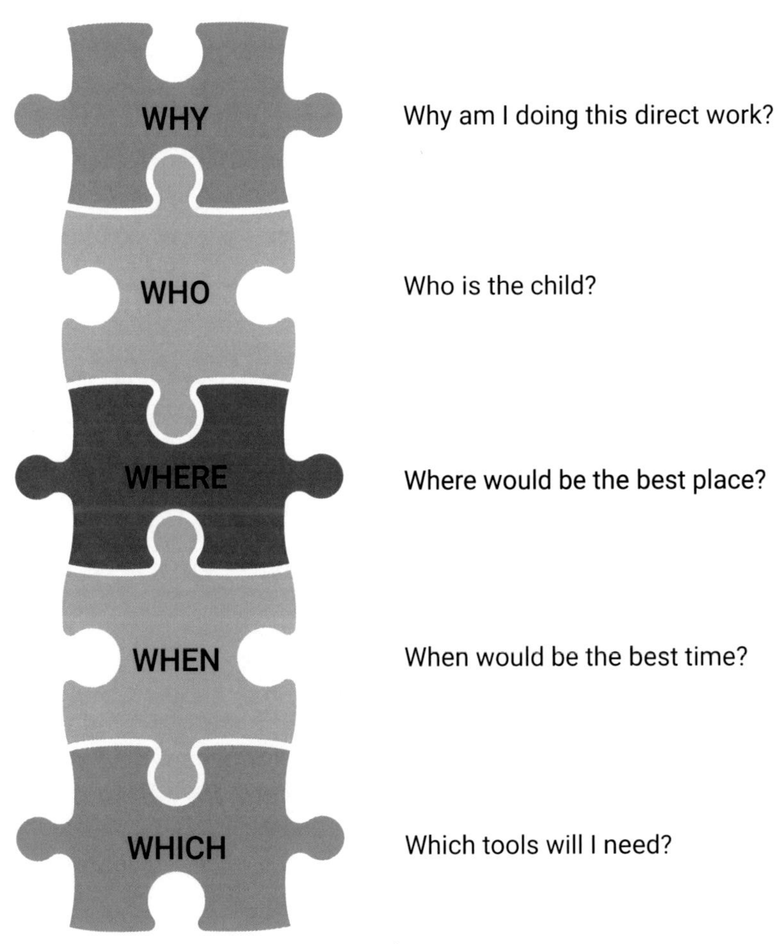

WHO?

Direct work should always be planned around the individual child or young person. What will work with one person may not work with another.

Who are you working with? Who are they as a person? What have their experiences been? What are they interested in? Do they have any additional needs that you will need to consider?

On occasions, it may be appropriate to involve others in the direct work (for example foster carers, or siblings). So thinking about who, would also consider the involvement of third parties.

WHERE?

Social workers take a person in environment perspective and so they need to have an in-depth environmental awareness. This environmental awareness should be used to think through the best place for the direct work to take place. There are pros and cons to every environment, and it is important that the practitioner thinks these through.

Working with a child in their own home is common for practitioners but the child may have experienced trauma in the home environment and being surrounded by memories of this may negatively impact on the child and their connection with the direct work. Alternatively, it could be that working with the child in their home environment may enable the social worker to further develop their understanding of the child's world.

Sometimes it may be appropriate to undertake direct work with a child in school or college. For some children school is a safe place, sometimes the only safe place they have. To enter their safe place and talk about trauma may take away this feeling of security. It is vital that social workers work closely with schools/colleges to form safety nets for children on departure from the school environment, ensuring that children have a safe designated person they can talk to. For some children attendance at school is a concern, if a social worker then takes a child out of lessons to undertake direct work this can give inappropriate messages about the value of education.

WHEN?

Timing and timescales are both important to think about in terms of direct work. Direct work with a set target or topic should be undertaken with a 'short and fat' approach, lots of input over a set small period of time, aiming for six to eight weeks for a targeted piece of work. Balance that with how often is right for the child? How many professionals are they working with and what appointments do they have to attend? Is all this work at the same time too much to handle and process? This, together with the level of risks in this child's life, will give an indication of your pace in undertaking the work.

The success of the sessions you undertake will also be dependent on the timing in the day and length of your sessions. Meeting children straight from school, for example, is not always going to work because children may want some down time to relax.

Where direct work is taking place in school, timing this effectively is vital. Think about the times the children will be having lunch breaks or play time. Regardless of all the planning and your time restraints, a child should never miss a meal, or their time to play. Check out times and lesson plans with school to determine when is best so that there is minimal disruption to the child.

In terms of how long direct work sessions should be, think through the child's concentration span. You are not the only person involved in working with the child or young person – speak to others, such as teachers, to determine how long you will need to structure your session to gain optimum success.

WHICH?

Questions which begin with which are always about specifics. So, this is about thinking through the specifics of the activity:

- Which tools will I need to have ready?
- Which of these might the young person have done before?
- Which activity will I use as Plan B?

PAUSE TO REFLECT

Think about a child or young person you are going to do some direct work with and work through the following questions to develop a plan:

What? *(What will you do? What is the purpose?)*

Why? *(Why are you working with this child?)*

How? *(How will you do the work? How will it impact?)*

Where? *(Where is the best place to do the work?)*

When? *(When is the best time?)*

Who? *(Who is the child? Who else might you involve?)*

Which? *(Which tools will you need?)*

Sophie Gilbert is an Advanced Practitioner in Dudley. She has been a social worker for ten years.

Sophie has worked in child protection for a number of years and has a particular interest in working with victims of domestic abuse and their children to repair relationships and secure safety. Sophie's current role is lead of staff learning and development in Dudley's innovative Centre for Professional Practice. Sophie has developed tools and training around good practice in direct work with children and young people.

Here in Dudley we recognise that we are working to achieve positive outcomes for the children and young people that we work with, they are at the heart of what we do, so we have focused on how we can achieve good practice by listening to our children and young people and letting them tell us what they want from us.

In June 2018, Dudley held a Voices for Choices event. 25 Children and Young People in our care, aged between 8 to 13 years, attended and engaged in expressive art sessions of comedy, rap/grime music, dance and street art to share their experiences and views about:

- Contact with family
- What makes a good social worker
- Understanding more about your past
- Most memorable times in care

The session was supported and attended by staff from the Children's Commissioners Office, to use the findings on a new Online National Hub for Children in Care.

The outcomes of the day fed into the development of our direct work and "Voice of the Child" training session, and the messages we deliver to our staff in best practices of direct work.

The graffiti session looked at what a good social worker is, giving us ideas about how we need to behave and key pointers for building rapport.

From this, we took that our staff need to be mindful of how we behave with children and young people and put more onus on what they want from us when we work with them, encompassing our restorative approach of working together to achieve. Identifying what children and young people want from us, allows us to be more self-aware and build successful rapport.

For us here in Dudley, remembering children's birthdays has hit home. If someone did not remember your birthday, it is something you remember about them. You question why not? Aren't you important to that person? This is not the message we want to give. It is important that we celebrate the children and young people that we work with and make them feel as important as they are. Remembering their birthdays is a simple small step we can take as social workers to continue on the journey in building a rapport and making a difference. We are not saying that we need to give extravagant presents or throw big celebrations; it is about acknowledgement and the relationships between us. Dudley have developed practice guidance for staff to encourage birthdays and celebrations of children and young people that we work with to support resilience and build self-esteem.

Our involvement with our Children in Care has continued to explore how we can get things right for those that we work with. Through fun days, we have explored the use of direct work tools and what works well and what doesn't.

Often a perception is that young people of14, 15 16 and above are "too old for direct work". This then results in social workers only speaking to young people, and not undertaking activities or using interaction tools to aid rapport and engagement. Yet some then say this is the hardest age group to engage with. So surely it is this age group that we should be pulling out all the stops to engage?

In our direct work training programme in Dudley, we play games build things and make things. This is a classroom setting of adult staff from all backgrounds, experiences and roles, engaging in craft and games throughout the day. As facilitator, I see in each session the smiles, the engagement and driven focus to complete tasks, whether it be making something out of a toilet roll or role playing air guitar. I hear laughs and voices from even those who are usually reserved, and the atmosphere is always positive. If it works for a class of adult learners, why not for young people?

Fun days in Dudley with our young people have had a variety of age ranges up to the age of 18 years, but our findings have shown that the older the child/young person the more they have engaged. At our last session, an 18 year old young man did not want sessions to end and he always stayed behind from one activity to the next to continue to play, craft and have fun. Messages from our young people were that they want to have fun. Our learning in Dudley is, no matter the age, more practical activities to engage in will support any rapport and relationship. This in turn has results with the quality of work improving the outcomes for the children and young people we work with. Building a Communi-crate.

A Communi-crate is a toolbox for staff full of direct work tools and resources as a readily available base line support in direct work. Here in Dudley we have introduced the use of Communi-crates to teams within our assessment, care management and children in care services.

Workers can build their own individual Communi-crate boxes or have a team crate to be on offer for staff to widen their practice and support in their engagement of the children and young people they are working with.

Having a selection of tools and resources to hand for a social worker makes direct work easier.

Since our direct work and Voice of the Child training where the use of Communi-crates was introduced into Dudley, our residential services have built tailored Communi-crates for all our residential homes that our Children in Care are able to access on a regular basis. The residential services Communi-crates add in more tailored resources and tools for the age ranges and regular issues of self-esteem or conversation topics. Such as games, mood cards and conversation cubes as physical visual tools to engage young people. Some of the resources are around relaxation because in Dudley we are keen to encourage mindfulness for our children and young people. This is a personal tool once learnt, that can be carried wherever they may go.

Staff within our residential services began using the tools quickly on implementation and have continued to do so. Feedback has been very positive with young people engaging well in conversations and in activities. All our children in our residential homes have worry monsters and these continue to be used. The worry monsters are checked regularly by staff for shared worries to ensure that our children and young people are supported appropriately.

All five family centres in Dudley have taken on the same principles and have Communi-crates that have tools and resources available to staff to use in their practice as a family unit. These Communi-crates have games and resources that can be used in activities with parents and carers as well as the children and young people we work with, to encourage their engagement with services and to support bringing about change.

A range of direct work tools are available, but don't forget that some basic toys and books can be just as useful and are much less expensive.

In a number of areas there are now individuals and small enterprises who will help knit or make direct work tools too. Keep an eye out for what you can add to your own direct work kit.

As Sophie has described, a number of local authorities provide direct work bags and there are a wide range of direct work kits available. However, these can (and probably should) always be added to. For example, I always liked to grow cress with children I was working with. An egg cup or even a broken egg shell can provide a good base, children can draw a face on the egg, pop a cotton wool ball in the egg and place some cress seeds on top. The cress grows quickly. You can comment on how the cress has grown on any subsequent visits and it's a cheap and easy activity providing lots of space for talking to children. A packet of cress seeds is therefore a cheap and easy thing to add to a direct work kit.

What is in your direct work kit?

What would you like to add?

What might you be able to make or get hold of cheaply that could really add something different?

Chapter 1

MESSAGES FROM RESEARCH

An ethnographic study (Winter et al, 2017) looked at how social workers can effectively communicate and build relationships with vulnerable children and young people under the age of 18. It identified factors such as:

- reflecting on shared past experiences
- use of compliments
- combining challenging with safer topics of discussion
- being responsive to the interests of the child or young person
- practitioners reflecting on what works in engaging children and young people
- practitioners being open about their preferences for the kinds of children and young people that they like to work with.

A persistent finding in investigations of cases where children have died or been seriously harmed is that social workers and other professionals have not adequately engaged with, or related to, the children concerned (Ferguson, 2016).

A literature review followed by small-scale qualitative research with practitioners (Lewing, Doubell, Beevers and Acquah 2018) found that whilst there is a strong logic for thinking that trusted relationships between a practitioner and a child can protect vulnerable young people from Child Sexual Exploitation or Child Sexual Abuse, as yet there is no evidence to support this.

In a study of social workers' engagement with children (Whincup 2015) children described how they appreciated social workers who cared for them, listened to them (which was linked to social workers' subsequent actions), were playful (or fun), and were motivated to work with them (this was interpreted as prioritising spending time and meeting with them).

The Talking and Listening to Children Project (TLC) is a UK wide study focusing on social workers' communication with children and young people. It found that most social workers engaged well with children and used a variety of methods and skills in their practice. There were also occasions when social workers seemed unwilling to communicate except through talking. Few social workers had their own play materials and when they did, they had usually paid for these themselves (Morrison 2016).

Survey based research, which had 350 responses found that on average social workers spent just over 20% of their working week in face to face contact with children, young people and their carers (BASW 2018). Some of the quotes from respondents included in the research final report include:

"There's no balance. I complete 'direct work' to satisfy targets, it's not meaningful by any stretch of the imagination. I'm basically a data input clerk."

"I don't feel I have enough direct time with children to build relationships and gain an accurate representation of their voice."

"When I am able to spend time with children on a 1 to 1 basis I am able to remember why I do this job."

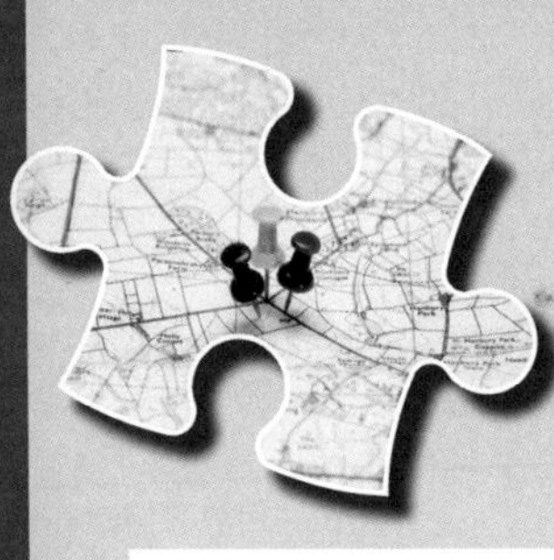

WHERE AM I NOW?

Revisit the start of the chapter. Look again at the KSS standard. Then consider the following questions:

What has surprised me in working through this chapter?

What three things would I highlight as key learning?

What do I still need to do in working towards being fully confident with this KSS statement?

What single next step should I take in working towards an improvement in my practice?

Chapter 2
COMMUNICATION

This chapter considers three different forms of communication - verbal, non-verbal and written communication. Communication is often seen as a basic skill and many social workers pride themselves in being a 'good communicator.' However, communication is often complex and challenging, these and a range of other Cs in communication are considered in this chapter. Working through the What? the Why? and the How? in terms of communication this chapter illustrates that (as in many areas of social work) the *why* is a major starting point and recurring theme throughout.

THE KSS REQUIRES PRACTITIONERS TO:

Communicate clearly and sensitively with children of different ages and abilities, their families and in a range of settings and circumstances. Use methods based on best evidence. Create immediate rapport with people not previously known which facilitates engagement and motivation to participate in child protection enquiries, assessments and services.

Act respectfully even when people are angry, hostile and resistant to change. Manage tensions between parents, carers and family members, in ways that show persistence, determination and professional confidence.

Listen to the views, wishes and feelings of children and families and help parents and carers understand the ways in which their children communicate through their behaviour. Help them to understand how they might communicate more effectively with their children.

Promote speech, language and communication support, identifying those children and adults who are experiencing difficulties expressing themselves. Produce written case notes and reports, which are well argued, focused, and jargon free. Present a clear analysis and a sound rationale for actions as well as any conclusions reached, so that all parties are well informed.

Take a look at the standard above in detail. Highlight key phrases and anything that jumps out at you. Then take some time to reflect on the statement.

- *What are your immediate thoughts?*
- *What might you want to discuss and clarify?*
- *How will you clarify meanings?*
- *Who will you discuss it with?*

GETTING FEEDBACK ON PRACTICE

Who can give me feedback on my practice in this area?	*How will I get the feedback?*

Make sure to keep a record of any feedback you receive.

INITIAL SELF-ASSESSMENT

What do I already do well?

How do I know? (What's my evidence?)

What do I need to work on?

How will I work on this?

COMMUNICATION: THE WHAT? WHY? AND HOW?

The What? Why? How? Framework is particularly important in relation to communication.

As a basic framework this chapter will explore:

- What is communication?
- Why do we communicate?
- How do we communicate?

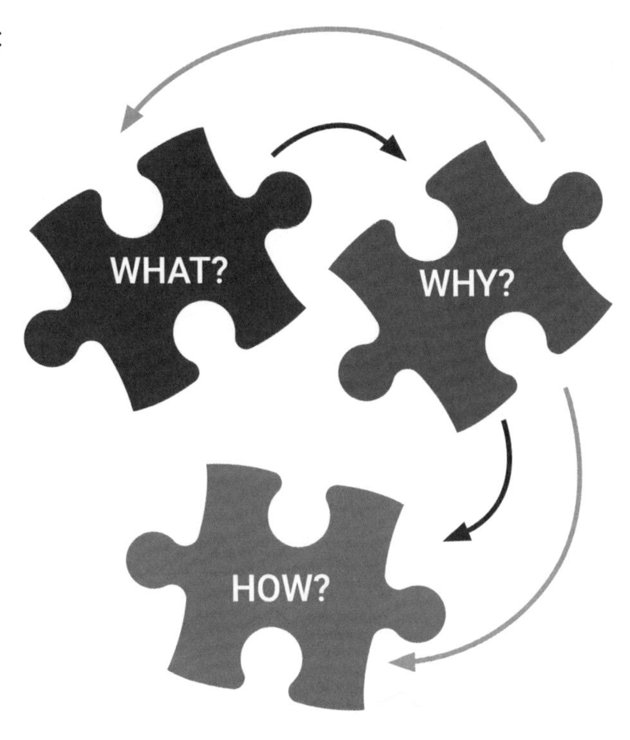

However, it is important to recognise that the connections between the What?, Why? and How? are extensive. In social work, communication and relationships must always have a purpose. This means that the 'why' question is central. Understanding why we are communicating is essentially about recognising the purpose of the communication. The purpose of the communication will then impact on what communication we use as well as influencing how we communicate.

WHAT IS COMMUNICATION?

This is a very basic question and of course one which we all think we have the answer to. Essentially communication is a two-way process. It is about the giving and receiving of a message. The message we are giving or receiving can be varied and therefore communication can be categorised in a variety of ways:

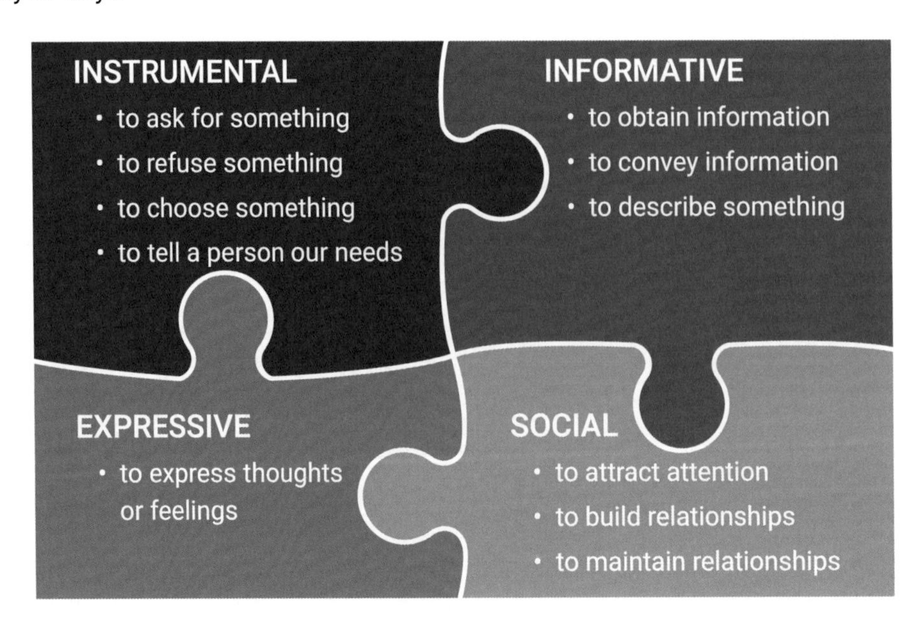

WHY DO WE COMMUNICATE?

It is essential that social workers are clear about the purpose of their communication. Everyone involved in social work refers to the importance of communication and indeed research indicates that the quality of communication affects a worker's ability to engage with families and impacts on parental evaluation of relationships with social workers (Forrester 2019). However, research by the Children's Social Care Research and Development Centre suggests that these same communication and engagement skills seem to have little impact on other outcomes in social work practice with children and families. In a blog, exploring these research findings Donald Forrester (2019) explains that the findings are not what he would have expected.

"It was the other dimensions of skill that seemed to have a much stronger relationship to outcomes. Good authority – a combination of purposefulness, child-focus and clarity about concerns – was a much better predictor of positive family change. This is really interesting: engaging parents is not enough. In child and family social work, purposeful and authoritative practice is crucial"

We are back to the importance of understanding why? Whilst in general, communication is divided into instrumental, informative, expressive and social, in social work communication must have purpose and needs to have depth and it generally connects each of the four functions of communication.

So, if you are communicating with someone in order to develop a relationship. Why? What is the purpose of the relationship? What are you hoping to achieve in that communication? Matching the style of the communication with the purpose of social work practice is vital. Therefore, at times communication needs to be authoritative, at times challenging, at times compassionate. Matching the purpose and practice of communication is about connecting the Why? and the How?

Which five words would you use to describe your communication in practice?

PAUSE TO REFLECT

What are the last three things you communicated at work?

What was the purpose of that communication?

What was the impact of your communication?

Communication between social workers and families is one of my favourite subjects and I've written extensively about it, so I'm really delighted to be able to get my two-penneth in here.

It's one of those go-to phrases we all put on our CVs, or eulogise about in interviews isn't it?

"I'm an effective communicator".

Well, Joan, that's great and I'll tick my box to say you are...but what on earth does that mean for families?

I'm going to shock you here; communication is a two-way street. I know - this is ground-breaking stuff. But communication means being able to speak and to listen.

Let's start with the latter: Listening. I remember starting a Counselling course many moons ago and being agog that there was a whole week on "listening". I felt I'd been jipped. I wanted my money back.

What does it mean to listen, as a social worker? Well, first of all, it means listening to families. And really listening; not just waiting for your turn to speak, or waiting to cut in and answer the question that your manager wants you to, or that's circled on your notepad to ask so you can tick a box when you get back to the office and fill in your reams of paperwork.

Actively listening is not an easy skill to master, it requires real concentration, patience and energy. It's not just about listening to what the parents, or child/young person are saying; it's the way they are saying it and the language they are using (I don't just mean the colourful stuff). Most of all, it's what they are not saying. But we'll come back to that.

So, what do we need from you when you listen to us?

- In my experience, a basic many professionals forget about is around taking notes. When you're listening to us, in the main, we understand it's going to help you to take notes, so you can accurately record what we're saying. However, it doesn't hurt to explain that to us, or to check out our understanding of the role of note-taking.

It's also common courtesy to ask if we're okay with you taking notes, and it's transparent and honest professionalism to then show us the notes afterwards so that we can agree they do accurately reflect what we've said. This is going to help you to build trust and a good relationship. It's a small thing to you, but a big thing to a family.

- Let us tell you our story. As human beings we are inherently conditioned to be story-tellers, and if you give us the space, we will do just that. I never felt that anyone ever cared enough to listen to me, that I was never important or relevant enough. Be that person who does care.

- That being said, don't be afraid to keep us on track every now and again with gentle prompts. We're not daft, we know you can't sit for four hours whilst we tell you everything that's ever happened in our lives. You're there for a reason. Be confident in your communication skills to keep that reason the focus of the conversation.

- Active listening is a skill you have already been taught. It's not an easy one, and it's tiring, but it's essential. Try to be patient with us and don't interrupt unless it's necessary to keep the conversation on track or to probe further.
- On probing, listen to what the family are saying...but what are they not saying? Where are the gaps? Which are the questions they are reluctant to answer? Why could that be, and could you re-frame the question to make it safer for them to answer? Be curious, and be bold, yet measured.
- Silence is golden! Or, in this case, it's a useful tool at least. If you've asked your question, and the family member has answered it – don't feel you have to fill the ensuing silence and jump in with your next question. Let the silence "be". It's powerful, and sometimes it can open up a space for families to tell you a little bit more than perhaps they were originally going to. It might feel a bit awkward at first, and go with your instinct as to whether it's going to work with each family member, but it's worth a try.
- Put your phone away. It might seem really obvious but having your phone out of sight sends a message to us that we are more important than it. If you are expecting an important call, tell us. If we are interrupted, keep it short if at all possible.
- Body language techniques really do work! We notice if you're sitting with your arms folded; it feels judgemental and defensive. Conversely, if you take your shoes off and put your feet up (yes, I have experienced this), it sends us the wrong message; it feels like you're trying to be our friend. Again, it seems obvious, but relaxed, open body language from you helps us to feel relaxed and open. When we're talking, lean forward to listen, and maintain eye contact. The little things aren't little.

So, that's listening. And as it turned out, that week on my Counselling course was useful after all.

Turning our attention to the other side of communication, how do you effectively communicate with families? How do you build a relationship with a family through communication? What about families who are hostile, or who don't want you there? How do you manage these tensions?

- The first time you meet a family is where their first impressions of you are informed. Pulitzer-winning stuff isn't it, this? But it is true. Whether you're going in at a time of crisis, at a time where you need to undertake a child protection investigation, or at a time where the family are asking for support, the way you introduce yourself and the first questions you ask will form the basis of our working relationship. Keeping calm, quiet, professional and courteous will help.
- With that in mind, it is essential you explain your role and why you are there. This may seem like a very basic standard, however, it is not the experience of many families. Some families don't understand exactly what you do, particularly if they've never had involvement before and their only experience

of social work is what they've seen on 'Corrie' or in the Daily Mail. Some parents are frightened of you and will be terrified you are there to take their children. Some parents think you are there to fix all of their problems. You need to be very clear why you are there and what you are going to or intend to do.

- Jargon. My all-time, number one pet hate, other than people who stand in the aisles of supermarkets chatting. It has absolutely no place in your conversations with family members, unless you are explaining a particular term, such as a Section 20, or a Section 47. Using jargon creates a barrier, an "us and them" dynamic. It's a tower to wield power. It enables some of you to hide behind words. It is absolutely, unequivocally unhelpful. When you think about the language you are using with parents, ask yourself if the average man or woman on the street would understand it. When you think about the language you are using with children or young people, ask yourself if your own children, or your nieces/nephews/cousins/friend's children would understand it.

- We don't all learn in the same way. I'm quite a visual person, I need to be able to see what I'm being told. I like a diagram. I bloody love a pie chart (and pie, for that matter). Other parents or family members will need to read what they're being told. Others will need to interact with what they're being told. It's imperative you probe to discover the most effective way of working with a family. Sometimes, we as family members won't know, because we've not been through this before, and it might take a few attempts to find the right way of communicating together. But it will make the difference between us understanding you and being able to better communicate back to you.

- Technology can be a wonderful thing. My 10-year-old daughter can do things on her laptop I didn't even know existed. She does Power Points for homework and can nail an Excel workbook. My five year old can download games on his tablet with aplomb, bypassing the need for my password (a one-off experience which cost me over £50 on the App Store...). My point is this, there is technology out there to be used which may help families to communicate with you. We shouldn't be restricted to the traditional method of calling your office number and leaving a message if we don't get an answer. Text messaging can be useful, email even more useful, and there are a wide range of apps which can be really effective and enable us to communicate with you in a way that helps us to feel safer.

Families don't always want to talk to you. There are a few reasons for that; fear being one – and when we are fearful, we get defensive and angry. We may not find it easy to trust anyone, professional or personal because of past life experiences. So, we shut down and we avoid you, hoping you'll get sick and go away. There may be stuff going on for us; a controlling partner who doesn't want us to engage with you, for example. We might not want to accept that we need a bit of help and support or believe that anything needs to change. We might find it very difficult to hear that we are failing our children, or that our care for them is not "good enough". We might want to offload the blame for our problems on to others. We may be frightened that what we tell you will be used against us.

Having been one of those parents myself, my advice to you to manage these situations is:

- Keep yourself physically safe
- Keep calm and stay in control of your own reactions
- Remain respectful, professional and dignified at all times
- Try to see things from the family's perspective; practice empathy
- Don't take anything the family say personally
- Know that our anger and aggression is often borne out of frustration and fear
- Have your own personal strategy for dealing with the aftermath of experiences like this. Gin doesn't help. A warm bath, some mindfulness and some self-care does.

Ultimately, communication is your biggest tool to engage with families. You can have all the fancy practice models and all the learning in the world under your belt (note: this would be a large belt) but it all stands for nothing if you can't communicate effectively, humanely, and respectfully.

What changes might you make to your practice after reading Annie's Advice?

BARRIERS TO COMMUNICATION

There are a range of barriers to effective communication. These can be separated out into a range of forms, as follows:

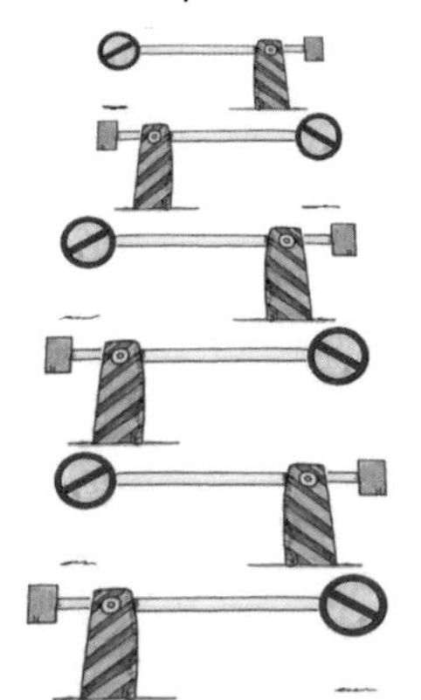

- Environmental barriers
- Clinical barriers
- Emotional barriers
- Attitudinal barriers
- Cultural differences
- Bureaucratic barriers
- Organisational barriers

ENVIRONMENTAL BARRIERS

The environment we are in can affect communication both in terms of being able to pass on a message or being able to receive a message. This could be as basic as:

- In noisy surroundings, people may not be able to hear what is being said, or even be able to formulate a message to pass on ("It's so noisy I can't even think!")
- In environments which are not private, people may not raise certain issues which they see as very personal
- If people are not comfortable, are too hot or too cold etc. This can affect the quality of communication taking place.

Power can be a very significant influence in terms of environmental barriers. For example, some 'spaces' carry with them specific power barriers – for example, court settings or social work offices communicate where the power lies before anyone has spoken at all.

CLINICAL BARRIERS

According to the Royal College for Speech and Language therapy, there are a range of clinical barriers to effective communication:

- Genetic or medical conditions
- Trauma
- Mental health problems
- Learning difficulties or disabilities
- Speech (clarity, stammering etc)
- Voice (lack of voice, hyper-nasality etc)

- Fluency (processing the delivery and receipt of language)
- Language
- Psychologically based communication disorders
- Social skills
- Problem solving skills
- Literacy issues or dyslexia

When considering specific clinical issues and the barriers that can be created, it is vital not to pathologise people (i.e. blame the individual for the communication problem). Social workers must find ways to communicate effectively taking into account any specific communication needs an individual has.

Clearly, it is important for social workers to understand the potential clinical barriers to communication so that they can work on improving their own ability to communicate with children and young people and their families. It is also important, however, so that they can support communication within families and to enable children to experience optimal development. According to the Communication Trust more than a million children and young people have some form of long term and persistent speech, language and communication difficulty, and in areas of poverty more than 50% of children begin school with delayed communication skills. Extensive research evidences that these communication difficulties can impact on the life chances of children and the Communication Trust is seeking to address this by equipping parents and professionals with more information about communication development and sources of support. The Communication Trust has developed a range of resources for teachers and early years professionals, but they are beginning to publish resources which will be specifically supportive for social workers, so a visit to their website will be useful (www.thecommunicationtrust.org).

The Bercow Review of Services for Children and Young People with Speech, Language and Communication Needs (2008) found that 77% of parents who responded said they did not get the information they needed when they needed it. Ensuring that parents have the information that they need to support language development and improved communication with their children is a vital aspect of the social work role.

EMOTIONAL BARRIERS

A range of emotions can have an impact on communication. This can be very basic or can be layered in its complexity. For example:

- Embarrassment: If someone is embarrassed about an issue, they may avoid discussing it
- Stress/Distress: The impact of stress on communication is particularly significant
- Anxiety: If people are particularly anxious, they may find communication difficult. Having to communicate about certain issues can create anxiety in itself and then the impact on communication becomes 'chicken and egg'.
- Shock/Anger: People can be shocked or angry about what is happening to them. This may result in a significant impact on communication. It particularly impacts on how a person hears others.

- Fear: Fear creates a fight or flight type response which impacts widely on effective communication – both in the giving and receiving of a message.
- Powerlessness: Sometimes people may feel that they have no control over their environment, choices or opportunities, so they may feel that communications can offer no new information or insight.

ATTITUDINAL BARRIERS

The barriers created by attitudes and bias are perhaps the most concerning when we see them in social work practice. Where people have negative attitudes towards the person they are listening to, then the quality of 'hearing' will certainly suffer, but attitudinal barriers go much further than this.

Morris (2017) highlighted statements made by social workers about certain areas of deprivation. For example, she quotes a social worker as saying, "you hear that they are a family from that road and you just think 'urgh'." This exemplifies how attitudes can have an impact on the way that a social worker might approach working with a particular family simply on the basis of what they have heard.

Prejudice, lack of respect and arrogance create significant barriers to communication. The barriers created by such attitudes are often referred to by professionals in relation to the service users they are working with ("he's got a real attitude problem in terms of authority figures") but it is important to recognise that such attitudinal barriers often lie with professionals.

Social workers need to take a whole system approach to understanding the barriers that can be created by attitudes:

- What is the ethos, atmosphere or culture of the organisation?
- How do individual practitioners reinforce that or cut across it in their own communication style?

CULTURAL DIFFERENCES

Where there are cultural differences between people communication can be adversely affected. For example:

- Assumptions may be made, which can effectively prevent open communication
- There may be differences in language, the use of words, accent, dialect etc.
- Non-verbal communication can be culturally specific
- Interpreters may need to be used which will clearly have an effect on communication

Culture is often viewed as being about race and ethnicity. Don't forget that "culture" covers a range of areas and could include generational differences etc. Indeed, in many ways each of the Social GGRRAAACCEEESSS (see Chapter 1) can have a major influence on culture.

The models of communication taught on social work training, often come from a very North American base and the inherent lack of cultural awareness within these is recognised by the American National Association of Social Workers (NASW 2017).

Victoria Climbie's aunt, Kaoau, and indeed Victoria herself, were first language French speakers having come from Cote d'Ivoire through France to the UK. The Laming Inquiry concluded that there was miscommunication and poor communication arising from the fact that no interpreters were used. This left the social worker limited ability to speak directly with Victoria.

BUREAUCRATIC BARRIERS

There are a range of bureaucratic layers in social work, many of which create barriers to communication. Morrison (2016) identified a body of research (for example Broadhurst et al, 2010; Munro, 2010, 2011) illustrating how the systems in social work can have a negative impact on how effectively social workers hear children and young people. The factors identified include heavy case loads, high levels of staff turnover and a preoccupation with bureaucratic, administrative and technical aspects of the contemporary social work role.

Ruch (2014) explored the practice of six social workers in relation to communication with children. Social workers described:

- Children did not communicate in the linear way that formal assessments, thresholds, evidence gathering or procedures require, which created a mismatch between the demands of the social work role and practicing genuine hearing.
- Feeling that they were forced to withdraw from cases before they felt their work was done, leading to feelings of anxiety and stress on the part of the worker.
- Feeling distressed by the content of what children said and feeling unable to share this because of concerns that emotion may be treated as a sign of 'weakness or professional inadequacy' rather than professional sensitivity and attunement to the child's circumstances.

ORGANISATIONAL BARRIERS

The barriers created within organisations are multifaceted and are generally about a combination of the barriers already covered within an organisation. So, for example:

- The environment of the organisation will create barriers.
- Attitudes are often shaped and promoted within organisational contexts.
- Organisations have their own cultures which can promote or hinder communication.
- The emotional context of social work may not be adequately addressed within organisations which may create emotional barriers.

When these different barriers compound within an organisational context the barriers may become more compacted, more powerful and ultimately more difficult to overcome.

PAUSE TO REFLECT

What are the main communication barriers you face?

How might you best overcome these?

USE OF LANGUAGE IN COMMUNICATION

The language that social workers use can be problematic in a range of ways and it is important that we keep the language we use under regular review. In Chapter 1 we covered the 3Ps. This framework can also be used to think about language: we may well different language in the different Ps. For example, we might use some language in our private P that we would not use in our professional P. At times though language used in our professional P can be used as a source of power. There is a great deal of professional jargon that others outside of the profession may not use at all. How many times have you sat in a meeting when someone has used an acronym or abbreviation for something and you haven't felt able to ask what that means, because asking may make you look like you don't know what you are doing? Thinking about how that made you feel can, to some extent, help you to imagine being a child or a family surrounded by language which is unclear. Sometimes professional language feels clinical, sometimes uncaring or lacking in compassion. It is almost always 'othering'.

The word othering is increasingly being used to describe the process of marginalisation where an individual or group of people become seen as 'not one of us'. Spivak (1985) originally used the word 'othering' since when it has grown in use. It is really important for social workers to understand othering because it can have a significant impact on children and families who experience social work involvement. Othering can impact on a person's sense of self, their self-esteem and confidence. Othering can also eat away at a child's sense of belonging. When someone is 'othered' they are viewed as different to 'the rest of us.'

TACT have produced a really helpful brief and accessible guide to appropriate language in social work with children and young people (March 2019). This has been produced by children and young people with care experience. It is laid out like a dictionary where the young people explain what language they would prefer to be used. In the introduction Ashley, who is care experienced, states that replacing professional language might be difficult but continues:

> **"However, I believe social workers and other care professionals should leave the big words for other professionals who understand them, and adopt the words provided in the new dictionary when talking to both young people and children and make the language they use around them more accessible, clear and sensitive."**
>
> **(TACT 2019: 4)**

One of the most widely used abbreviations used in children and families social work is LAC (looked after child). The dictionary calls for the LAC acronym to be removed altogether. Children and young people should be referred to by their names, the use of LAC could be understood as a suggestion that a child or young person is 'lacking' something.

Some of the words that are referred to in the TACT dictionary appear below. As you work through the table, reflect on your use of language in practice as widely as possible:

	Do I use this in practice? Why?	Why is this a problematic word?	What might I use instead of this word?	How might this impact on children and their families?
Contact				
Difficult to place				
LAC visit				
NEET				
PEP				
Challenging behaviour				

PAUL'S PERSPECTIVE

Effective communication sounds like it should be instinctive. But all too often, when we try to communicate with others, something goes astray. We say one thing, the other person hears something else, and misunderstandings, frustration, and conflicts ensue.

This can cause problems at home, school, work and relationships. As a child, growing up in the care 'system' I understood very early on in life that anything I had or wanted to say held no importance to anyone, and therefore this belief, combined with growing up in a brutal regime taught me silence. Not having any avenues where I could talk or be heard, I began to struggle with any form of expression, refusing, and eventually, avoiding any scenarios that meant I was required to say something about me or what I was feeling. Physically I became unable to hold eye contact, and my responses became quiet, flat and lacked emotion or expression. This even spilled into my school work and I offered minimal participation in anything creative. My belief that I didn't matter by that time was so ingrained! What I did learn however, was to interpret 'non-verbal' communication and the ability to listen, both for the spoken and unspoken. I learned to watch, and I noticed everything. (Quite a common trait for children to develop when living in 'difficult' situations).

What I needed, was someone, who would allow me time to talk at my pace, some reassurance and then to act on how I was feeling. Then I would have known I was being heard! Sadly this wasn't the case and the difficulty for me and others, when the only communication heard or felt is negative, one sided, misunderstood and violent, is that the outcome and impact on the receiver (in this case me) is wholly negative and destructive, resulting in poor or stunted emotional growth and intellect with little self-esteem and belief. This manifested and resulted in a lot of self-blame, loathing and shame for me.

Children, like me, in this setting needed to know and understand that these are circumstances out of our control and should never be made to feel it's our fault or to be blamed. Confidence alluded me and I never felt confident to ask questions or voice what I was thinking or feeling. The style of 'care' wasn't encouraging of children speaking in this manner, and for me, knowing no one was listening (even when I disclosed various assaults and abuse) taught me to no longer bother, that I didn't count, ...and I wondered why I struggled with relationships in my late teens and early adult life. I wasn't just 'clueless' around speaking about how I felt, I was frightened!

So, communication contributes to those life experiences we all face each day. It has the ability to create positive experiences and outcomes or the potential to gift self-loathing, lack of self-belief, esteem and self-worth. It can be something we look forward to (as it offers rewards, support, encouragement and confidence) or dread with trepidation and fear (as it's used to bully, undermine and silence individuals).

Me, the child, knew very little as to why I was living in a children's home. Those that should have been looking after my wellbeing reminded me that I needed to be 'good' all the time (I think it was an ideal I could never achieve), then I wouldn't get into so much trouble. Often the language used was not only negative but 'barked' as orders or instructions. I wasn't given or allowed a space to respond and when I did (I couldn't always control my temper or tongue) their response was physical chastisement with brutal consequences, and so I learned silence and knew not to 'rock the boat'.

From those that came to visit me and check my welfare, I needed to be seen as more than the file they clung onto. Some even looked fearful as if they were coming to see a caged beast or perhaps it was fear of those who 'cared' for me? (Interestingly, despite the regular visits and the clinging of my file, little or any evidence is recorded. Between aged 5 – 10, nothing is documented of value, the only 'noteworthy' remark is written across my medical record card "This boy is always in trouble" (I haven't yet found the correct medical terminology for these words but I'm open to offers!) As an adult, I still haven't decided if this is a good thing. A part of me wants to hold the thought that my spirit remained lively and wanted to protest! It may have been a truer comment if it had read '*This boy is troubled*', as emotionally, looking back, that's when I existed! I needed to be seen as more than a 'file' or bunch of papers. I had feelings, needs and wants, and more importantly I needed a way to express myself, somewhere or with someone I felt safe with or at the least, confident that 'they' had my interests at heart....Otherwise, as my own file states:-

"He only ever says fine."

"He rarely smiles, a sullen looking boy"! ...And no one inquired why?

When I was older, and feeling a little courageous, I wanted to discover something about me. Aged 14 I asked my social worker if I could be told about my background. I probably guessed why I was in a home, but I never knew, apart that is, from what those in charge said. I only hoped that I wasn't so bad and there may be some answers which would hold some sort of meaning for me. The conversation that followed is a memory that is still very clear, as it almost felt as if I was an inconvenience for asking and my social workers response felt contemptible, almost scornful in its delivery. "*Your father was a Mohammedan and had no plans to marry your mother*" (I didn't even know what a Mohammedan was! I had never heard the word before, so it meant nothing, except it was said in a way that made me think it was bad!)

"*You're here because, you're what we call a 'paki', a half caste, and wouldn't have been accepted out there*" wherever 'out there' is, isn't perhaps the best way of communicating to a hormonal, misunderstood, troubled teenager, wanting to understand the language used at him and his need to understand the basis of his own identity? The most interesting comment noted in my file regarding this particular event, probably reflects my own ambivalence, and again sadly no follow up to explore or discover what I really thought took place. "Paul, showed no emotions at being told, he doesn't seem surprised about being a half caste. I told him the society chose his name because he would have sounded too foreign."

What of that file that was regularly hugged? Like all children of the state, the paperwork trail followed me prior to birth and for the whole period I remained within the system. It attaches itself as if it's your shadow. Within the file, notes are written, opinions stated, reviews, medical details, development, educational, family details, assessments, lists of moves/periods 'farmed' out, etc are all kept. Details to ensure I was safe and kept safe, that my interests were monitored, and steps were being taken so that I reached my full potential. Sadly, this wasn't the case, my file is less than detailed:

(12mm represents 18 years!)

As a current foster carer I often have children's social workers come to visit. Sadly, I still see files being pulled out and held onto as they try to speak with the children they've come to visit. Some struggle to engage with the children and appear uncomfortable and therefore use the visit to write copious notes. Some have asked why the children are reluctant to speak or seem uninterested in them? My wife is probably a little more tactful than I but I have suggested that as they are coming to see the child, they perhaps could get down to the child's level, maybe play a game, or bring an activity for the child to get involved with etc. The child needs to understand that it is them, they have come to see. That they are important to this person.

In the past I've pointed out that perhaps they may want to consider a change of approach and not project or use a 'barrier' (file/paper work) to 'shout out' 'I don't really want to speak with you', as it isn't the physical picture I think any child wishes to see and the only outcome can be a reluctance to engage. It's not always received in the spirit that it's offered! However, to give some balance, there have been some social workers who just get it. They arrive at the house with a bag full of smiles and goodies. They actively engage with the child and even bring stuff for the child they promised from previous visits. (Little things like promises being kept go a long way for a child who may have trust issues) Some social workers enjoy it so much they don't want to finish their visit. I can't help but notice and see how fully engaged 'our' children become. They chatter away, as a child should, showing toys, precious items, talking about their latest achievement or speaking positively about important people in their lives. Later, when reading write ups, it becomes clear to me that the social worker has got a real sense or essence of the child, which I find encouraging and makes me want to work together more (There's a message here!)

I have suggested that using the communication style we adopt with our friends, 'informal, friendly', is the way forward. It makes the other person comfortable and more likely to respond. Social workers must also be mindful of the 'professional' language used. This form of language needs to only be with other professionals and shouldn't be any part of a child's vocabulary. Recently two very young and very bright children (aged 1 and 2) joined our household. Part of their placement plan involved visiting with their birth and extended family three times a week. On the first day we told them they would be seeing their family, the older child (2yr old) stated "I'm having 'contact time' with mommy and daddy' whilst their younger sibling began singing 'contact, contact'. Both spoke about it matter of factly and appeared to view it as something that happens. We were a little shocked by their ambivalence and told them we don't call it 'contact time', we say 'family time'. We mentioned this to their social worker, who said that's what the birth family call it but when questioned further agreed that the family had taken their cue from the professional services they were currently involved with. We spoke with the birth family and asked them if they minded if we referred to all future meetings with them as 'family time'. They were delighted and stated it felt 'right' and not so 'clinical'. It also went some way to build a working relationship with the birth family as they felt part of the 'communication' link. I guess what I'm saying is bad communication sends a certain type of message to all those involved. In this example, the children spoke clinically about having 'contact' with their family, as if it's something that happens, there wasn't any emotion, just a factual comment. By changing the approach and narrative the children and birth family developed a sense of excitement regarding the time they began spending with each other. It contributed to the children feeling happier about having 'family' time, they started to see it as fun and it enabled us and their social worker to have conversations with the children about their experiences.

Sometimes communication breaks down due to bureaucracy and processes and as we all know can lead to devastating consequences. That said I have been involved with children, their birth families, their social workers, IROs, medical and health visitors where everyone has been kept informed at all stages and the experience is very noticeable. Things happen when they should. All involved get heard and it meant that unavoidable delays or inconsistencies were reduced significantly.

Sadly, this isn't always the norm and workloads are often used as a means of this breaking down, but it does feel good when everyone is on the same page.

So, here's a few things that I would have liked as a child. They are very similar points to those I made about relationships and direct work. Of course they are – communication and relationships are inextricably linked!

- Talk to me, after all it is me you are coming to see not my carers. If you're running late, I get it, it happens. Ring and speak with me. It'll make me think I matter enough to be told by you. It helps build my trust and belief that you are committed towards me.

- Use words that I understand. I don't need professional jargon. I'm a child and I use words that are around me and my peers. Sometimes the words you say make me know that I am different and not the same as others. It makes me feel less than. Please use the same words you would use to your own children.

- When you see me, don't rush me by asking lots and lots of questions. I don't always want to say how I feel about my losses, or about me. It scares me a little because I don't always understand what's going on. I need time, so visit and spend time. You may learn a lot more about me without all these questions by just playing with me and having some fun. (p.s... I start to get to know you this way. I may even begin to like and trust you.)

- Remember our conversations, what I like or don't. I'll know you listened to me if you remember because I remember everything you say, including the times you let me down or don't show up or don't carry out your promises. When that happens, I stop believing in you.
- If you have to write stuff, tell me why you have to. Let me contribute, after all it's supposed to be about me. When I'm older I don't want to read opinions, I want to read about me and what I was like. I need this so that I have a sense of who I was and am. Keep it real, keep it about me.

As a foster carer and as an adoptive parent. One piece of advice really does stand out in my mind:

- When distributing a placement plan make sure the details are specific to the correct child. Others' stories shouldn't take precedence. We understand cut and paste. Read it before you send it and remember this copy is retained on the child's file. When they are older, they may want to read it. Make sure it's factually accurate because at best it feels for the reader you didn't care and at worst it can feel contemptible and highlight not being good enough to warrant your attention.

Paul has concluded with advice to social workers about effective communication. What advice would you give to other social workers to help improve communication?

Pauline Hilling is a social worker with twelve years' experience in child protection. She is currently working with looked after children.

Eight of the children I work with were going to be long term matched. This is a great thing to happen because it is an undertaking between the Local Authority and the child for a plan of permanence. What this means for me as a new worker with them is that I would only see them every 12 weeks instead of the standard 6 weekly. My dilemma was how I was going to build trust and bridge that gap and develop my relationship with them?

At this point it might be worth saying that I am blessed with being dyslexic so it's part of who I am to look for solutions and to not realise there was a box to think outside of. I had an idea to send postcards once a month by first class post. All postcards are addressed and handwritten by me.

There have been a number of benefits to this:

- Each child knows I have thought of them and taken the time to draw or decorate the postcard, finding a quote, phrase and positive message relating to them.
- Every child gets post for them which is not about looked after reviews or events that are coming.
- No matter what happens even when they are upset or angry, they still get these messages so they know I am there.
- The children who are young and also in the household are included because looked after children are, after all, part of their family.

Unexpected benefits include:

- Children have written back using all sorts of media. I have had emails, WhatsApp messages, phone calls and drawings. Sometimes the children are cross and want me to know how unhappy they are but this is brilliant because they are communicating. The message I take from this is that they know I will listen.
- I have experienced two of the girls I work with not wanting to speak to me and this has gone on for a number of visits. I keep showing up and I keep sending the cards to show them that they can be angry with me. I am willing to listen, and I will dig in and show up so when they are ready I am there. I will not be an adult who will give up on them. They can speak to my manager at any time if they want to convince them that they want a new social worker, but I will continue to show up and let them see that they matter to me.
- I am working with an eight-year-old on the autistic spectrum who now asks most days. "Any post for me?" He puts the new postcard on the fridge and the old one is saved for him.
- Even the foster carers, connected carers and others look forward to seeing what is coming next, so this has enhanced all my working relationships.

CONNECTED CONVERSATIONS: THE TEN Cs

The importance of conversations has long been widely recognised in social work. For example, Welbourne (2012:72) asserts *"If social work has a defining characteristic, it is perhaps the intensely conversational aspect of the work. What is done in 'doing social work is largely having purposeful conversations."*

There is a great deal written about different types of conversation (Mager 2017), and a number of models have been developed to explore the importance of conversations. These tend to fall into the following three Cs:

Crucial Conversations: Crucial conversations are widely referred to in terms of leadership models. The concept was developed by Patterson et al (2012) and refers to conversations where the stakes are high, there are opposing opinions and strong emotions. Clearly many of the conversations that social workers have with families would fall into this category.

Coaching Conversations: Coaching conversations centre on the delivery of feedback in a conversational style to support individual learning and development (deHaan and Stewart 2008). Whilst coaching conversations are very often referred to in terms of adult learning, coaching can be seen as a vital aspect of social work with children and families. Supporting parents to improve their parenting, motivating people through cycles of change and ensuring that families understand processes for example can all benefit from the use of coaching conversations.

Courageous Conversations: The notion of 'Courageous Conversation' was developed by Beddoe and Davys (2016) in relation to social work supervision. It is helpful in considering conversations in social work more widely. Some conversations are avoided, because we know that they will possibly cause hurt, conflict, and a range of other difficult emotions, namely shame, anger and anxiety, in both oneself and the receiver. According to Beddoe and Davys (2016) there is a need to be courageous in starting these conversations.

In social work we can add further Cs, as follow:

Critical Conversations: In many ways (as explored at the very start of this resource) in social work the word critical can be read as 'power' – for example critical reflection includes a consideration of power dynamics and the impact of power on the situation. Social workers need to be power sensitive in their practice and communication. The head, heart and hands of power sensitive practice is about understanding power (head), owning power (heart) and using power effectively (hands). Effective conversations in social work are power aware.

Constructive Conversations: Most people know what constructive feedback means – supporting people to learn and change calls for constructive communication. This is communication which balances strengths and needs and is purposeful and clear. Conversations should be useful to people, they should be able to reflect on what was said and look towards how they might be able to use this in the future.

Child-centred Conversations: It is vital that a social worker's communication always remains focused on the child. The child's circumstances and wishes and feelings should be at the forefront and communication must be tailored to the communication needs of the child or young person.

Concerns Focused Conversations: Where a social worker has concerns about a child or young person, everyone involved should be clear about exactly what those concerns are and how they can be addressed. Clarity of purpose is vital in supporting parents to effectively care and support their children. Where a parent understands the concerns clearly then they are much more likely to be able to address these.

Clarity in Conversations: Ensuring clarity in conversation is vital. Does the other person understand what you have said? Do you understand what they have said? How clear are things? Concluding conversations with a summary can really help ensure clarity. Asking the other person how they would summarise the conversation helps to clarify understanding further.

Change Based Conversations: Motivational interviewing techniques clearly identify that it is only where a person is clear about their reasons for change that change will occur. Behaviour changes come from a combination of internal and external motivators. Communication should support people to identify their own reasons for change and should keep progress towards permanent change under review.

Complex Conversations in Social Work: All of the above Cs come together in social work in what could be termed complex conversations. Social workers have complex conversations with children and families but also with colleagues, managers and other professionals. Conversations become complex when:

- The stakes are high
- There is significant conflict about the issue under discussion
- There are a range of emotions involved
- There are a range of compounding barriers to communication
- There are significant issues about power and its use

These complexities should be dealt with by effectively connecting the first nine Cs. Being power conscious, courageous, clear, constructive and focused on change, will address aspects of complexity creating **connected conversations**.

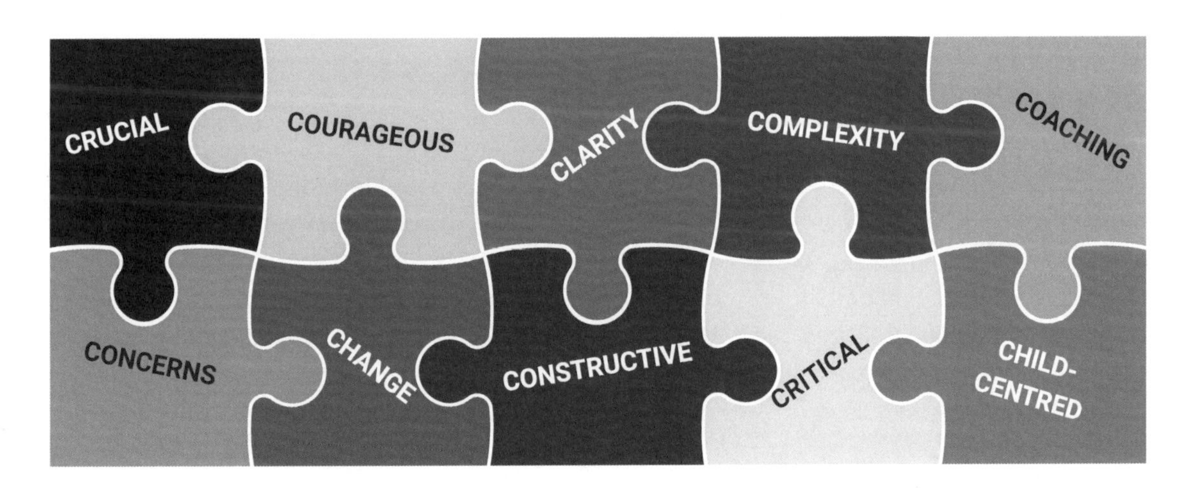

BEHAVIOUR AS A FORM OF COMMUNICATION

When asked to list forms of communication people will generally say things like speaking, writing and signing. However, one of the most powerful forms of communication humans have is behaviour. In everything we do we are communicating something. When we go to sleep we are communicating that we are tired or bored or ill. Children and young people particularly communicate through behaviour.

Communication is a two way process, so when someone is communicating via their behaviour the success of the communication is to a great extent reliant on the way that the other person "reads" the behaviour. Think about a baby crying. Often the parent has no idea why the baby is crying and they need to explore this through trial and error. Is the baby hungry? Are they cold? Are they thirsty? Do they need their nappy changing? When it is an older child or an adult who is communicating through their behaviour, working out the answer to the question, "What are they communicating?" can be very difficult.

This is where truly active listening comes in. We don't just listen with our ears, but also with our eyes and minds. What do we see? How do we interpret this? This is perhaps best illustrated by the following poem written by a young person with learning disabilities in Canada.

To work with me

You have to listen to me

And you can't just listen with your ears

Because it will go to your head too fast

You have to listen with your whole body

If you listen slow,

Some of what I say

Will enter your heart.

The more vulnerable someone feels, the more confused they are, the more change they are experiencing, the more likely they are to communicate through behaviour rather than words. Understanding communication beyond words is therefore vital for social workers who often become involved in a person's life at these key stages. Social workers also need to be able to support others to understand this and to be able to "read" behaviour as a form of communication.

LEE

You receive a referral about Lee. Lee is 15, he was adopted when he was a few months old. His parents divorced several years ago and both remarried. His father lives some distance away with his wife and two stepchildren. You are not sure from the referral how often Lee sees him. Lee's mother has recently had a daughter with her husband. The referral comes from Lee's mum, she said Lee's behaviour is "out of control." The referral states that Lee is smoking cannabis, he is missing school regularly and he is screaming at his mother. She said she doesn't feel safe and she is very worried about the new baby's safety.

How might you approach this referral? Why?

ACTING RESPECTFULLY WHEN PEOPLE ARE ANGRY, HOSTILE AND RESISTANT TO CHANGE

This is a specific phrase taken directly from the standards. Social workers with any experience will know that it is common to work with people who are angry and hostile. I am amazed that sometimes even the most experienced social workers will comment, "I haven't done anything to them. I have always been.....", demonstrating a real lack of understanding of the impact of trauma, service involvement and power dynamics. Sometimes services let people down, sometimes people become angry as a result of loss, or the fear of loss, sometimes people are hostile towards social workers because of preconceptions they have. Of course sometimes people are angry and hostile as a tactic to cover abuse. As always, understanding the 'why?' can help in planning the how? So working through "why is this person angry or resistant to change?" helps a social worker to think through "How do I handle this?".

It is an ordinary human response to "fight or flight" in the face of change or challenge, indeed research on brain function suggests that resistance to change creates not just a psychological response but also a physiological response. This can often be communicated through aggression or withdrawal and can be challenging for social workers who may have a limited amount of time to engage with a family and support that family to make changes. It can be helpful here to draw on learning from research and theory around leadership which has a significant focus on change management. In business leadership a range of models to support change management and address resistance have been developed. Common factors in all the models include the need to:

- Communicate the need for change clearly – so that people understand WHY the change is needed.
- Ensure a focus on current positives to motivate change.
- Engage leaders as visible sponsors or role models of the change.
- Have advocates of change throughout the organisation.

This can be easily applied to thinking about helping families work towards change. The process begins and ends with good communication – the social worker must communicate effectively the reason why the change is needed. A clear strengths-based approach can help a family to see that their strengths are being clearly recognised by the worker. Other professionals and wider family members can be visible 'sponsors' of the change and everyone who comes into contact with the family can continue to advocate the need for change. This approach may address aspects of anger and hostility, but equally it may not.

Some of the specific methods covered in the following pages can help aid communication where people are angry, hostile or resistant to change.

Of course it is vital to remain respectful and calm when people are angry, it is important to be persistent in the face of hostility and authoritative about involvement, but as human beings social workers may not always find this easy. Taking such situations to supervision can be helpful.

PAUSE TO REFLECT

Reflect back on a situation where you faced anger, hostility or significant resistance. Use the What? Why? How? Framework to reflect, as follows.

What did you do?

Why did you do that?

How did it impact on the situation?

If you could have done something differently what would it have been?

LISTENING AND HEARING

Hearing and listening are two different things. You can 'hear' without meaning to, for example, by overhearing something, but listening requires purpose, commitment, attention and an effort to understand what is being communicated. It is also possible to listen without actually hearing, since fully hearing what someone is saying can be really difficult. So, the link between hearing and listening is complex.

Active listening is a phrase often used in social work training. It involves demonstrating to the 'speaker' that you are listening. It is not enough to have heard what someone has said; you need to show the person that you have heard them through your actions.

Egan's work around 'micro-skills' in counselling, particularly the SOLER model (2002) can be helpful in considering active listening. Egan believes that basic non-verbal skills improve active listening, and developed the SOLER model around:

Sit squarely in relation to the service user - this is said to demonstrate that you are ready to listen.

Open position - open body language indicates more attentive listening. This means not folding arms etc.

Lean slightly towards the service user - this is said to encourage the speaker as it shows you are interested in what the person has to say.

Eye contact - maintain good eye contact and encourage the 'speaker' to maintain eye contact. This can create a human connection and more empathic listening.

Relax - it is important to be relaxed and to sit still without fidgeting to demonstrate attentive listening.

Whilst this is a useful model in terms of considering early skill development in active listening, it is important to recognise that cultural difference impacts on communication and Egan's model was developed based on North American culture. In some cultures, for example, eye contact can be seen as threatening or rude. It is also vital to remember that using the SOLER model is only the very beginning of listening. It might demonstrate attentiveness to the person 'speaking' but it doesn't mean that you will really hear what is being said. In fact, if you are focusing too much on whether you are sitting fully squarely, whether you are holding eye contact well enough etc... then you may not allow yourself the space to truly hear what is being said.

Active listening is often understood differently by different stakeholders. For example, McLeod (2008) explains that a social worker may believe that they are actively listening to a child, because they are nodding and making affirmative noises and therefore actively showing that they are listening. However, the child may have a very different view, believing that they have not been heard, because nothing changes and what they want to happen doesn't come about. Active listening is therefore about much more than the kind of 'micro-skills' referred to by Egan, listening must be linked to action". If you really hear what a person is saying then this should be demonstrated to them through your actions.

The following poem written by Paul can be helpful in exploring listening and hearing from the perspective of a child. Reading this aloud can aid in reflecting on whether you are truly listening - hearing the words is important!

ARE YOU LISTENING?

Please don't tell me my fears are silly, for me they are terribly real.... You can do much to reassure me if you try and understand.

Don't forget that I don't have all the words to explain myself as well as I should like. This is why I am not always very accurate.

Please try not to ever suggest you are perfect. It shocks me greatly when I find out you're not.....I become confused about your expectations.

Please try not to be upset when I say " I Hate you" It isn't you I hate but your power to thwart me, as sometimes I feel helpless, it's not personal... My loss of control scares me, I've told you this before, were you listening?

Don't correct me in front of people if you can help it...I'll take much more notice if you talk quietly in private, I don't like to feel ashamed.

Never think it is beneath your dignity to apologise to me. An honest apology makes me feel surprisingly warm towards you. I may start to believe you care.

Try not to be inconsistent ....That makes me confused and makes me lose faith in you.

Don't make rash promises...Remember that I feel badly let down when promises are broken, haven't I been let down enough. Never let it be by you. Be the difference for me!

Please don't put me off when I ask questions, even the ones you think are silly or I should know the answer to. If you do, you will find that I stop asking and seek information elsewhere.

Don't keep secrets about me and my circumstances away from me. You may find that I can cope with a lot more than you think...... just be empathetic and actually acknowledge my feelings, I really need to be heard, I can see through pretence!

And finally ....never forget that I can't thrive without lots of understanding, patience and love (I need to hear and know that I am!)

...But I don't need to tell you...do I?

UNDERSTANDING THE CYCLE OF CHANGE

Originally developed in relation to smoking cessation (Prochaska and DiClemente 1983), the six stage cycle of change is now used widely in relation to a number of areas. Drawing on the cycle of change is particularly useful for social workers as it helps in understanding people's readiness to make changes. It works from the premise that nobody changes things by force and change occurs best and most sustainably when it is something which people genuinely desire for themselves. It links particularly closely to motivational interviewing and the worker's role in encouraging and supporting change to occur. The cycle is as follows:

1. **Pre-contemplation** This is where a person is not ready to consider changing the behaviour. The idea that 'ignorance is bliss' is key and the worker's skill here is about clarifying that the decision is theirs, explaining the risks in not changing, and providing encouragement. A person in this stage will not respond to action, but this is more about them being able to explore the situation for themselves.

2. **Contemplation** A person who is in the contemplation stage may be perceived as ambivalent about making changes and reluctant to set a timescale for doing things differently. The worker's techniques here are similar to in stage one but may move towards looking at the costs and benefits both of the individual's current situation and of a scenario where things were different.

3. **Preparation** This is characterised by 'testing the waters' and may be where a person might set themselves a target date for making changes. Here the worker needs to look at problem solving to support the person to remove the barriers they feel exist to making change occur and identify resources which they could access to support them to move forwards. The idea of small steps is key and further encouragement that everyone has the skills to make changes if they want to.

4. **Action** As the name suggests, this is where the person begins to practice a new way of behaving. Again, here the worker could focus on the support which is available to the person and on encouraging the person to note their successes. Feelings of loss may be apparent for the person in moving away from their old way of living, so the idea that there are benefits to the new situation should continue to be encouraged.

5. **Maintenance** This is the process of the individual continuing to act on their changed behaviour and sustaining this over time. Support from the worker would reduce at this stage in a planned way and would focus on discussing and agreeing strategies to prevent relapses.

6. **Relapse** Many people will relapse and return to the previous behaviour and here the worker would focus on reassessing the motivation of the person and the barriers they face, evaluating the reasons for relapse and promoting strategies for the person to continue with the change. Sometimes a relapse can be so significant that the person will feel that they are right back at stage one of the cycle, so different strategies may be needed for individuals in this situation.

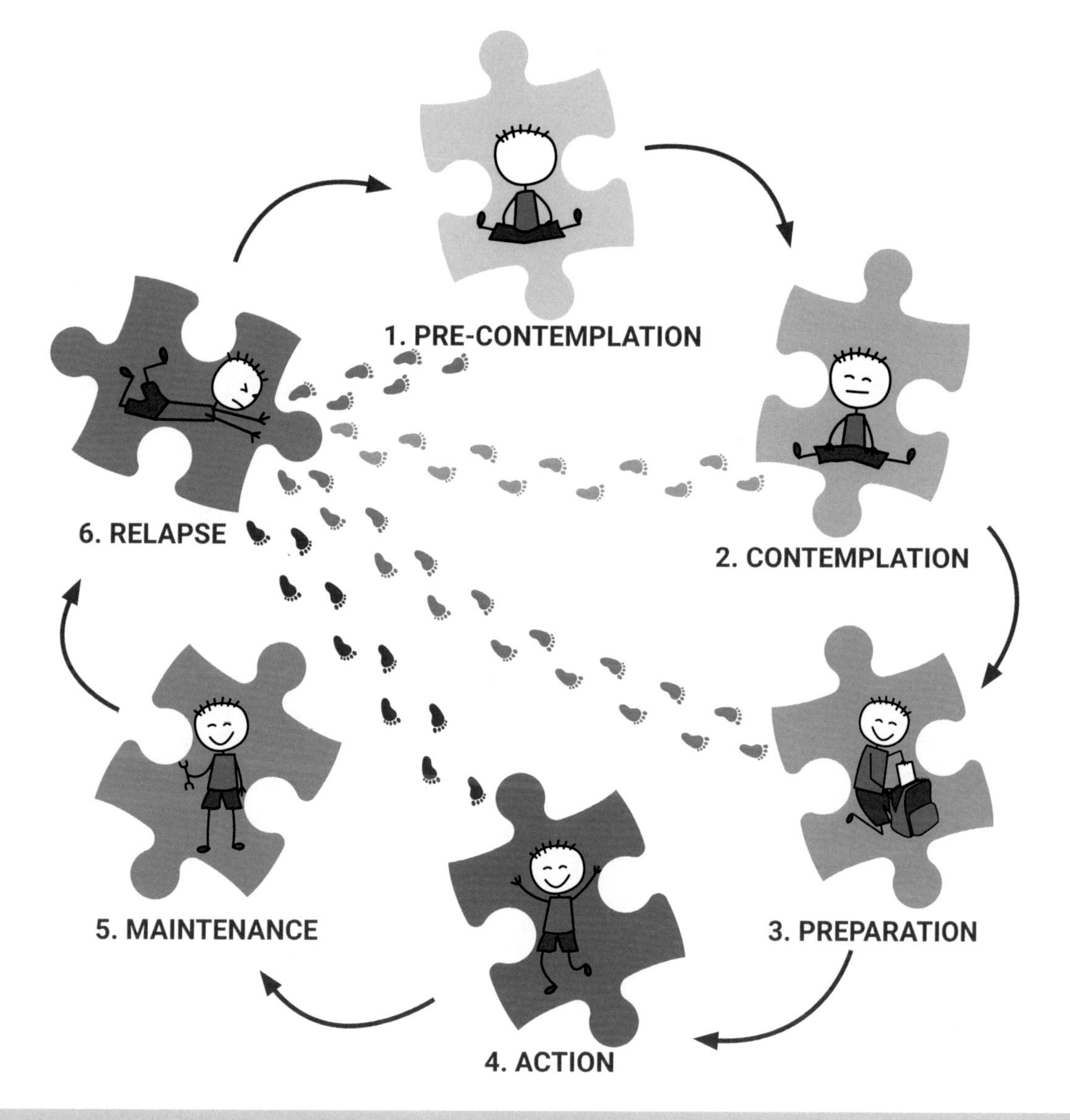

PAUSE TO REFLECT

How do you use the cycle of change in your work?

MODELS TO SUPPORT PEOPLE TO MOVE AROUND THE CYCLE OF CHANGE

Prosci's ADKAR model, widely used in supporting individual change within organisational contexts is a particularly useful one in terms of transferability to social workers working with families. ADKAR is an acronym which stands for:

Awareness: Social workers should ensure that families are clearly aware of the need to change. They need to understand where they are now and where they need to get to.

Desire: Social workers should work with families to help them understand why the change will be good for their child/children and their whole family. People are much more likely to change when they WANT to change.

Knowledge: Social workers need to ensure that people have the knowledge they will need to make changes. Does a parent understand what change is needed? Does a parent know how to do what is required?

Ability: Knowledge and skills are separate issues. Do people have the skills (ability) to make the change? Will support be needed? How can that support be effectively provided?

Reinforcement: Regular reinforcement is needed to support people to create change in their lives. (Hiatt 2006).

MOTIVATIONAL INTERVIEWING

This is an applied form of Cognitive Behaviour Therapy, which originated in services for people with drug and alcohol addictions but is now widely applied. Motivational interviewing involves the worker having an empathic, non-confrontational approach. Aspects of the technique include:

- Educating the person about the situation they are in.
- Encouraging the service user to list the benefits and costs of their present lifestyle or situation. This should be concretely expressed (written down). The benefits and cost of an alternative lifestyle (if the person were to change their behaviour) should also be listed.
- Exploring barriers to potential goals. The professional should support the service user recognise that there will be difficulties but acknowledge that many or all of these can be addressed. Again, it is best to be as concrete as possible, listing the difficulties and stating how each will be overcome.
- Re-framing past events. When discussing barriers, it could be that the service user said they "tried that before and it didn't work" or similar. Past experiences may need to be explored and viewed from a different perspective. This re-framing of past events is a key cognitive (thinking or ideas) skill. For example, if a person was a drug user and they said they tried to give up before (many times) and it didn't work, then rather than the 'didn't work' being emphasised the worker could point out that the service user has shown the determination to try and that it appears to be a heartfelt goal of the service user to give up.

There are five key principles to motivational interviewing:

- Express empathy through reflective listening.
- Highlight discrepancy between a person's goals or values and their current behaviour.
- Avoid argument and direct confrontation.
- Adjust to resistance rather than opposing it directly.
- Support self-efficacy and optimism.

Open questions, affirmation, reflective listening, and summary reflections (OARS) should be used early and often to support people to move towards change. But there will be challenges along the way – the old phrase "a Smooth sea never made a good sailor" is very true!

Use OARS to move towards change.

To support change in the following situations, how might you respond:

A parent says to you "I don't see the problem. We've always done it like that."

A parent is talking about their drinking. They say "I have tried to stop lots of times the last few months. I went a week the first time, then ten days. This last time I went nearly two weeks, but I always start drinking again."

A grandparent says "we just don't know where to turn when that happens."

WRITTEN COMMUNICATION

Perhaps the key difference between written communication and other methods of communication is that written communication is more permanent than any other form. Whilst what someone has said may be forgotten or confused what is written is permanent - it can be read time and time again perhaps for years! Written work remains 'on file' for years and can therefore influence future actions. Social workers must therefore recognise the vital importance of recording and ensure that they work to continually develop their skills in this area.

In 1999, a manager quoted in an overview of inspections of case recording in Social Services said "My staff are good at what they do, not what they write down" (Goldsmith 1999). Almost twenty years ago it may well have been acceptable to separate out 'recording' and 'doing'. However, it is now recognised that recording and reporting (writing down!) is an essential aspect of social work practice; in many ways it is the 'doing'. The records you keep can be seen as the main legacy of your practice - they record your practice for the long term and may enable a person to understand pieces of their own jigsaw in years to came.

A range of concerns about recording in social work practice have been raised over many years. In his report into the death of Victoria Climbie, Lord Laming (2003) highlighted a range of concerns in relation to reading and recording, as follows:

- Nobody in Haringey - not even [the social worker] - ever read Victoria's case file in its entirety, (p59).
- We cannot be certain what passed between the two because of the lack of recorded information - indeed in the case of the hospital there was none whatsoever (p177).
- It is unlikely that Ms R read any of this material because she said she found it illegible and 'could not read it' (p185).
- Resolving this conflict of evidence has not been helped by Ms K's poor note taking. There is certainly no record of a telephone conversation between Ms A and Ms K in Ms A's contact notes on Victoria's case file (p284).

Concerns such as these led to a renewed focus on the importance of good recording in social work practice, linking the 'doing' and 'recording' more closely together within the realm of 'practice'. In fact in social work teams it is not unusual to hear the phrase "if it's not written down then it didn't happen".

Pritchard and Leslie (2011) assert that social workers often do not understand the purpose of recording, resulting in them seeing recording as a chore. This means that they may not commit to the continuous development of their recording; they effectively create an attitudinal barrier to good record keeping.

It is easy to understand why this might be the case, as recording can be seen like part and parcel of defensive practice, perhaps justifying actions and decisions made in case of future concerns. It may also take away time from direct work with individuals and families. It is important though that the time spent on recording is recognised as valuable because records serve to:

- Provide information to deliver the highest possible standard of service.

- Enable staff to assess intervention, plan, monitor and evaluate work with service users.
- Provide continuity of service when workers change.
- Communicate information.
- Enable managers to monitor the work of staff and give appropriate advice, support and direction.
- Provide a means of accountability, so that actions and decisions that have been taken can be understood and justified.
- Meet specific legislative requirements.
- Provide information that may be needed as evidence in court proceedings, judicial reviews, internal and external enquiries and complaint investigations.
- Enable information and data to be collected as a basis for evaluating service delivery, managing resources and future planning.
- Provide information to people about professional involvement if they wish to have access to their records.
- Support people in understanding their life from a range of perspectives.

The first ever care experience conference took place in Liverpool on 26th April 2019. The conference explored 'The care experience - past, present and future?' and brought together people of all ages with care experience. The following image was created as part of a workshop at that conference. It presents a very powerful perspective on the key question of 'why' in relation to record keeping.

Reproduced with the kind permission of the conference committee.

Case recording is often viewed by busy social workers as bureaucratic and cumbersome, taking precious time away from direct work with children and their families. However, comprehensive case recording is integral to demonstrating the quality of work undertaken, to enhance reflection and planning, and provide transparency to families. Case recording refers to all the written material contained in the child's social work file, which may be wholly or partly electronic. It is essential to become familiar with your own organisation's recording system.

Rebecca O'Keefe has been a social worker for 14 years; she has held a variety of roles in child protection and is currently a Child Protection Conference Chair. Here she shares her thoughts on case recording.

WHAT IS THE PURPOSE OF CASE RECORDING?

In order to produce high quality case records, it is first helpful to consider their purpose. Fundamentally, case recording documents the day to day life of the child. It tells the child's individual story, including the strengths within the family, the areas where support is required, and states any concerns raised. It ensures accountability. It evidences the child's wishes and feelings. Case recording is essential for hypothesising, analysing and planning. It forms the basis for the child's chronology, assessments and any formal reports needed. Case recording assists in making sense of the available information, ultimately impacting on decision making, asking what is going on within this family? Have we got the right plan for the child?

Up to date, accurate records are vital to the day to day running of the service. Imagine the frustration of a duty social worker or team manager in the event a query is made, and the social worker is unavailable. It can be problematic to find even the most basic information or make sense of the case when recording is inaccurate or incomplete. Case records are often audited by management within your organisation, and externally. Case records can be requested for Court. Would someone unfamiliar with the case obtain an understanding of the child's world? Would they get a complete sense of the work you have undertaken?

Ultimately, the child may wish to access their information in the future. What would they read? Would it tell an accurate, clear and coherent story? Case records can help the child piece together their life experiences much later on, helping to aid understanding, heal and empower.

Maintaining comprehensive day to day records sounds simple and obvious. However, there is expertise in writing for a variety of readers simultaneously - the child, their wider family, colleagues, professionals in partner agencies, managers, auditors, and sometimes Court. Case recording is therefore multi-functional and a social work skill in its own right.

WHAT MAKES GOOD CASE RECORDING?

- The very basics need to be present. Names, addresses, significant dates and key professionals' details need to be accurately recorded, spelt correctly, and be up to date. Check these important details on a regular basis with the family as they can change over time. For each home visit or phone call recorded, state who was present or spoken to, and include their relationship to the child. For professionals, include their job title and contact details, such as office base or phone number. Make sure the correct date and place the event took place is recorded, and include the exact time if appropriate. This makes records easily understood, accessible and clear for anyone who needs to access them. A colleague or team manager can clearly see what work has taken place, exactly when, and with whom. Information can be obtained quickly in the absence of the allocated social worker, and accuracy in sharing information is essential. Remember if the case recording is not complete, there is no evidence for the interaction taking place.

- The child is always at the centre of case recording. All actions taken affect the child's life. Make sure you record the child's wishes and feelings explicitly, and say how these views were obtained. Record the child's own words or upload their pictures where possible. Ensure you have recorded your observations for younger children, or children without verbal language. Ask yourself would someone reading the file get a sense of the child's personality, opinions, likes and dislikes? Would the child, or their care giver, recognise themselves in your recordings?

- Consider the use of social work terminology, jargon and acronyms. Such language may not be easily understood by the child or their family, and this impacts of the power differential between social worker and family. Some services or ways of working may be local, and language can become lost in translation. Would another Local Authority understand the case file if the child moves to their area? Language also changes over time. Consider if a child accessing their file in 10 years' time would understand what work has been completed, and why decisions have been made about their life.

- Information should be recorded as close to the event as possible. Case records can lose their validity if written days later. Handwritten notes will provide a prompt, but memory will fade if there has been a delay in recording, especially given the busy nature of the job. If a disclosure is made by a child, write it down as soon as you can and ensure this is in the child's own words. Remember that contemporaneous, hand written notes can be requested by your organisation or Court, so keep these safe.

- Always highlight strengths to ensure fairness and balance. What is going well for this family? What have you seen or heard which corroborates this view? Building on strengths is integral to decision making and future planning, and also impacts on a positive, relationship with the child and family.

In conclusion, case recording is a complex, yet necessary social work skill with lots to consider. Being reflective and thoughtful will ensure you are respectful and sensitive when writing about the child and their family. Remember social workers are privy to very personal information, so a final question to ask yourself when recording is how would you feel if this had been written about you and your family?

How do you ensure that the child's voice is central in your case recording?

MESSAGES FROM RESEARCH

The Talking and Listening to Children project (TLC) identified that all the social workers involved in the research knew that communication with children is important and necessary (Morrison 2016). However, they reported finding this difficult at times because of three main factors:

- Structural factors (which included aspects of workload)
- Practice-related factors (including the apprehensions of children and their families)
- Personal factors (including for example, levels of confidence)

Harry Ferguson observed child protection home visits and reported on this and his conversations with social workers (2014). He notes that while some social workers were confident in relating to children, others were not and said that they wanted further training and to develop skills on communicating with children and their parents.

There is considerable research about parent - child communication, but Kranstuber Horstman et al (2016) found that there is very limited research on communication in diverse families (they give examples of divorced/stepfamilies, adoptive, multiracial, LGBTQ, and military families). They assert that changes in society such as advances in technology, the aging population, and differing parenting practices are also transforming the parent–child relationship and therefore communication within families, arguing that this is now poorly understood with little evidence about familial communication.

Forrester, Kershaw, Moss and Hughes (2007) analysed 24 taped interviews between social workers and an actor playing a parent. They report finding that most social workers asked many closed questions and often raised concerns. They used few reflections and rarely identified positives. In all but one interview, social workers were rated as achieving clarity over issues of concern; however, they tended to demonstrate low levels of empathy. The responses of the simulated client were rated for resistance and information disclosure. The factor that most strongly influenced simulated client responses was empathy. Empathic social workers created less resistance and increased the amount of information disclosed by clients. This was not associated with failure to identify and discuss concerns. They concluded that empathy, appears to be central to good social work communication in child protection situations.

Lefevre (2015) reports some of the findings from a UK-based empirical study into factors and processes which support students in developing the self-efficacy and applied understanding they need to undertake effective direct work with children. This found that there was a 'superficial' focus on the actual 'doing.' The research concluded that social work education needed to focus more on helping students to learn the skills needed for effective communication.

Lynch, Newlands and Forrester (2018) used a mixed methods analysis of 110 audio recordings of meetings in a child protection service between workers and parents, applying a coding framework for analysis. They found that workers who demonstrate higher levels of empathy skill:

- Use more open questions and reflections in their communication.
- Demonstrate curiosity and attempt to understand parents' experiences.
- Have a focus on emotions.

The research paper clearly identifies a high level of empathy is linked to motivational interviewing and supporting change in families. However, most workers in the study were found to not demonstrate a high level of empathy in the recordings.

WHERE AM I NOW?

Revisit the start of the chapter. Look again at the KSS standard. Then consider the following questions:

What has surprised me in working through this chapter?

What three things would I highlight as key learning?

What do I still need to do in working towards being fully confident with this KSS statement?

What single next step should I take in working towards an improvement in my practice?

Chapter 3
CHILD DEVELOPMENT

Understanding child development is important for social workers. This chapter explores some of the basic theory around child development, considering the impact of this theory on contemporary social work practice. Working through this chapter you will revisit some of the basic frameworks underpinning this aspect of practice. You will consider how you keep your knowledge of child development up to date and how you use this understanding in your practice. If you haven't looked at reflexivity for some time (see 'How to use this resource') it might be worth refreshing your understanding of this again because in child development theory seeing the connectivity between the I and the E is particularly helpful.

THE KSS REQUIRES PRACTITIONERS TO:

Observe and talk to children in their environment including at home, at school, with parents, carers, friends and peers to help understand the physical and emotional world in which the child lives, including the quality of child and parent/carer interaction and other key relationships. Establish the pattern of development for the child, promote optimal child development and be alert to signs that may indicate that the child is not meeting key developmental milestones, has been harmed or is at risk of harm.

Take account of typical age-related physical, cognitive, social, emotional and behavioural development over time, accepting that normative developmental tasks are different for each child depending on the interactions for that child between health, environmental and genetic factors. Assess the influence of cultural and social factors on child development, the effect of different parenting styles, and the effect of loss, change and uncertainty in the development of resilience.

Explore the extent to which behavioural and emotional development may also be a result of communication difficulties, ill health or disability, adjusting practice to take account of these differences. Seek further advice from relevant professionals to fully understand a child's development and behaviour.

Take a look at the standard above in detail. Highlight key phrases and anything that jumps out at you. Then take some time to reflect on the statement.

- *What are your immediate thoughts?*
- *What might you want to discuss and clarify?*
- *How will you clarify meanings?*
- *Who will you discuss it with?*

GETTING FEEDBACK ON PRACTICE

Who can give me feedback on my practice in this area?	*How will I get the feedback?*

Make sure to keep a record of any feedback you receive.

INITIAL SELF-ASSESSMENT

What do I already do well?

How do I know? (What's my evidence?)

What do I need to work on?

How will I work on this?

CHILD DEVELOPMENT THEORY

There are various theories of child development. Having some understanding of the theories and how they developed is helpful. In a very general sense, the main theories can be separated out into those which see child development as being nature (biologically) based and those which see child development as being nurture (environmentally) based.

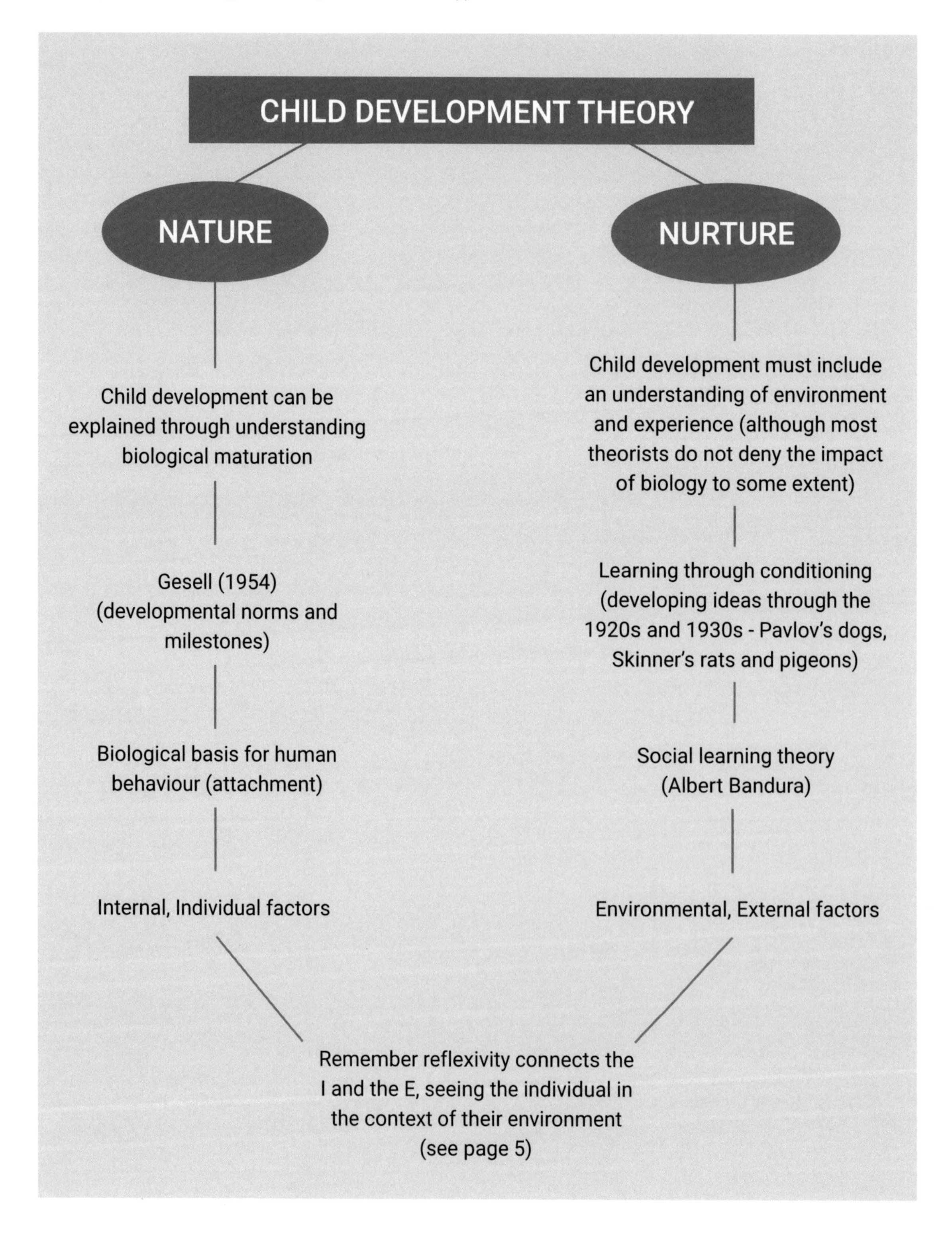

UNDERSTANDING CHILD DEVELOPMENT IN TERMS OF NATURE

ARNOLD GESELL

Perhaps the theorist that has had the most significant impact on how child development theory is used is Arnold Gesell. Working in the 1920s in America, Gesell (with his colleagues) established a very popular (still to this day) idea that child development is based on biological maturation. Gesell felt that genetic coding and developmental sequencing are much more important than external experiences. From this basis the idea of developmental norms and developmental milestones was developed.

Gesell and his research team observed babies and young children, recording their findings in fine detail. Their descriptors were very age specific. Gesell described his belief that environmental, external issues were supportive to development, but that the push towards change was internal to the child. Gesell's work influenced specific advice given to health professionals and parents during the 1940s and 1950s and continues to influence advice around child development today, particularly in terms of the measurement of developmental milestones.

JEAN PIAGET

Piaget developed his stage theory of intellectual development from the 1920s onwards (see for example Piaget, 1928.) Initially, his ideas did not have a significant impact on understanding of child development, but over time his theory became more popular.

Piaget identified four stages of child development and asserted that a child moves from one stage to the next as a result of various factors that aid development. These factors are:

- Maturation: This is the physical and cognitive growth that occurs as the child grows up.
- Experience: This is acquired by the child as they engage with the physical world around them.
- Social interaction: The child engages with other people. Piaget was particularly aware of the influences of other (often older) children.
- Equilibration: Is the way the child draws the first three factors together to establish logic and consistency.

So, whilst Piaget saw development as being very significantly influenced by maturation (nature), he saw the role that external factors (nurture) had on the child.

The four stages of development Piaget identified are:

SENSORIMOTOR STAGE. Aged 0 to 2 years. The child uses their senses to actively explore their world. The child becomes aware of their separateness from the world around them. Towards the end of this stage, the child is starting to experiment with objects to see how they fall or move.

PREOPERATIONAL STAGE. Aged 2 to 6 years. During this stage, the child is egocentric. They are largely focussed on their own perspective. Early on in this stage when children play together, it can be as if the children each play their own game, even though they could be side by side. The child has a view of the world that is objective. Rules are absolute.

CONCRETE OPERATIONAL. Aged 7 to 12 years. The child begins to develop their own logic and can organise thoughts in a consistent framework. Abstract reasoning is still too difficult but physical objects and mathematical problems can be worked on (adding, subtracting and multiplication). The egocentric outlook comes to an end in Stage 3.

FORMAL OPERATIONS. Aged 11 to 15 years. The young person is able to grasp hypothetical ideas and abstract thinking. The young person can test out theories or hypotheses. Abstract thinking can extend to algebraic mathematics. This stage continues into adulthood.

ERIK ERIKSON

Erik Erikson (1950) developed a model of human development titled the 'Eight Ages of Man'. Erikson described each stage as a struggle between two emotional opposites. The first stage is characterised by the emotions of trust and mistrust. The child's experience would result in the child adopting one of these emotions as a dominant (unconscious) outlook. Continued experiences can impact on previous stages - for example, if the child came through the first stage trusting people, there is still a chance that future negative experiences could result in the child losing trust in those around them.

Five of the eight stages identified by Erikson relate to children. As follows:

TRUST VS MISTRUST. Age 0 to 1 year. The child will feel able to trust the world and people in the world if their needs are responded to and the child is cared for. Emotional warmth and a sense of belonging from adult caregivers are crucial to building up a sense of trust. Inadequate and rejecting care from adults will result in the child being suspicious and fearful of adults and others.

AUTONOMY VS DOUBT. Age 1 to 3 years. Erikson argues that this is the first opportunity the child has to develop a range of life skills. Encouraging this is key to building up the child's confidence. If the child is not positively supported to develop their own skills, or is mocked or criticised when they do learn new skills then the child will be riddled with doubt and lack confidence.

INITIATIVE VS INADEQUACY (OR GUILT). Age 3 to 6 years. The child has already got control over their body and their life skills are being increased. In stage three, the child feels able to initiate actions, both physical and verbal. Children who are supported to initiate physical activities, such as bike riding or swimming will have their sense of initiative reinforced. Emotional and intellectual initiative will be reinforced by the child's questions being answered whilst conversation and play are encouraged. If the child's initiative is not encouraged the child will develop a sense of guilt or inadequacy over self initiated activities.

INDUSTRY VS INFERIORITY. Age 6 to 12 years. The child has a strong interest in matters of detail. How things work, why events happen, how things are made are all key questions and points of interest for the child. Children will need to be encouraged in their activities of making, sewing and baking. The end products need to be praised. It is in this sense that the child is industrious. However, if the child's making activities are dismissed as 'making a mess' then this can instil a sense of inferiority in the child. This is also the first stage where the child is really aware of other children. The child's sense of industry or inferiority can be shaped by their relative achievements in respect of their peers.

IDENTITY VS ROLE CONFUSION. Age 12 to 18 years. The child is developing into an adolescent. There are significant biological changes resulting in new feelings and sensations. The adolescent is also increasingly aware of the importance of what other people may think of them. Intellectually, the adolescent is also able to generate ideal images (of family, friendships and society) and contrast them with the imperfections they experience on a daily basis.

MELANIE KLEIN

Klein was an Austrian psychoanalyst working in London from the 1920s, she focused almost exclusively on the impact of the mother and child relationship on child development. Klein observed children playing and saw that children were preoccupied with what went on inside themselves and their experiences of an 'inner world'. Kleinian theory refers to an 'internal' object to describe a child's understanding of their external world. The inner world is seen as being populated with inner objects which are based on the child's inner emotional and mental image of an external figure and their experiences of that external figure.

SUSAN ISAACS

Susan Isaacs worked in England from the 1920s, she focused on the unconscious life of children drawing on emotional conflicts underpinning identity development. The main aspect of Isaacs' work which has been influential is her understanding that for children play is both an emotional release and a source of intellectual development. Early years practitioners claim that the content of her writing still has a great deal of relevance for today (Graham 2009) and her work has certainly been influential in play therapy. In many ways Isaacs' work was the start of a professional understanding of trauma informed practice with children.

PAUSE TO REFLECT

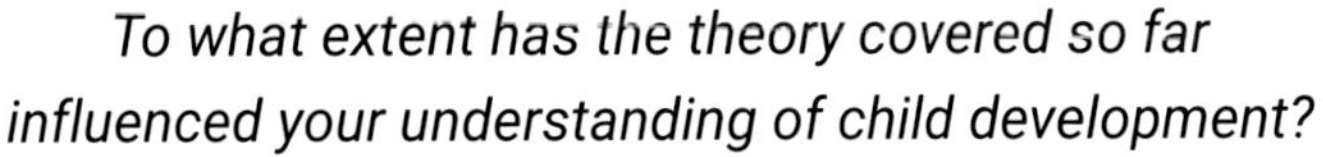

To what extent has the theory covered so far influenced your understanding of child development?

How do you draw on this in your practice?

UNDERSTANDING CHILD DEVELOPMENT IN TERMS OF NURTURE

Most child development theory which focuses on the importance of nurture comes from behaviourist and learning theories. These theories do not deny that biology (nature) has an impact on development, but they focus on the major role of environmental factors (factors which are external to the child).

CONDITIONING

Conditioning is drawn from behaviourist theory. It attempts to explain behaviour as being the result of stimulus, so it explores the cause and effect of behaviour.

CLASSICAL CONDITIONING

This is most well known through Pavlov's experiment where dogs were given food at the same time as a bell was rung. After a short while, the dogs would salivate when the bell was rung even though no food was presented. One example of the use of classical conditioning in child care is where a child who persistently wets the bed may have a sensor under the groundsheet of the bed. When the sensor detects urine, a buzzer or alarm sounds. This wakes the child. The theory is that after a short while the child should wake when their bladder is full without the need to urinate in bed.

OPERANT CONDITIONING

Skinner's rats experiments were the basis of this theory. Skinner placed hungry rats in a box. The box had a lever on one side, when the rat knocked the lever, a food pellet would drop into a food container. Whilst the rats knocked the lever accidentally at first, they quickly learned to go straight to the lever when they were placed in the box. This illustrated that positive reinforcement strengthens a behaviour (Skinner 1971).

Operant conditioning recognises that the environment (both human generated and natural) has an effect on our behaviour. This has had a significant influence in psychology and in one form or another is used regularly in social work.

Operant conditioning also highlights that most behaviours are a response to a stimulus. To try to capture the processes involved in how behaviour is influenced or shaped the A:B:C continuum was developed. 'A' stands for 'antecedent' – an event happens and as a result the person engages in a behaviour, (B), which is a response to 'A'. Immediately, or soon after the behaviour, the consequences (C) occur. ABC charts are commonly used in a range of settings. Antecedent ➔ Behaviour ➔ Consequence.

SOCIAL LEARNING THEORY

One of the principle writers of social learning is Bandura (1977). Bandura noted that children based their own behaviour on observing the behaviour of other children and of adults. Crucially, Bandura noted that it is not just behaviour which children learn through observation. They also learn about ideas and expectations, developing their own standards – providing them with their framework of behaviour. This means that behaviour is not simply copied.

Bandura based his work on an understanding of conditioning, but felt that a more sophisticated understanding of human behaviour was required. He recognised that behaviour can be strengthened by positive or negative reinforcement, and also introduced the idea of partial reinforcement.

POSITIVE REINFORCEMENT	Positive reinforcement might be something as basic as a smile or a hug, but could extend to a range of 'rewards' such as a favourite food, a prize etc.
NEGATIVE REINFORCEMENT	Negative reinforcement refers to where something unpleasant (or negative) is removed from a situation. This can reinforce a behaviour. Imagine a child being told not to do something over and over again (the child may view this as nagging). After a while, the parent stops telling the child not to do it, and simply allows the behaviour (for a quiet life). The child is happy that the 'nagging' has stopped and they will continue to behave in that way.
PARTIAL REINFORCEMENT	This refers to where there is a lack of consistency in the way that a behaviour is responded to. The behaviour is neither reinforced positively or negatively. Bandura states that behaviour which is reinforced partially is stronger than any other. This behaviour, he argues is more resistant to change than behaviour which has been consistently reinforced (one way or another). So a lack of consistency from the adults surrounding a child can lead to behaviour becoming embedded and very resistant to change.

Reinforcement is seen as strengthening patterns of behaviour, increasing the likelihood of the behaviour occurring. On the other hand, in behaviourist theory, 'punishment' is seen as weakening patterns of behaviour. Punishment may be the removal of something that is viewed as pleasant by the child, it may be verbal criticism or negativity. Bandura recognised that children who experience punishment are likely to hide their behaviour rather than change it. The behaviour, he argued, will only change through reinforcement. Punishment will simply lead a child to learn that they should hide their behaviour or become secretive, so that it cannot be observed and subsequently punished.

In social work negative reinforcement is sometimes seen as referring to negative attention for example, a child being shouted at. However, in the theory this would be seen as punishment. The negative reinforcement would be when the parent stops shouting and allows the behaviour (this is the removal of the negative for the child).

INTRINSIC / INTERNAL REINFORCEMENT

Bandura stresses the importance of children working towards intrinsic (internal) rewards. If a child is always rewarded with an external reward then they will become motivated only by external factors. A sense of achievement and feelings of self worth are important motivators for children. In trying to work effectively with children in the short term, many childcare professionals argue that external rewards which create internal rewards are the most powerful. For example, in early years and education, it is common to use stickers which provide an external (tangible) reward but are designed to promote internal reinforcement (a sense of pride or personal achievement). Again this demonstrates the importance of connecting the I and the E in working with children.

BRONFENBRENNER'S ECOLOGICAL MODEL

Urie Bronfenbrenner's work is key to the development of systemic thinking as it involves an in depth understanding of how systems form part of all human development. First published in 1979, his work sees child development as being at the centre of multi-layered systems which interact with each other, which influence the child, and which are in turn influenced by the child.

Bronfenbrenner's work took the knowledge and understanding from fields as diverse as psychology, anthropology and sociology, and located the child at the centre of multifaceted and interacting systems. The quality of the interaction between those systems (for example, between family members, between the family and the educational setting, between the child and their peer group, between the family and their community etc) is seen as influencing the child's own (ecological) development.

There are five levels of system defined in Bronfenbrenner's (1994) work:

1. **Microsystems:** For example, families, educational or community settings.

2. **Mesosystems:** Defined as the ways in which microsystems link – for example, how the family interact with school, or how the family link with others.

3. **Exosystems:** The way in which other settings or systems influence the systems around the child. For example, the parent's workplace as a system will have an impact on a child, as will the family's own social networks and the local community.

4. **Macrosystems:** Broadly defined as the cultural norms, beliefs, structures and lifestyles around the child. Bronfenbrenner calls this "a societal blueprint" (1994: 40).

5. **Chronosystems:** The impact of change and consistency as the child grows up and also crucially as the society and structures around them change with time.

A further dimension to Bronfenbrenner's work lies in the notion of 'heritability', meaning the extent to which human development is genetically determined, or the 'nature/nurture' question. His work argues that research shows that the environment and conditions (or 'proximal processes') around the child play a far greater role than he himself previously thought.

It is helpful when working with children and families to view the child at the centre of a variety of systems as described in Bronfenbrenner's work. For example, the child is part of a family microsystem with its own structures, and the way the child is viewed within this system is crucial to that child's development and wellbeing. The community networks can also be mapped out and the child's access to these (how the mesosystem works) is again significant. Children are also part of the education system, and again the success or failure they experience within this is key to their development. If this system is failing the child, how far can a social worker go in attempting to address this, and which aspects of the system are outside of the worker's, child's and family's control? The child and family may also end up having to navigate systems such as those around health, mental health and youth justice.

Each system has its own set of terminology, and its own values, norms and expectations, and is surrounded by the macro and exosystems around the family and around how society, community and culture operate, as well as being influenced by the chronosystem over time. It can be helpful to see these various systems as interlinking circles, as the interface between the family and each system is again key to the child's development and opportunities. Systemic thinking requires the worker to see the child in the round in order to understand the impact of social and familial structures. Only with this understanding can a plan be formed which attempts to effect change in the areas where changes and choices are possible.

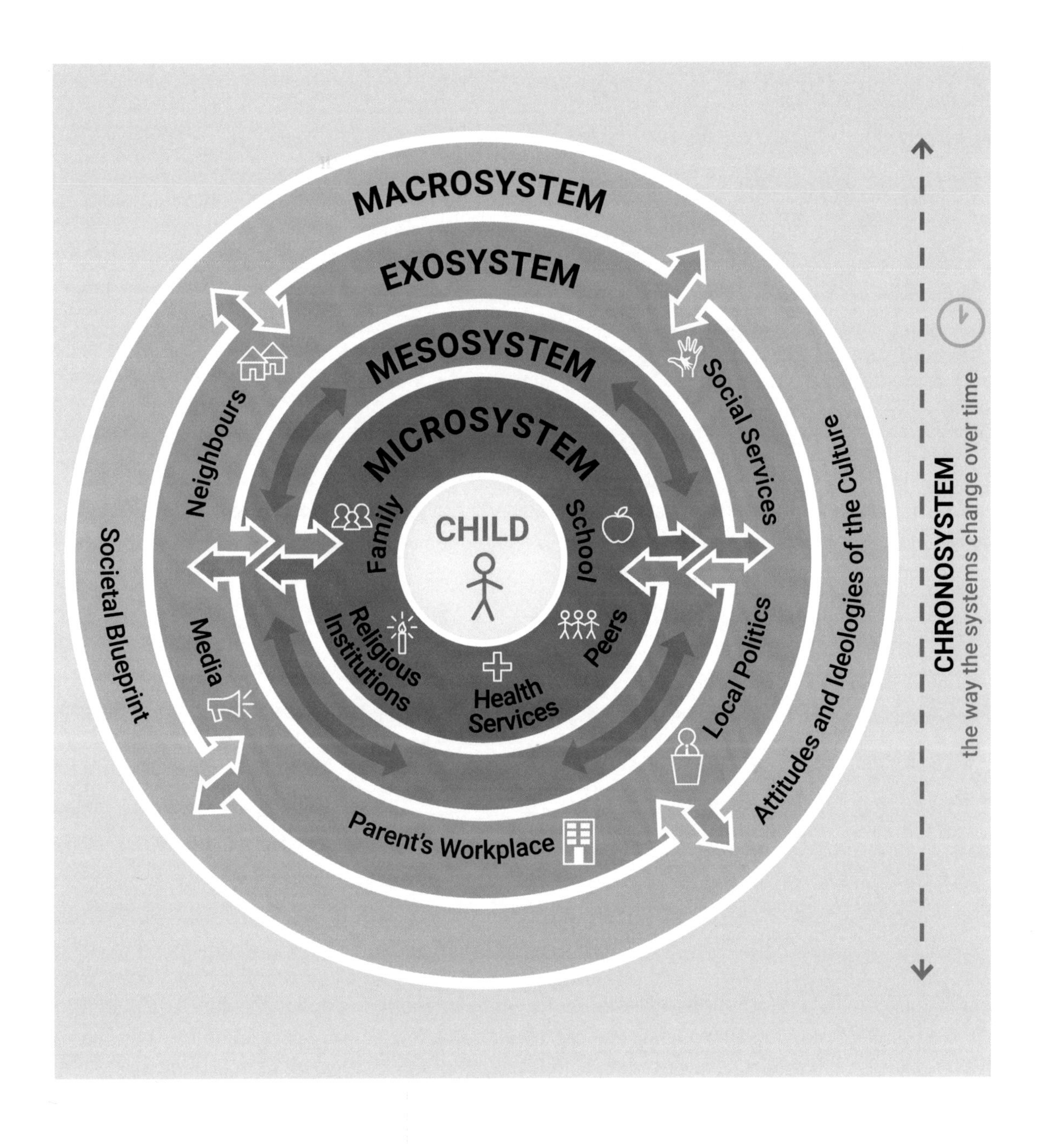

CHILD DEVELOPMENT MILESTONES

Developmental milestones are drawn out of child development theory. Essentially they describe things that most children can do by a certain age.

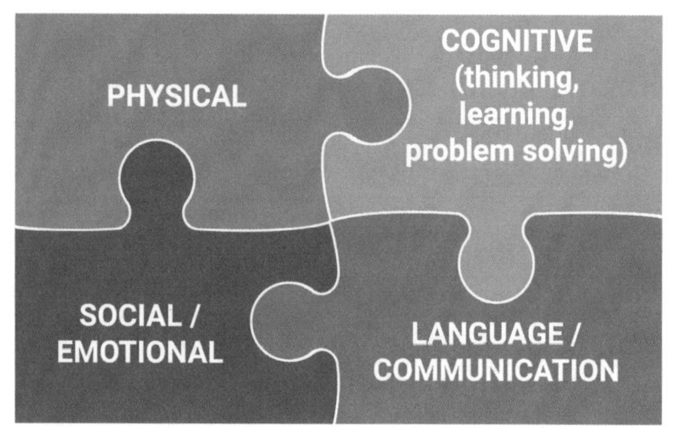

Developmental milestones are generally broken down into the four key areas of physical, cognitive, social/emotional and communication.

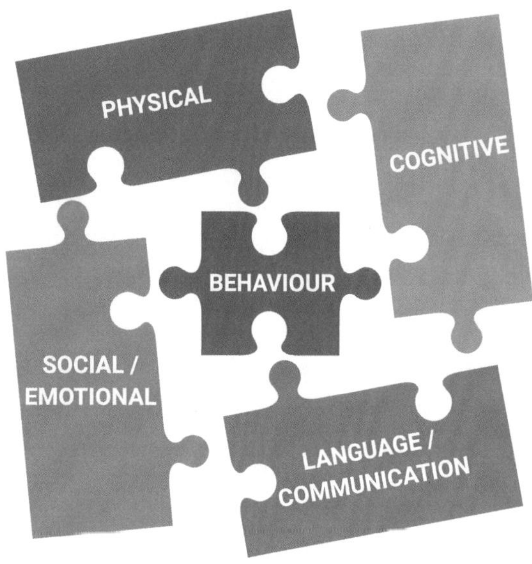

The knowledge and skills statement also refers to behavioural development, although behaviour can be seen as a direct result of the other four areas of development.

There is widespread difference in how children develop, although there are considered to be 'normal ranges' for many key milestones. However, the ranges can be significant, and many things might impact on these developmental milestones.

So, for example a baby is expected to:

 Be able to smile between 6 and 10 weeks.

 Be able to sit independently between 4 and 7 months.

 Be able to crawl between 6 and 10 months (but some babies bottom shuffle and some babies skip this stage altogether).

 Take their first steps between 9 and 12 months.

Knowing this can be helpful, but there are so many variables that can impact on whether children reach these 'milestones', and it would not be outside of expected 'norms' for children to meet one or two milestones later than expected, equally they may do some things earlier than expected.

DEVELOPMENTAL DELAY

Developmental delay is a phrase used to describe when a child continually misses key milestones. Developmental delay is usually considered in relation to the four key areas of child development, with a fifth aspect of skills of daily living added in (this would include things like eating, dressing and using the toilet). The term global developmental delay usually means that a child is delayed in more than two of the five areas. Developmental delays can be caused by either internal or external factors:

Complications at birth: For example, premature birth or a lack of oxygen at birth.

Medical conditions: Short term delays can be caused by infections such as hearing infections. Longer term developmental issues can be caused by long term conditions.

Environmental issues: A wide range of environmental factors can impact on development.

Advice on child development from the World Health Organisation, which is widely used in health care, suggests that developmental delay can be identified through positive or negative indicators. A positive indicator refers to something that is happening, whilst a negative indicator refers to something that is not happening.

POSITIVE INDICATORS	NEGATIVE INDICATORS
Problems with vision	Not smiling by 10 weeks
Hearing loss	Not reaching by 5 months
Persistently low muscle tone or floppiness	Not sitting by 9 months
Persistent tiptoe walking	Not walking by 18 months
	No single words by 18 months
	No 2-3 word sentences by 30 months
	Not running by 30 months

REGRESSION OF DEVELOPMENT

The World Health Organisation asserts that the most significant red flag in terms of concerns around child development is regression – the loss of skills which a child has previously mastered. This, they say, requires urgent investigation.

Developmental regression is regularly referred to by medics. Developmental regression is generally demonstrated through behaviour. Regression can indeed indicate that there are significant concerns. However, there can also be some legitimate reasons for children regressing to behaviour which they have previously grown out of. The reasons for regression in child development can include:

- Medical conditions – some very serious medical conditions are initially picked up because of significant regression (often in the domain of physical development). There is an increasing amount of research which suggests that children diagnosed on the autistic spectrum experience developmental regression in the early years.
- Illness – short term illness can create regression, particularly in terms of behaviour.
- Lack of sleep or poor diet – where children do not get enough sleep or sufficient nutrients from a healthy varied diet then they can exhibit regression in all developmental domains.

- Change and transition – changes in routine or caregivers often leads to regression in child development. Children who have contact with social care services often experience more change than others and this should be considered when exploring child development issues.
- Stress – any kind of stress can lead to regression at any stage. For example, young people who are experiencing exam stress often find solace in being supported in ways they enjoyed when they were younger.
- Distress – when children experience distress and trauma this can lead to either developmental delay or developmental regression.
- Ordinary response to developmental demands – some early years practitioners believe that regression in one area is perfectly ordinary for children. Often development, especially in the early years occurs in 'spurts'. A child may need to put all of their energies into one area to develop in that domain, this can lead to some regression in another area.

Any concerns about regression in development must be assessed holistically. What are the environmental factors? Is the regression in one domain or is it more global? Is the regression long term or is there regular short term regression? There may be a range of reasons for any regression in a child's development, which highlights the vital importance of hypothesising drawing on knowledge and expertise.

PAUSE TO REFLECT

Think about a situation where you noted developmental delay or developmental regression in a child

How did you identify the issues?

What impact did your response have for the child?

EMILIA

Deryn and Lucy are new foster carers. They are caring for Emilia who is 30 months old. Emilia has come to foster care from her mother's care. This is Emilia's second time in foster care. She was looked after for a short time when her mother lived in a different Local Authority. You have only recently started to work with Emilia as she recently moved into your area. Deryn and Lucy tell you that they are worried that Emilia makes no attempt to help when they are dressing her, she stands or lies very still. When you are visiting Emilia, Lucy and Deryn tell you that they have noted that Emilia has some delay in other areas, they feel that her lack of physical interest in getting herself dressed is very concerning. They ask what you think. Do you know if Emilia used to be more physically engaged in getting dressed?

How do you respond? What might you want to do?

CHONGAN

Chongan is 16 months old. He is currently in hospital having recently had meningitis. Nursing staff have some concerns about Chongan. His parents stayed with him the first day he was in hospital but they have only rarely visited since. Chongan's paternal grandparents, who speak very limited English, have visited regularly, but he has been left alone at the hospital for periods of time. Chongan is doing well and is ready for discharge, but he will have some long term disabilities and health needs and a referral has been received from the hospital ward raising concerns about whether Chongan's needs can be met by his family.

What are the issues here?

CHILD DEVELOPMENT THEORY AND PRACTICE: CHANGING PERSPECTIVES

Reading through the child development theory covered so far, have you noticed that most of the theory development is drawn from the field of psychology or medicine? Did you reflect that most of it is attributed to men (although the research teams were very often more gender balanced)? This is where the role of expertise is interesting. The recognised 'expert' voice often goes unchallenged. However, there are many occasions where 'experts' have got child development wrong.

During the 1970s and 1980s parents were informed that sleeping children on their backs was risky as this created a choking hazard, and were advised to sleep children on their stomachs. By the 1990s there was a clear statistical rise in what was often termed 'cot death' and parents were told that the safest way for babies to sleep was on their side. I had my first child in 1991, I remember being given really firm direction from a health visitor to sleep the baby on her side. I had towels and blankets to keep her on her side. I recall vividly waking up one morning to see my daughter had rolled back and she was sleeping on her back – I panicked completely, thinking she must be dead. When the advice to parents was reversed to babies sleeping on their back then the incidence of unexplained infant death dropped very considerably. Exploring the research behind this initial advice it is clear to see (with hindsight) what 'went wrong'. The initial 'evidence' which indicated that sleeping on the back increased the risk of choking was based on research with a small number of very premature babies, this was then incorrectly generalised to all child care practice.

The use of evidence and prevailing 'expertise' has significantly changed child rearing advice and therefore the way that children are brought up, over time. It is therefore vital that social workers are fully aware of contemporary practice in terms of parenting and child rearing. It is also important, though to recognise that at times the prevailing advice may need to challenged. Contemporary child care practice in the early years in the UK is very focused on getting children to be 'school ready'. There is often an artificial divide between early years education and child care in this context. In Scandinavia, however, this is significantly different. Here there is a publicly funded early years service which combines education and care and does not focus on 'school readiness'.

"Childhood is experienced in a time and place" (Lindon and Brodie 2016) and social work is also practiced in a time and a place. If time and place is not open to question, then poor and dangerous practice can occur. For example, in the 1930s, 40s and 50s (in fact right up until the 1970s) social workers were involved in child migration programmes. Thousands of children were shipped from the UK to Australia, New Zealand, Rhodesia and Canada. Many of these children were abused systematically. They were put to work, so that children as young as seven were working on building sites in Western Australia, with resulting serious injuries.

The 'time and place' of childhood must be connected with the time and place of social work practice if social workers are to make use of best evidence in child development. Being child focused at all times is essential.

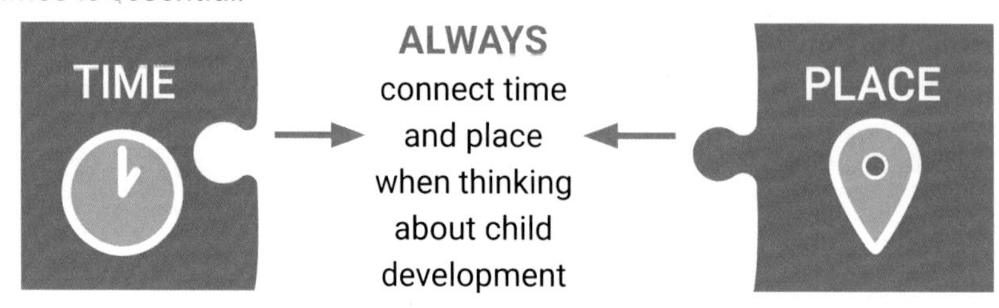

KEEPING KNOWLEDGE OF CHILD DEVELOPMENT UP TO DATE

With theories and ideas changing regularly it is vital that practitioners keep up to date with the changing understanding and advice around child development. Many social workers have access to services such as Research in Practice or Community Care Inform both of which provide up to date information on child development and the latest advice.

There is a series of three child development apps devised specifically for social workers. These apps are a free resource available from the Appstore on your mobile phone. They were first developed in 2013 in a partnership between Ulster University and Queen's University Belfast and the child development app steering group convened by the Northern Ireland Social Care Council. The apps were fully updated in 2018.

©Shutterstock/THE YOOTH

The three apps cover:

 0-6 years

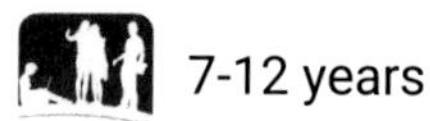 7-12 years

 13-18 years

The apps have some context-specific information about law and policy which will clearly not be relevant for social workers in England. However, the information on child development theory and the skills required to draw on child development in social work practice is universal. The apps have won several awards and every social worker I know who has downloaded them has found them useful.

PAUSE TO REFLECT

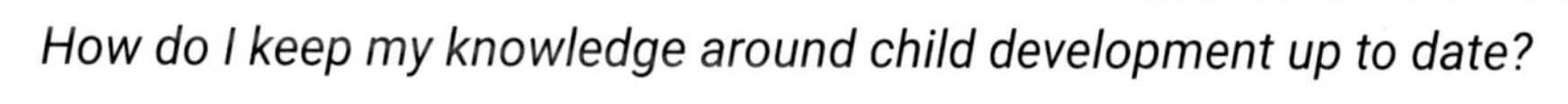

How do I keep my knowledge around child development up to date?

ACEs

ACEs is an acronym in widespread use in contemporary social work. It stands for Adverse Childhood Experiences and originates from a research study in South Carolina in the 1990s. Since then, ACEs have become very commonly referred to and used in public policy development in America. In the UK ACEs have only become commonly discussed in the last few years.

According to Corcoran and McNulty (2018) adverse childhood experiences are traumatic events or chronic stressors that cannot be controlled by the child. The original ACE questionnaire focused on two areas of abuse and household challenges. A third area of neglect was added during the second wave of the research.

The original ACE categories are outlined in the following table:

ABUSE	HOUSEHOLD CHALLENGES	NEGLECT (added in second stage)
Physical	**Mother treated violently**	**Physical neglect**
Emotional	**Household substance misuse**	**Emotional neglect**
Sexual	**Mental illness in household**	
	Parental separation or divorce	
	Criminal incarceration of member of household (prison)	

The original categories of ACEs made a distinction between what was happening in the inner life of the child and what happened externally (so effectively the first ACEs focused on experiences within a family household). A number of studies have added to this, bringing in "community level adversity" (Crinholm et al 2015). This includes issues such as whether a child has witnessed something but not personally experienced it. Other studies have added in abuse from people outside of the household (for example bullying). There is regular criticism of the original study and what were identified as ACEs, with a particular focus on what was missing and there is still debate about what should and shouldn't be included as an ACE.

A widened understanding of ACEs brings together the I and the E – what is happening in the child's internal world or individual situation with what is happening in the environment or issues that are external to the child.

- Domestic violence
- Substance abuse
- Physical, emotional and sexual abuse
- Maternal depression
- Physical and emotional neglect
- Divorce
- Mental illness
- Incarceration

- Poverty
- Discrimination
- Community disruption
- Lack of opportunity, economic mobility and social capital
- Poor housing
- Violence

IMPACT OF ACEs

The original study found that the more ACEs reported by participants, the more the risk of the following occurring in adult life was raised:

- Alcohol abuse
- Chronic lung disease
- Depression
- Early initiation of smoking and continuation of smoking
- Early initiation of sexual activity, multiple sexual partners
- Unintended pregnancies
- Foetal death
- Increased risk of sexual violence
- Increased risk of intimate partner violence
- Lack of physical activity
- Drug abuse
- Poor performance at work and / or missing work
- Obesity
- Diabetes
- Suicide attempts
- Sexually transmitted diseases
- Stroke
- Cancer
- Heart disease
- Poor academic achievement

The theory behind ACEs is that adverse childhood experiences lead to neurobiological changes. They actually change the formation of genes. In simple terms the science is based on an understanding that genes provide instructions for making proteins in our bodies. Some genes are referred to as 'control genes' because they give instructions to proteins that actually regulate the activity of other genes, through complex connections. Epigenetics is the study of the way that our genes are used, turned on and off or expressed. The actual genetic code isn't changed but the way that genes are expressed can be changed and epigenetics studies this. Those that promote the concept of ACEs claim that life experience can change genetics.

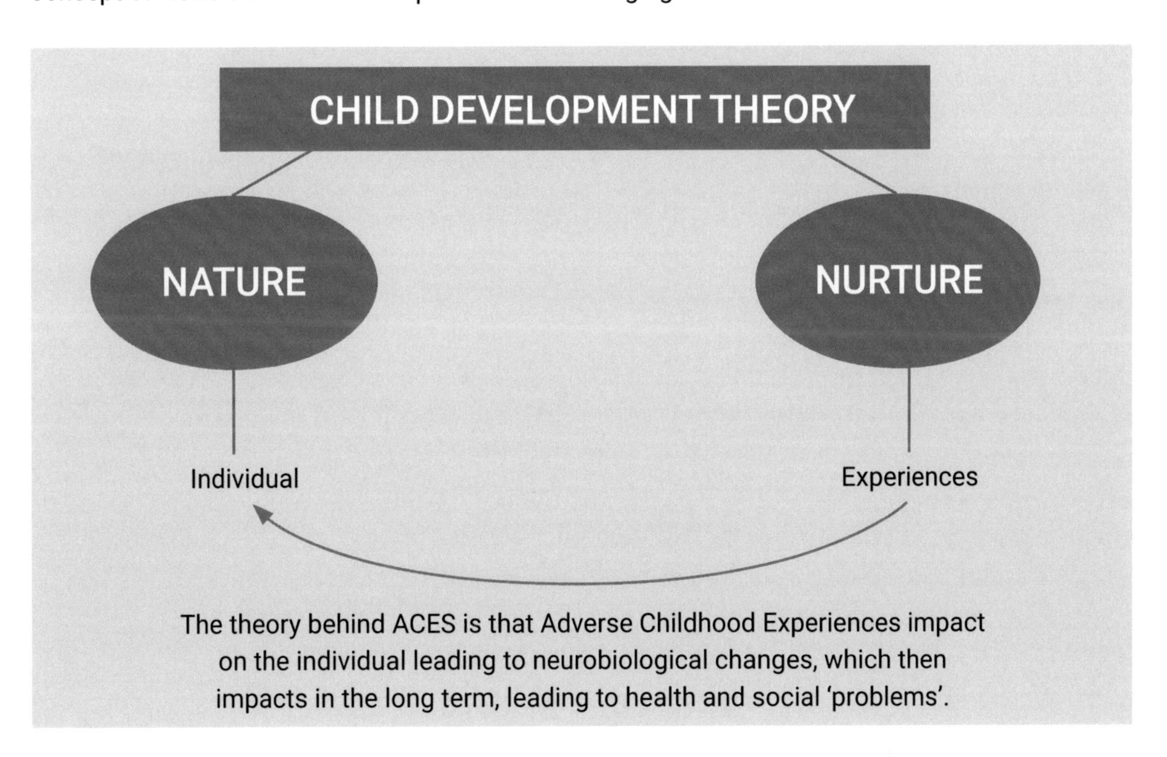

I look back and can measure my milestones by acts of violence or abuse, as I learned, I represented little of note or value. Very little in my file refers to any achievements I mastered. If it wasn't for my own memories of the times I was successful, my whole childhood could have been a write off!

Today, I suspect those who champion ACEs (Adverse Childhood Experiences) would be pointing and proclaiming that I will be damaged for life both physically and of course mentally. They would suggest that my experiences would impact my development and any chance I had of attaining 'normality' would more than likely be compromised, they certainly would 'map' out all the routes I'd be likely to follow, none of which would be my choice! Instinctively when I hear people banging on about ACEs, I want to create an iconic picture (Kes) from my childhood and stick my two fingers up. Don't get me wrong, I get it that new ideas are developed as we increase our learning and understanding but ACE feels unbalanced and a whole blanket approach. It feels like a new wave, the 'New Romantics' (I'm giving my age away here!) movement, everyone is talking about it and the impact it has on child development and everyone wants to jump on the bandwagon because it's easy to do so!

Actually, I don't have a massive problem with some of the research that has been undertaken, except at best it means we have an awareness of events that have occurred in and during childhood which may have had a negative impact. My difficulty is in accepting this narrative as the 'whole picture' as it references how the impact is long lasting and will impact on future generations. I haven't seen any convincing research on this, and I have looked!!...

The thing is this, we all are aware that 'stuff' happens. How we get past it and move forward is what's relevant or as some may view it, developing resilience. Therefore, a child like me growing up in what can only be described as barbaric conditions has to develop their own coping mechanisms. Yes of course events can impact but it doesn't have to be all negative. Statistics around those that have 'care experience' centre around the negative aspects. Numbers in prison, numbers with poor mental health and so on and yes it paints a bleak picture and influences 'new' ideas? It was, after all, the expectation for me and others that these were the 'dizzy heights' we should reach for! Fortunately, I'm a stubborn sod and like the majority (the statistics no one refers to) I got on with life. My success, I suppose, is measured by my long term relationships, the ability to parent (you'll have to ask my kids, how well) that I maintained and progressed in my career and developed my emotional self. Normality is how I see it and yes I may have taken a little longer as I did have to learn some things. Ultimately, I get the starting point of ACEs, I just don't think it is reflective of me, or my cultural difference or the vast majority of people who have grown up in difficult situations.

THE ACE-AWARE MOVEMENT

The concept of ACEs has spread widely, with some organisations describing themselves as ACE Aware. Finkelhor (2017) identifies that, in fact, there has been "much excitement" about ACEs. However, he argues that we should be cautious about a widespread use of ACEs until there is further evidence on a range of issues. The use of ACEs is still under widespread debate. Many find the ideas useful and the theory compelling, whilst others argue that ACEs is overly deterministic and offers little that an awareness of the impact of socio-economic factors cannot.

Gary Walsh (2018) argues that instead of referring to 'adverse childhoods' using a narrative of 'hopeful childhoods' would be more helpful. Certainly many in the care experienced community have referred to finding the idea of ACEs difficult. The concept suggests that negative outcomes are pre-determined and many people have referred to a sense of guilt about passing on their own ACEs to their children (Turner 2019).

PAUSE TO REFLECT

What are your thoughts about ACES?

RESILIENCE

There is a host of theory around resilience in children and young people, such that even definitions of what it is are debated. It is generally seen in one of two main ways:

As a trait, characteristic or ability (the ability to bounce back from difficult experiences or adversity)

As an inferred capacity to adapt to challenges, situations and stressors (how well a child is felt to be doing)

Most theory focuses on individual or family resilience, with systemic thinking connecting the two. Where connections between child and family resilience are made, these almost always focus on the importance of the parent-child relationship. Other factors which are seen as important in the development of childhood resilience, often referred to as the 'short list' are:

- Capable care giving
- Good quality wider relationships
- Problem solving skills
- Self regulation
- Motivation
- Faith, hope, a belief that life has meaning
- Effective schools and education
- Wider communities which function effectively

In many ways these are all connected, building on the prevailing professional understanding that systems in a child's life are embedded and interact in an interdependent way (Masten 2014). Promoting a child's developing resilience must build on this understanding.

Most resilience theory suggests that there are three basic steps, or strategies, to support the development of resilience in children and young people:

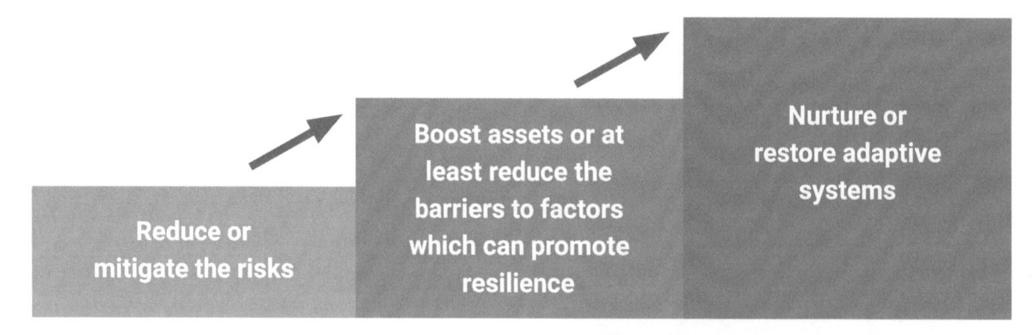

Resilience theory seeks to understand why some people thrive in difficult circumstances and others don't do so well. In many ways the theory is very incomplete and still leaves us with a range of questions around why some children thrive in spite of (or perhaps because of?) a range of adverse experiences whilst other children do not.

©Shutterstock/PopTika

The two most popular models of resilience in children and young people, both come from America. They demonstrate in many ways, the struggles in resilience theory: one focuses very much on factors internal to the child, the other focuses on what services can do (drawing on factors external to the child).

THE 7Cs

Kenneth Ginsburg, an American paediatrician, developed what has become an incredibly popular model of resilience for children and young people. The 7Cs are:

COMPETENCE: Children and young people need the opportunity to develop skills, they also need to have acknowledgement of when they are doing something well.

CONFIDENCE: Confidence is linked to competence, since children will develop confidence when they do something well. Confidence can be easily undermined, but can be enhanced by setting goals that challenge but are within reach of the child.

CONNECTION: Being a part of a community and having wider connections is important to help children develop resilience.

CHARACTER: Children need to develop a clear understanding of what is right and wrong and need to be able to follow a 'moral compass'.

CONTRIBUTION: Children benefit greatly from helping others. Ginsburg also argues that an experience of helping others makes asking for help easier.

COPING: Children and young people need to learn a variety of coping mechanisms so that they have choices when they need to problem solve. This includes helping children and young people to learn about what isn't important and can be 'let go'.

CONTROL: Children need to feel that they have a degree of control over their lives and their environment.

(Ginsburg 2011)

THE 5Ms

Ann Masten, a psychologist by background, is Professor of the Institute of Child Development at the University of Minnesota and writes widely on resilience in children. She developed the 5M model of resilience (2014). Rather than focusing on individual children and young people, this provides a framework for policy makers and practitioners to look at what helps in terms of supporting resilience for children and young people:

MISSION: Develop and work towards a clear mission for intervention which is framed around positive goals.

MODELS: Draw on models and measures which include promoting and protecting factors which build resilience, as well as using positive criteria to measure success.

METHODS: Utilise methods which mitigate risks, boost assets and maximise preventative and adaptive systems.

MULTI-SECTOR AND MULTI-LEVEL INVOLVEMENT: To create meaningful change professionals at every level across multiple disciplines must work together.

MAXIMISING: To build on each of the first four Ms timing and targeting must be considered.

Helen Taylor is an experienced social worker currently working in child protection.

I am a social worker, a job role I think of as a privilege. I've worked in the statutory sector for most of my social work career, currently that is in child protection, in the past I've worked in fostering and adoption, including two years at BAAF, now CoramBAAF.

Assessments are at the core of social work, they being the method we use to work out what families need, and how those needs can be met. They also give us an overview of the way that everyone is functioning within their world and encompass a multi-agency perspective of the child, with the expertise of health, education and other professionals. I might have to look at a book or a chart to tell you exactly what a child should be doing at any given age (I'm not a health visitor after all) but understanding child development is critical to an understanding of that individual child's needs, both physical and emotional, and their lived experience.

Ensuring we capture 'the voice of the child' isn't always verbal; it also emerges from observations of interactions at home, school and with family, friends and their peers. Whoever that child is, their behaviour is communication. One of the most useful tools I use regularly is undertaking an observation in a nursery environment. Not only will that inform you about the child you are observing, it will also give you confidence in your memory, (a key part of an observation being that you remain fully engaged, don't take notes, and write it up as soon as you leave the setting). I no longer take my notebook out in any visits, unless there is a particular detail that needs recording. It's a barrier and means I'm not making eye contact.

One of the most common ways I currently use observations is for sibling together and apart assessments for permanency, particularly to assess whether there is a sibling relationship, or if there is a trauma bond. I also often support substitute carers who need help with how to ensure children understand their story. Any carer can be quite discombobulated by the way children puddle jump, one minute asking about something really significant, the next asking if they can lick the cake bowl. Giving people a script for difficult conversations with children is always helpful. It is something you can think about together, and they can pull out on the spot when they need to.

A child who is not functioning on a par with their peers is one of the most fundamental uses of child development in my work, allowing for the fact that children do things at a slightly different point in time. Even if we know a child has a diagnosis, additional needs, or even complex and multifaceted needs, we may also know that their family has been open and closed to children's services repeatedly on grounds of neglect. That will be the child who wasn't on the receiving end of motherese and the serve and return communication which developed their neural pathways and made them feel safe and secure. Children who have additional needs or a disability are more vulnerable in such circumstances and we now know a lot about the impact of long-term neglect.

Sometimes we might be completing a jigsaw puzzle, but on other occasions we might wonder if we need to take pieces out and see if they belong somewhere else. I won't be the only social worker who has been allocated a case with an ADHD diagnosis attached to a child, and I use that as an example simply because it has been so common throughout my career. The test is relatively subjective, being partly reliant upon scales completed by parents, who will understandably experience their own child's behaviour more acutely than others would. Having spent the early part of my career in social work working with children in care, there were many occasions that the indicators of ADHD disappeared once children were placed with alternative carers, because the cause was environmental. I always tell people to read the Coventry Grid, which details the overlap between autism and attachment (Moran, 2010).

Some of the children I work with have been subjected to neglect, trauma or abuse, which can cause developmental delay. I've also worked with children who have experienced a one-off event, which has had a cataclysmic impact upon that child's ability to trust the adults around them to consistently meet all of their needs. In one such case nobody knew what the event was, but the professionals could all see that there were behaviours which reflected developmental trauma, and a psychologist helped us to determine a highly insecure attachment style. Sometimes that takes a while, but in the meantime. It helped that we were able to work with the family to develop their parenting strategies in a way that would work with a child with ADHD, autism, or issues related to their attachment style. (One of my soapbox topics is how the autism friendly school would actually work really well for all children). I don't want to make this about labels, but they are really only useful if they signpost us to specific targeted support or services.

It's a bit of a cliché to say that families are the experts on themselves, but they are, you will never know them as well as they know each other. Social work does however have an eclectic theory base and access to other disciplines. That holistic overview supports us to assess strengths and difficulties, to identify any antecedents, and the impact of that child's world upon them. That analysis is essential to any social work assessment, whether it be a single assessment, or your statement for a final hearing.

As much as there is simplicity in looking at stages of development, there is also a complexity in the neurobiology, genetics and epigenetics. I think the more we know the more we become aware of what we don't know. There are for example some cases where we know alcohol consumption is problematic, but the child escapes the impact in embryo, and foetal alcohol syndrome is bypassed.

Assessments are an ongoing process, rather than an event. They require us to be child centred, to assess capacity for change where that is necessary, and necessitate both having a clear understanding of how this child that we are looking at now is developing, and why. It probably won't surprise you to know that I think the most useful theory of child development is Bronfenbrenner's (1979), because he believed that a person's development was affected by everything in their surrounding environment.

How do you ensure that child development is a key aspect of your assessments?

ATTACHMENT

Attachment theory has had a very significant impact on social work with children and families, so you are likely to have a good level of understanding in this area. It is, however, sometimes worth revisiting the basics.

Attachment is basically a theory based on psychological perspectives about how babies use their relationships with their main carer to set-up an expectation about themselves and their relationships with others.

A securely attached child will learn that their parents/carer will comfort them when they are distressed, and they will develop a sense that they are worthy of being consoled and loved. This is essential for healthy child development.

Where a child has parents who do not make the child feel secure or where attachments have been ruptured there is a significant risk of the child having difficulty with a range of relationships and their problem solving and coping skills can be poorer. There is also a risk of the person, when they are adults (and parents), failing to provide secure attachments to their own children (and so the cycle continues).

The evidence around the effect of secure and insecure attachments is clear. Secure attachments:

- Promote security.
- Enhance a child's development particularly in terms of independence skills.
- Foster a child's ability to establish social relationships.
- Enable a child to explore and investigate the wider world.
- Facilitate play as children develop and mature through play.

Attachment theory makes clear that when a child senses that their attachments to their adult caregivers are not secure then they focus their emotions and behaviours on trying to re-establish their attachment (attachment behaviours are activated).

Attachment theory has established that there are three insecure types of attachment, each of which generates certain responses in the child:

1. AVOIDANT/DEFENDED ATTACHMENT ANXIETY:

- Child is rejected, may just be emotional rejection, but this rejection may include physical violence from the caregiver.
- Child downplays attachment.
- Child minimises expressions of distress. The child knows that when their parent is shouting at them if the child is distressed this results in further parental rejection.
- Child acts happy even when frightened.
- Child shows aggression when they are dominant. For example, at school with weaker children or with younger siblings.

2. AMBIVALENT/COERCIVE ATTACHMENT ANXIETY:

- Unpredictable/insensitive care giving. Often characterised by neglect or disinterest in child. But there are times when child feels cared for and loved.
- Child maximises expression of distress, especially when parent about to leave.
- Child engages in attention seeking behaviour. This can include the child ignoring the parent when back together, the child is communicating (but not saying verbally) "show me you love me".
- Child desires close relationships but is anxious over the risk of withdrawal of affection. This can include child hanging around the parent for long periods of time.

3. DISORGANISED/CONTROLLING ATTACHMENT ANXIETY:

- A child finds this type of parenting the most difficult to adapt to.
- Caregivers are unpredictable and rejecting – this may just be emotional rejection but can include violence.
- Caregiver is frightening or frightened – a source of distress for the child. The caregiver (parent) may have a drug or alcohol dependency or mental health problems. This affects the caregiver's personality which causes the child distress.
- If the child gets closer to the caregiver the child gets more distressed since the child becomes more aware of the impact of the parent's drug or alcohol dependency etc
- Child feels they are unloved and the child feels they are the cause of others anger.
- Child flooded with emotions of fear and anger.
- Child has fear of being in danger and feeling out of control. The child's behaviours can be inconsistent and destructive.
- Only predictable aspect is the child, therefore they try to control themselves. Child develops defences and inhibitions to maintain control.
- Child can see themselves as strong and powerful but also bad. View of child as bad is impressed on child by parent who labels child as a bad child.
- Child can stop fearing danger.
- Child fears losing control – fears their feelings may overwhelm them. Child gives impression of being strong, assertive, even arrogant. This is a heavily defended façade. Behind the façade is emotional turmoil.

There needs to be a clear awareness that attachment behaviours change as the child becomes a young person, but the reason and intention behind them remain the same. A teenager who is experiencing ambivalent/coercive attachment anxiety is also likely to engage in behaviour which may seem counter-productive, but is actually designed to seek attention and closeness. Unlike a seven year old, who may lie on the floor kicking and crying, a teenager may engage in self-harm, sexual activity or consume alcohol and then make sure that their parent is aware of this.

THE IMPORTANCE OF RELATIONSHIPS IN CHILD DEVELOPMENT

Whether they believe child development to be based on nature or nurture, almost all child development theories stress the importance of relationships for child development. Generally speaking the issues of relationships expand as a child grows older, so in the very early years the most significant relationships impacting on the child are parental relationships (parent-child and inter-parental) and as a child grows older other relationships become vitally important, such that for teenagers often the relationships which have the most significant impact are peer groups relationships.

Parent-child relationships: The emotional tone of the parent-child relationship is a fundamental factor in predicting children's long-term emotional and behavioural development, the links with attachment here are clear. While research has tended to focus on the mother-child relationship, the role of fathers is increasingly recognised as an important influence on a child's development.

Inter-parental relationships: Where conflict levels between parents are high, research indicates that children are not only directly affected by the experience of acrimony between parents, but parenting practices are in themselves disrupted Harold and sellers (2012).

Wider relationships: Children grow in a complex web of relationships, as Bronfenbrenner's ecological model demonstrates. A wide range of research demonstrates that the quality of relationships that a child has with siblings, wider family, peers and relevant adults is a vital aspect of their development. For example, children who develop warm, positive relationships with their early teachers are more excited about learning, more positive about education, more self-confident, and achieve more educationally (National Scientific Council on the Developing Child 2009).

Peer relationships: Peer relationships are important throughout childhood, but they become particularly important during adolescence. At this point peer relationships become more complex and young people are seeking to develop more intimate relationships outside of their family circle.

A key aspect of a social worker's role is about promoting the quality of relationships in a child's life. This is important for a range of reasons, not least because it will enhance the child's development in a range of ways. Social workers know that relationships are at the heart of social work practice and this is recognised throughout the knowledge and skills statement. In an overview of research Winter (2015) highlighted that:

- Before they come into care, children and young people's relationships are often fractured, chaotic, frightening, violent and abusive.
- Being in care provides opportunities for children and young people to experience loving, secure, stable and safe relationships.
- While in care, children value opportunities to build positive and meaningful relationships but experience difficulties in building and maintaining them.
- Transitioning out of care is a challenging time and access to supportive relationships is critical for young people in helping them manage the demands of this experience.
- Throughout the different stages of their care journey, access to positive and meaningful relationships is likely to lead to better long-term outcomes for children and young people.

Natasha Langleben is a team member of one of two leaving care teams in Brent Council. Here she outlines some work undertaken with young people.

At Brent Council, the Care Leavers teams decided to put some creative ideas in place to meet one particular need: to combat isolation and increase emotional support for care leavers. Research shows that loneliness is one of the biggest challenges facing care leavers, gaining householder responsibilities at such a young age and often feeling that none of their peer group can relate to their lifestyle.

We therefore implemented a number of initiatives. The first was a weekly football group who met every Wednesday at the Powerleague opposite our office. This has now been running for over 6 months to huge success. In that time there has been a care leavers vs staff match, which included service managers and an assistant director playing football. We have played against other local authorities and we have had sponsorship so that Brent now have their own kit. Young people travel up to an hour across London each week from their accommodation because they love playing.

We created the Hub as a monthly social for care leavers. This started in a venue opposite our office where we ordered pizza and put on a film night, organised games and generally helped introduce care leavers to each other. From there we organised a Xmas meal and other meals. All the events have been well attended and it has been fantastic to see young people meeting and connecting over shared experiences.

©Shutterstock/begalphoto

Finally, we created a WhatsApp group for care leavers. This is an opportunity not just for staff to post about events, jobs and participation but for young people to chat amongst themselves. This led to young people choosing to go outdoor ice skating on Boxing Day, five young people who had met once via the Care Leavers hub enjoyed a day out, at a time of year when isolation can be particularly prevalent.

What do you do in your practice to address the development needs of young people?

CHILD DEVELOPMENT FOR OLDER CHILDREN AND YOUNG PEOPLE

Social workers, as most people, tend to think about child development very much in terms of babies and younger children. However, we all continue to develop throughout our lives and so child development of course covers development throughout the whole of childhood. It is important to continue to recognise development in the domains of physical, cognitive, social/emotional and language/communication development throughout childhood. Each of these areas is likely to connect and they will all have an impact on a child / young person's behaviour.

ADOLESCENCE

It is perhaps during what is often referred to as the adolescent years that child development becomes more diverse. In the early years most children develop in similar ways in terms of the different aspects of development. The stages of adolescence are generally seen as:

- Early adolescence which begins with puberty - around 11 to 14 years
- Middle adolescence - around 15 to 17 years
- Late adolescence – around 17 to 21 years

PHYSICAL DEVELOPMENT

At this point physical development does not relate to being able to physically do new things, although lots of young people will develop their physical abilities through practising new skills. Generally, at this point physical development relates to changes in the body related to puberty. Puberty can begin as early as nine for girls and is often weight and size related. Young people may find the physical changes scary or they may be concerned that they are not changing as quickly as others around them.

COGNITIVE DEVELOPMENT

Young people's cognitive development may take them to key philosophical questions about the meaning of life, but where they concentrate their thinking will largely relate to their developing sense of self and self-identity. They may become very focused (almost to the extent of obsessive) about certain things which they see as making up a part of identity which they wish to explore. Neuroscience research suggests that brain development in young people can lead to an increased tendency towards risk taking and a lack of ability to think through consequences of behaviour. However, there are concerns that research drawn from this area can reinforce negative stereotypes about young people (Sercombe and Paus 2013).

SOCIAL / EMOTIONAL DEVELOPMENT

At this point peer groups and social networks become particularly important to young people. With the increasing use of social media "virtual" peer groups may hold particular significance at this stage of a young person's development. The development of identity is seen as a key aspect of this stage of development, Erikson identifies a role identity v role confusion stage.

Development psychologist James Marcia (1966) extended and refined Erikson's ides about identity formation at this stage of development and this has since been seen as the most helpful way of understanding identity development for young people (Pelco and Ball 2018). Marcia's theory is that there are five stages to identity development, as follows:

Identity Diffused: In this stage the young person does not seem to know or care about their individual identity. However, over time the pressure from peers, parents, and society help many to wrestle with the key decisions about identity.

Foreclosure: At this point there has been no crisis of identity, but a young person will have adopted the values and ideas of their parents or peer group or others with influence without any questions. Foreclosed adolescents are unable to distinguish between their own goals and interests and the ones that others have made for them.

Negative identity: At this stage the young person may adopt an identity simply to oppose the identity that they feel is being 'forced' on them. They may adopt a negative and exaggerated stereotype.

Moratorium: The word moratorium means a period of delay given where someone isn't yet ready or able to make a decision or move forwards. In this stage a young person experiences a pause in identity formation, and they explore various identities without making a clear choice. Adolescents in this phase are experiencing crisis, but many at once without making commitments. Consequently, they often feel perplexed, unbalanced, and dissatisfied. Young people in this stage are likely to experience anxiety and may express their identity crisis through a range of emotions.

Identity Achieved: This stage relates to there being an achievement of identity – a clarity of role and purpose. The young person begins to recognise their own unique identity, part of which may be made up of group belonging, but the identity is not reliant upon this. This may well not be achieved until into adulthood.

LANGUAGE / COMMUNICATION DEVELOPMENT

Linked to the previous aspect of development, the importance of peer groups and the development of identity means that young people often develop their own language forms. Generational language is not unusual. Language is a key part of identity and as identity forms so language can change and grow. Linguists widely agree that young people are the most linguistically innovative of any age group, which can subsequently have an impact on language more widely. Young people often see new language as a way of demonstrating belonging to a group. If someone from outside the group regularly tries to use that language it can create identity confusion for young people. This demonstrates why careful consideration of the use of language in social work is vitally important (see Chapter 2).

WHERE AM I NOW?

Revisit the start of the chapter. Look again at the KSS standard. Then consider the following questions:

What has surprised me in working through this chapter?

What three things would I highlight as key learning?

What do I still need to do in working towards being fully confident with this KSS statement?

What single next step should I take in working towards an improvement in my practice?

Chapter 4

ADULT MENTAL ILL HEALTH, SUBSTANCE MISUSE, DOMESTIC ABUSE, PHYSICAL ILL HEALTH AND DISABILITY

This chapter considers the impact of some adult factors on the lives of children and young people. As you work through this chapter you will read about some of the services that support children and parents with issues covered in this KSS statement. Children using one of the services share what they most want from social workers, such that the voices of children are central to your learning in this chapter. That reflects the fact that children should be central to any consideration of factors relating to adults. As part of working through this chapter you should reflect on the challenges you may face in working with other professionals, particularly colleagues working with adults.

THE KSS REQUIRES PRACTITIONERS TO:

Identify the impact of adult mental ill health, substance misuse, domestic abuse, physical ill health and disability on family functioning and social circumstances and in particular the effect on children, including those who are young carers. Access the help and assistance of other professionals in the identification and prevention of adult social need and risk, including mental health and learning disability assessment.

Coordinate emergency and routine services and synthesise multi-disciplinary judgements as part of ongoing social work assessment. Use a range of strategies to help families facing these difficulties.

Identify concerning adult behaviours that may indicate risk or increasing risk to children. Assess the likely impact on, and inter-relationship between, parenting and child development. Recognise and act upon escalating social needs and risks, helping to ensure that vulnerable adults are safeguarded and that a child is protected and their best interests always prioritised.

Take a look at the standard above in detail. Highlight key phrases and anything that jumps out at you. Then take some time to reflect on the statement.

- *What are your immediate thoughts?*
- *What might you want to discuss and clarify?*
- *How will you clarify meanings?*
- *Who will you discuss it with?*

GETTING FEEDBACK ON PRACTICE

Who can give me feedback on my practice in this area?	*How will I get the feedback?*

Make sure to keep a record of any feedback you receive.

INITIAL SELF-ASSESSMENT

What do I already do well?

How do I know? (What's my evidence?)

What do I need to work on?

How will I work on this?

UNDERSTANDING THE IMPACT OF ADULT EXPERIENCES ON CHILDREN AND FAMILIES

The areas covered in this statement have been identified as increasing the risk of harm to children and young people (Harold et al 2016 and Hedges and Kenny 2018). They have become widely referred to as the 'toxic trio.' Initially this phrase referred to the first three areas (mental ill health, substance misuse and domestic abuse) and the fact that the risks to children were significantly increased where there was a co-morbidity of these issues in a household.

The Association of Directors of Children's Services (2016) reported that 'toxic trio' issues, and the associated responses of frontline practitioners, are a significant driver impacting on increases in children's services caseloads and the numbers of children being taken into care.

TOXICITY, VULNERABILITY OR CONCERNS?

The word toxic is defined as meaning poisonous, noxious or destructive. In itself therefore the phrase toxic trio has been seen as potentially problematic and blaming. There are some arguments that the phrase is largely blaming of mothers (Hardy 2018). Despite the concerns about the phrase it is still in common usage, although a range of alternative phrases appear in different literature:

- Trio of vulnerabilities
- Trilogy of concerns
- Multiple and complex needs

POVERTY AS A HIDDEN TOXICITY?

The Child Welfare Inequalities Network is particularly critical of the concept of the 'toxic trio' identifying that whilst these three are undoubtedly very significant factors in the lives of children and their families, the impact of poverty and insecurity and the links between poverty and the three identified risk factors are not taken into account when the focus is simply on the factors identified in the 'toxic trio'. The Child Welfare Inequalities Network research is interesting to consider, particularly in relation to the risk factors explored in this chapter.

The Network identifies their initial key findings as:

- Very large inequalities in a child's chances of being on a child protection plan or looked after between and within local authorities are statistically related to measures of area-level deprivation. A child in the most deprived neighbourhoods nationally had an 11 times greater chance of being on a protection plan and a 12 times greater chance of being looked after than a child living in the most affluent.
- A social gradient in child welfare intervention rates across society. Each step increase in neighbourhood deprivation correlated with an increase in child protection and looked after rates.

- Large ethnic inequalities in the experiences of children and families in contact with children's services. Black children were less likely to be looked after than White children living in similarly deprived neighbourhoods, contrary to previous reports. White children were up to 6 times more likely than Asian children to be looked after or on a child protection plan.
- An 'inverse intervention law'. While a child's chances of being on a protection plan or being looked after increases substantially with a Local Authority's overall level of deprivation, for any given level of neighbourhood deprivation, rates of intervention were substantially higher in more affluent Local Authoritys.
- Misleading Statistics. Unless controlled for population, deprivation and ethnicity, variations in overall intervention rates can be a misleading measure of local services

(Bywaters et al 2017)

Poverty is certainly an issue which needs to be carefully considered in terms of impact on children and families and impact on social work practice. However, it is important that social workers recognise that more affluent families may be able to effectively 'hide' issues of concern. I have been aware of social workers talking about feeling intimidated by wealthier, well-educated parents and this can have a profound impact on social work thinking.

Triangles are very popular in theory and in a range of frameworks. Think for example of Maslow's hierarchy of needs and Karpman's drama triangle. In this chapter, in addition to the toxic trio we have also included the assessment framework. In Chapter 7 we include reference to the triangulation of evidence and in Chapter 8 we use a triangle to illustrate the layers of legislation. In fact when considering the impact of adult experiences on children all four triangles need to be considered.

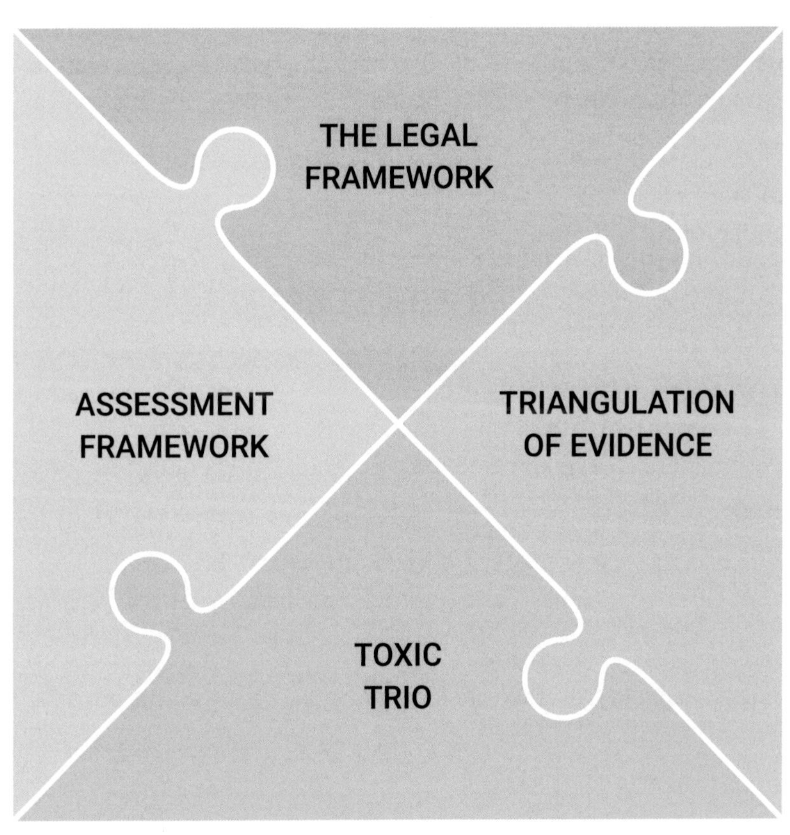

Young oasis offers a free service that supports young people aged between 5 and 18 years in Lincolnshire who are or have been affected by a family member or person close to them misusing drugs or alcohol.

Young Oasis meets with the young person on a 1-1 basis in school or other safe environments. The support offered by Young Oasis aims to develop the young person's understanding of issues that may be associated with drug and alcohol misuse and ways of coping with their circumstances. The Young Oasis team provides much needed emotional support, wellbeing advice and a non-judgemental listening ear to allow the young person to begin to work through the challenges in their situation. Young Oasis will also focus on other factors such as emotional health, self-esteem, social networks and family relationships. The young people accessing services from Young Oasis and the staff supporting them were asked about what they would want from a social worker.

Young people said:

- My dad doesn't talk to the social worker, but I need the social worker to think about our whole family.
- Social workers should not expect a child to act as the adult as very often the child has not experienced a childhood.
- Please try to understand how a child will worry about their parent due to the substance misuse.
- Focus on safety and neglectful parenting.
- Make sure that you are aware of the spectrum of stress for a young person affected by an adult's substance misuse. For example, we have the usual teenage worries but they are amplified (exams , friendship issues vs financial difficulties, safety, family dynamics, lack of rules and boundaries/structure and parenting).
- Understand the behaviours associated with various types of substance misuse e.g. aggression, neglectful parenting etc.
- Understand how a child's self-esteem can affect goals, both in terms of the goals we set and whether we achieve them.
- If a parent is not engaging with services please try to arrange some support for us. We need respite. Longer term respite would be useful to enable them to understand what emotional warmth FEELS like and what normal relationships FEEL like, not just what they should look like.
- The age of a child should not limit the amount of support they receive. You seem to think that as we get older we need less help. From our perspective it feels like it's the other way around.
- Emotional needs should be taken into consideration as well as physical/materialistic needs.

Feedback from staff about what is best practice when supporting children and young people affected by substance misuse:

- An understanding of emotional neglect which can happen with substance misuse and its impact on young people
- The importance of a focus on emotional safety, rather than just physical safety. Often staff find that when a child reaches the age of 14 or 15, children's services back off because they feel the young person can look after themselves. While this may be true on a practical level, young people at this age are incredibly vulnerable due to other stresses such as school, exams, thinking about the future, finding a sense of who they are etc, and therefore the importance of emotional support cannot be underestimated. In one situation staff worked with a family where the younger children were on a child protection plan but the older child in the family was a child in need. The two separate processes also meant double the meetings for professionals involved which was time that could perhaps be better spent directly supporting the family.
- An awareness of how young people may monitor their family members alcohol use and how this can lead to arguments and potentially unsafe situations.
- An awareness of how a person cannot just stop drinking/taking drugs as the cycle of change is a long process. Recovery is not a binary process whereby either someone is either using substances or not, it is a journey, and should not solely be about negative drug testing. In relation to this, a family member can be stable on methadone, for example, and still be able to parent very well.
- An awareness that the whole family may need ongoing support, even when the family member has started to engage with services.
- An understanding of the ripple effect that substance misuse has on the whole family with regard to emotional stress, changes to routine, and practicalities.
- Due care to making young people feel believed.
- The importance of understanding what a day looks like for the young person and for the person using substances. What are the issues and worries along the way? For example, does a child/young person have specific worries when they wake up in the morning as that is the time when a parent is poorly due to withdrawal effects or alcohol?
- The importance of avoiding labels.
- The importance of silences, allowing a young person to think and find a way of working through their fears and expressing themselves.
- A reassurance is required to young people that talking about the substance use of a family member does not automatically mean they will be taken away from them. Many young people fear this, and it stops them from opening up. In addition, they fear they will be in trouble for speaking up and, in some instances, feel the drug or alcohol use is their fault. In relation to this, there is a need to test and try out safety plans. Staff have experienced young people agreeing to safety plans out of loyalty to parents but then the plans are not followed.
- The importance of reviewing safety plans.

WHAT DO WE KNOW ABOUT PREVALENCE?

ADULT MENTAL ILL-HEALTH

Every seven years a survey which measures the prevalence of mental ill health is undertaken in England. It was last reported in 2016 (McManus, Bebbington, Jenkins and Brugha 2016). It is important to recognise that the survey does not include people in hospital, prison, sheltered or supported housing or people who are homeless. The actual figures are therefore likely to be much higher. Even so, the survey indicates:

- 1 in 6 people living in England report experiencing a common mental health problem in any given week.
- Nearly 6% of people experience generalised anxiety disorder.
- Over 3% of people experience depression.
- Almost 2.5% of people report experiencing phobias.
- 4.5% experience Post Traumatic Stress disorder.
- Almost 8% of people have mixed anxiety and depression.

MIND 2019 report that certain conditions are measured over a person's lifetime rather than at set points, and that estimates vary considerably. However, they report that the latest findings suggest:

- 2 in a 100 people will be diagnosed with bipolar disorder.
- 3.3 in a 100 people will be diagnosed with anti-social personality disorder.
- 2.4 in a 100 people will be diagnosed with borderline personality disorder.

Drawing on research studies across England and Wales, MIND calculates that only 1 in 8 people with a mental health condition is receiving treatment at any one time.

SUBSTANCE MISUSE

The latest Government statistics on drugs misuse suggest that around 9% of the population had taken an illegal drug in the last year (2017/2018), whilst statistics for the misuse of prescription drugs are almost impossible to find. In terms of alcohol it is estimated that there are 589,101 dependant drinkers of whom more than 80% are not receiving treatment. Alcohol misuse is the biggest risk factor for death, ill-health and disability amongst 15 to 29 year olds in the UK (Public Health England 2016).

DOMESTIC ABUSE

Women's Aid asserts that there is no reliable data about the prevalence of domestic abuse in England, but they do suggest that The Crime Survey of England and Wales offers the best data, This suggests that 1.2 million women experienced domestic abuse in the year ending March 2017. There is an increased awareness that whilst undoubtedly there is a gender difference in the rates and forms of domestic abuse experiences, men also experience domestic abuse. In the Crime Survey for England and Wales (reported 2018) 29% of women and 13% of men said that they had experienced some form of domestic abuse since the age of 16.

On average the police in England and Wales receive more than a hundred calls an hour relating to domestic abuse (Her Majesty's Inspectorate of Constabulary 2015).

One in seven (14.2%) children and young people under the age of 18 will have lived with domestic violence at some point in their childhood. (Radford et al, 2011).

61.7% of women in refuge on the Day to Count 2017 had children (aged under 18) with them. (Women's Aid, 2018).

PHYSICAL ILL-HEALTH AND DISABILITY

The Office for National Statistics states that more than one in three people in the UK live with a long standing illness or disability (Office for National Statistics 2015).

There are around 1.7million disabled parents in the UK, mostly with physical and sensory impairments (Best Beginnings online 2019).

NSPCC HOW SAFE ARE OUR CHILDREN 2014

The last time that the NSPCC Annual overview of child protection reported on the prevalence of these risk factors was in 2014, identifying:

- 1,796,244 children in England live in households where there is a risk of domestic violence.
- Between 250,000 and 978,000 children have a parent who misuses drugs.
- Somewhere between 920,000 and 3.5 million children are affected by parental alcohol problems.
- 50,000 to more than 2 million children are affected by parental mental ill health.
- The parents of 23,000 to 250,000 children have a significant learning disability which impacts on parenting capacity.

CHILDREN'S COMMISSIONER ESTIMATES

In 2018 the Children's Commissioner's Office (CCO) published a quantitative analysis on the potential numbers of children in England living in households where the 'toxic trio' of factors affecting adults may be present. The report identifies that there is very little "recent and representative empirical evidence on the prevalence of these factors, especially their co-occurrence within the same household" (Chowdry 2018: 3). This report recognises that there are a number of limitations to the statistics identified, but ultimately report that:

- 100,000 children in England (0.9% of all children in England) are in a household where a randomly selected adult faces all three 'toxic trio' issues to a severe extent.
- 420,000 children (3.6% of all children in England) are in a household where a randomly selected adult faces all three 'toxic trio' issues to a moderate/severe extent.

UNDERSTANDING IMPACT

The most important aspect of practice in relation to this KSS statement is recognising impact. Just because a child is living in a family where there is one or more concerning factor in terms of adult mental ill-health, substance misuses, domestic abuse, physical ill-health or disability does not necessarily mean that there is a significant impact on the child. Risks may be increased, but there could be a wide range of protective factors in place. Social workers must understand and be able to assess the impact of these (and other) factors on a child's life.

Drawing on the assessment framework is particularly helpful here. What impact does the risk factor have on:

- The child's developmental needs?
- The parenting capacity?
- How these risks are managed in terms of the family and environmental factors?

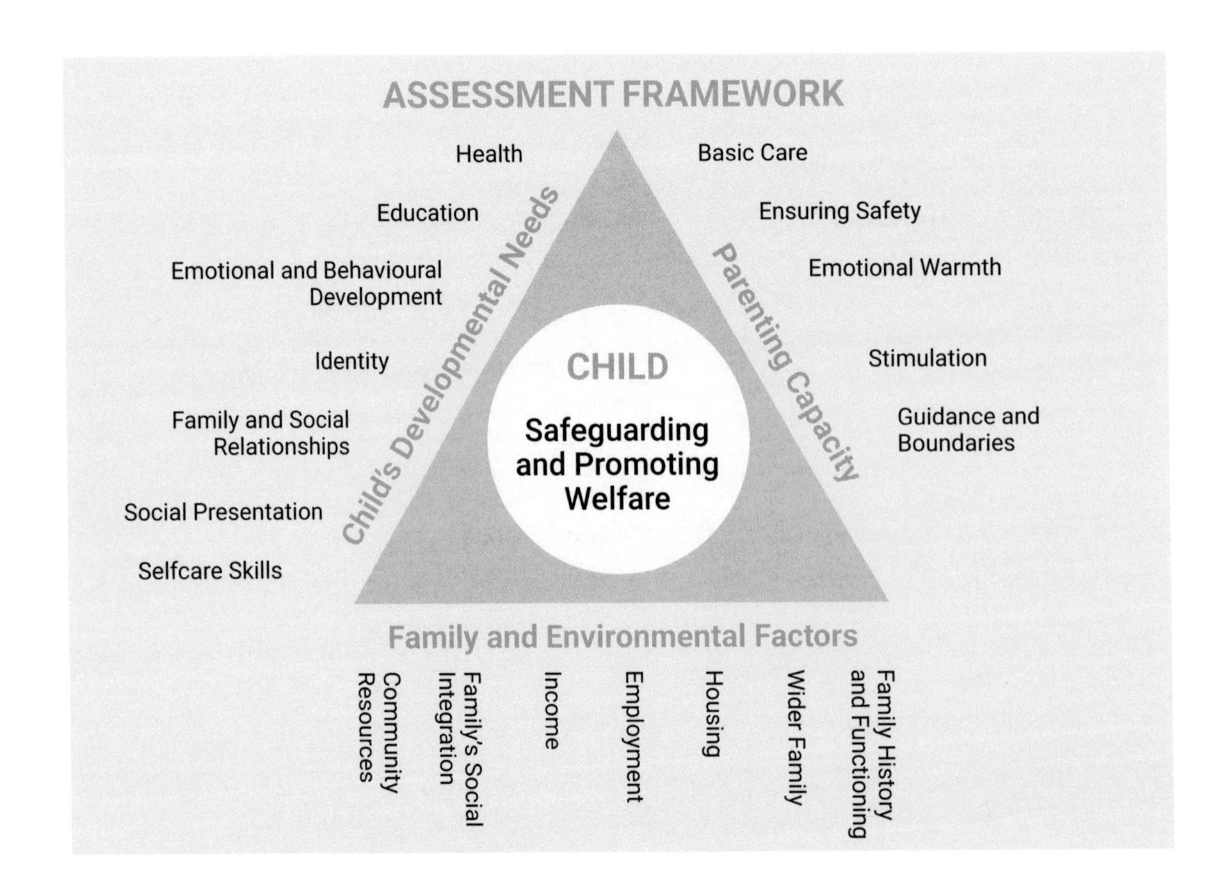

Impact is always uniquely individual and should be seen in the context of the inter-relationship between the risk factors and the supportive factors, drawing on the assessment framework triangle. That said it can be helpful to draw on the wider evidence of impact on children. The next few pages will work through some issues of impact which might be drawn on by social workers in their analysis of the information they obtain during an assessment.

THE IMPACT OF PARENTAL MENTAL ILL HEALTH ON CHILDREN

Mental ill-health is varied and many people will experience some mental health problems at some point in their lives. Where a mental health problem is either long term or very significant, then this can impact on children and young people in a range of ways. Clearly the impact will be varied, depending on the age of the child and their own needs at that time. For example, a teenager needs clear boundaries and parental guidance which may be impacted upon by parental mental ill health. Research, however, tells us that:

- Related stresses such as poverty, poor housing, family separation and lack of social support can increase the risk of children suffering harm.
- Children are most at risk of harm when their mother's mental health problems begin in pregnancy or the first year of life, especially if they are long-lasting or severe.
- The stresses of parenting can make it even more difficult for a parent or carer to cope with their mental health problem – such that there is a co-morbidity of problems (parenting impacts on the parent's mental health which in turn impacts on the child). It is vital that a child is never made to feel that their parent's mental ill-health is their fault.
- There are particular risks to a child when a parent is making threats to harm themselves, their children or other family members, or if they appear to be experiencing psychotic delusions.
- If the adult isn't accepting support offered by mental health services or isn't attending appointments, this loss or lack of support may impact on their children's wellbeing or safety.
- Children may be more at risk of harm if the parent or carer experiencing difficulties is living alone with them without the support of another adult.
- Consider if any of the children had to take on caring responsibilities for their parent, carers or siblings.

(NSPCC 2018)

The impact of a parent's mental ill-health can be mitigated by a range of protective factors including:

- Parents and carers who are willing to acknowledge their difficulties and accept support from services.
- Friends or relatives who are able to care for children and help with practical issues when needed.
- Sufficient benefits and advice available to families struggling with unemployment and poor housing.
- Regular school or nursery attendance, with someone the child feels able to speak to being identified in the educational environment.
- Children knowing who and how to ask for help in the event of a crisis with their parent.
- Good facilities in the wider community such as young carers' projects.

(Cleaver, Unell and Aldgate 2011)

THE IMPACT OF ADULT SUBSTANCE MISUSE ON CHILDREN

Jo- Anne Welsh is a registered nurse. She has worked at the Oasis Project for over 10 years. The Oasis Project takes a gender specific approach to substance misuse treatment and has a particular focus on the impact of parental drug use in children.

The impact of parental drug and alcohol misuse on children is significant, affecting their health and wellbeing at all stages of development, from pre-birth to adolescence and beyond. The impact of problematic drug use (mainly defined as heroin and crack use) was identified in Hidden Harm 2011 (ACMD). Alcohol use is no less problematic and subsequent reports have focused on the impact of this on children.

Drug and alcohol problems can and do affect people throughout society, nevertheless the impact of substance misuse is often greatest on those who are already disadvantaged and often experiencing problems with poverty, housing and social isolation.

Problematic substance misuse is generally surrounded with secrecy and a degree of denial. For parents there are generally high levels of anxiety around accessing services for fear of social services involvement. Some parents will avoid accessing support because they are worried about their children being removed from their care. This may not be an unrealistic assessment of the situation and may have been their experience in childhood. Services should attempt to communicate a message that accessing treatment services is a protective act. Where parents are found to be using substances it is key to engage them with local treatment services for assessment and support. Treatment services will be able to undertake a full assessment of use and undertake any specialist prescribing required. Whilst treatment services have traditionally been seen as being for people with addictions to heroin and alcohol, they can be of use for those with problematic use of other drugs such as cannabis or NPS (New psychoactive substances). There is an emerging issue of addiction to prescribed medication either obtained legitimately which then develops into a problematic pattern of use or obtained illicitly. There are a number of websites which give information about patterns of use and type of drugs. It is important to recognise that drug use trends can change rapidly as a result of changing legislation and supply issues.

Services should develop a treatment plan which may include 1-1 and group work. It may be that a period of engagement with services is required to fully understand the extent of drug use. The development of an effective trusting relationship between worker and parent should be the starting point for treatment. It is not unusual for the parent to be ambivalent about treatment and to minimise use. Motivational interviewing is a key plank of treatment. Where Children's services are already involved with a family as a result of concerns about the impact on children, the social worker should agree the goals of treatment with the treatment service. The first aim of treatment is stability and reduction of harm, including reduction of risks to children. Treatment services in the UK have been criticised for not focusing sufficiently on complete recovery, (for example, no longer requiring ongoing prescribing of opiate substitutes in the case of heroin addiction). A focus on recovery is an important goal of treatment and people should be encouraged to consider their aspirations post treatment so that they have an increasing pool of support and are building "recovery capital."

Structure is an important aspect of recovery from drug and alcohol misuse and children's social workers should aim to work with the parent to develop an appropriate timetable of activities which meet their and their children's needs, recognising that the parent may be under a great deal of stress and may be facing a high level of commitments such as legal appointments , housing issues and attending meetings with domestic abuse services .

It is common for the type of drug used to be seen as the focus of the assessment, but it is essential to place this in the context of the impact on the child. This will also need to be considered with reference to the child's age and developmental stage. Poly drug use involving both legal and illegal drugs is typical and use of both drugs and alcohol needs to be considered. Social workers should make use of supervision and reflective practice to ensure they are aware of their own experiences and lifestyles impacting on assessments of risk. For example, problematic use of alcohol is often assessed as being of less risk to children due to its widespread acceptance in the UK.

Problematic drug and alcohol use often co-exist alongside domestic abuse, although the relationship is complicated. Whilst drug and alcohol use does not cause domestic abuse it can exacerbate it. For women use of substances can be a coping strategy for dealing with abuse and violence. Using a gender informed approach to supporting parents is advisable. It is worthwhile noting that treatment services are generally male dominated with men outnumbering women 3-1. Women can be particularly vulnerable in this environment. There are benefits gained from accessing support alongside others and a women only environment can be particularly beneficial in addressing issues around relationships and parenting. Similarly, there is a tendency to ignore the role of men in treatment as fathers and it is important for social workers to try and engage them in any plan for children.

When there are problematic issues with drugs and alcohol children can be affected over a long period of time. They may be exposed to a range of risks, and usual routines and boundaries are unlikely to be maintained. This can include exposure to violence and illegal activities. Children may find themselves keeping secrets about their family from others either as a result of overt or tacit communication in their family. Children themselves may have concerns about being taken away from their parents. Children frequently express worry and concern about their parent which may include fears that they may die. The support provided to children in their own right should be considered. Social workers should consider what is communicated to children about their parents, offering age appropriate information and avoiding colluding with secrecy. Any support that can be provided which helps with the practical aspects of family life should be considered including providing childcare whilst parents engage with support. It is important to note that when the parent becomes abstinent, or is making progress in recovery this may be a difficult time for the child as they experience the introduction of boundaries and a re-assertion of appropriate family roles. Children may feel more comfortable and safer in "acting out "their feelings at this point which the parent may find very challenging in early recovery. Most parents in treatment will benefit from addition parenting support.

The Oasis Project offers community treatment to women with drug and alcohol problems. It provides a gender specific response in acknowledgment of the difficulties that women can face in accessing treatment. Our portfolio of services and our approach are almost unique in the UK, taking a family focus, providing both childcare and therapeutic services for children. There has been, for some time, a tendency for contracts to provide drug and alcohol treatment to be awarded to big national charities who adopt a "one size fits all approach". In services dominated by men there is a real challenge keeping a focus on the impact of children who are rarely seen.

The impact of drugs and alcohol on children and families is often overlooked in debates about drug use, yet at Oasis, we witness daily the trauma of intergenerational misuse which results in families being separated and early mortality. I would like to see much more focus on outcomes for women in treatment and for children.

THE IMPACT OF DOMESTIC ABUSE ON CHILDREN

The Royal College of Psychiatrists have put together some useful information for parents exploring the impact of domestic abuse on children and young people. This details that impact is varied, but can include:

- They may have difficulty sleeping.
- They are likely to have nightmares or flashbacks.
- They can be easily startled.
- They may complain of physical symptoms such as tummy aches and may start to wet their bed.
- They may have temper tantrums and problems with school.
- They may behave as though they are much younger than they are.
- They may become aggressive or they may internalise their distress and withdraw from other people.
- They may have a lowered sense of self-worth.
- Older children may start to use alcohol or drugs, begin to self-harm by taking overdoses or cutting themselves or have an eating disorder.

(Royal College of Psychiatrists 2019)

The United Nations has explored the impact of violence within the home on children and young people on an international level, first reporting more than ten years ago (UN 2006). This report and UN guidance suggests that the impact of domestic violence can be split into three main areas (UNICEF 2006):

Increased risk of children becoming victims of abuse themselves

The report states that there is international evidence that children who are exposed to violence within their home are much more likely to be physically and/or sexually assaulted than the national average.

Increased risk of harm to the child's physical, social and emotional development

There is international evidence that domestic violence impacts on child development, leading to:

- Delays in development.
- Behaviour changes including excessive irritability, sleep problems, emotional distress, fear of being alone, immature behaviour, and problems with toilet training and language development.
- Primary school age children may have more trouble with school work and show poor concentration and focus. They tend not to do as well in school.

- Personality and behavioural problems among children exposed to violence in the home can take the forms of psychosomatic illnesses, depression, suicidal attempts, and bed-wetting.
- Later in life, children are at greater risk of substance abuse, early pregnancy and criminal behaviour than those raised in homes without violence.

Some studies suggest social development is also damaged. Some children lose the ability to feel empathy for others. Others feel socially isolated, unable to make friends as easily due to social discomfort or confusion over what is acceptable. Many studies have noted that children from violent homes exhibit signs of more aggressive behaviour, such as bullying, and are up to three times more likely to be involved in fighting (Baldry 2003, Fantuzzo and Mohr 1999).

Increased likelihood of cycle of violence on an inter-generational level

UNICEF reports that there is significant evidence on an international level that children experiencing violence within the home may grow up to be either perpetrators or victims of abuse as adults. It is important however, to recognise that this should not be accepted as a deterministic factor in the lives of children and young people who experience domestic abuse.

PAUSE TO REFLECT

How do you ensure that parents are aware of the impact of domestic abuse on children?

THE IMPACT OF ADULT PHYSICAL ILL HEALTH AND DISABILITY ON CHILDREN

The impact of parental ill-health and disability is hugely varied. Adults with social care needs who are also parents should have their parenting responsibilities addressed as part of the assessment. It is important to recognise the impact of austerity on adult social care as adults are often receiving less support and there may be some reluctance on the part of adult services to consider the needs of the adult in terms of their parenting. In practice this can lead to significant challenges with adult social care.

There are a range of organisations that are able to provide advice to parents with disabilities. Those based on peer mentoring may be particularly useful. For example www.disabledparent.org.uk offers some really helpful advice and online support for parents. They also offer information and advice for professionals.

YOUNG CARERS

When the figures from the last census (2011) were reported it showed a 19% increase in the number of young carers aged under 18. Shockingly the figures indicated an 83% increase in the number of 5 to 7 year olds providing care for someone in their household. There was also a 25% increase in the number of young adult carers aged 16 to 25.

In September 2018, Nottingham University and BBC News released figures suggesting there were 800,000 young carers aged 11-16 in England.

The Carers Trust (2019) reporting on a survey they commissioned to mark Young Carers Awareness Day, stated:

- Of the young carers responding to the survey, 37% said they felt 'stressed' while 32% said they felt 'worried' because of caring for someone. And 50% of those who reported stress said they 'often' felt that way.
- Almost a quarter (23%) of young carers felt their caring role had, on at least one occasion, stopped them making friends.
- Less than half (44%) felt they got enough help with their emotions and feelings.
- 22% of young carers responding to the survey, who had negative feelings about caring, said they did not speak to anyone about their feelings. And just 6% said they would speak to a professional working in mental health services.

Children and young people who are providing care for someone else in their household (whilst this is often a parent it may be a sibling or another family member) are entitled to an assessment of their needs as a young carer. So, The Children and Families Act 2014 (Part 5 Section 96) contains the right to a young carers assessment, and there are Young Carers (Needs Assessments) Regulations 2015. Where a young carer is going to be making the transition to adult services then they should have a transition assessment under the Care Act 2014. This is particularly important since research clearly identifies that young people aged 16 to 25 who have care commitments at home are less likely to be in employment, education or training.

PAUL'S PERSPECTIVE

I looked at the title for this chapter and took a deep breath..."Where do I go with this one"? I suppose my starting point needs to reflect that at some point in all our lives we are impacted by our own mental health one way or another.

I understand that a lot of my thought process has been influenced by my childhood and I'm acutely aware that the mistreatment which I experienced potentially set me up to fail in life. I also 'get' that the physical and emotional violence I experienced impacted on the relationships I carved out, both in the care system and once I was in the 'outside' world.

I can see how I became more of a risk taker and why I flirted on the margins of the drug scene, participating with the belief that the people involved were more accepting of me and for the first time allowed me to feel I belonged. Many like me dabbled with every type of substance in order to create an illusion of a better life or feeling, to be able to hide away, when the hurt and mental anguish was too much as well as shielding ourselves from the past. The other appealing aspect to me was I didn't have to try too hard at relationships, as being 'stoned' allows an acceptance of others and allowed me in those moments 'get away' time, where I just didn't need to explain myself to people.

So how did I get involved in these scenes? I suppose I have to look all the way back and start at the beginning! The world I was brought into and witnessed was a scary place, any sense of trust or belief I had was snatched from me before it was allowed to grow. The intent and impact on my childhood and my emotional 'me' were threads I carried into my adulthood. It shaped my approach towards work, people and relationships, taking me years to 'make sense' of events, eventually learning how to recognise, like and value myself, and then, to be able to make positive and lifelong relationships, based on genuine feelings, and more importantly, on trust.

I bear witness that the effects of domestic violence can last a lifetime and I'm aware that studies do show that this can lead to 'life choices/styles' being repeated time and time again. The impact on relationships can become destructive and sometimes the need to 'block out' all memories may involve taking of substances, because trying to come to terms with events can be too much. The impact on mental health can be immeasurable. People often use the word resilience as a strategy, technique or coping mechanism that we, as humans, can apply....'The rubber ball effect', the ability to bounce back to your 'status quo' following setbacks, challenges and or problems we meet during the course of life.

Resilience for me isn't necessarily about overcoming huge challenges; each of us face plenty of challenges on a daily basis for which we must draw on our reserves of experience. Resilience, or as I prefer to call it, 'my bouncability' is a way of relying on, or using different skills. It draws on various sources of help, including rational thinking skills, physical and mental health, and your relationships with those around you. Some people state they can even teach it! But here's a thought, what if the ability or capability to be resilient already exists?...and experiences, finely tune that skill!

Unfortunately for me growing up in children's institutions meant that violence was the 'norm' and the overall impact it had on me was that I became a fearful, yet at times, a fearless child who lacked confidence or belief in himself on one hand and on the other was reckless...a bit of a conundrum. I was a child who was both sensitive and alert to the environment I was living in, and at times appeared to have very little regard for my own personal safety. Afterall, attention in whatever guise is attention!

Compliant to the point of being subservient to any authority or person who was deemed as being more powerful than me. I learned and developed 'mistrust', quietly questioning peoples' motives, but never verbally asking. I craved a held belief that 'big people' would be kind to me, and when that didn't happen, my responses slowly and eventually lost their enthusiasm and I took on the mantles of shame and self-blame, because I believed that everything was my fault!

Unable to control my destiny I even contemplated ending my life at the age of 6, but hadn't accounted for a 'Sunday' bus service, 2 hours is a long time to wait for a small child, especially a fearful and frightened child, who still worried someone might see him and report back. I remember crouching, hiding in a bush by the bus stop, praying desperately for the bus to arrive, before fear overtook me and the thought of retribution saw me returning back!...So I moved on to hurting myself, and I bit and pinched myself to release pain, occasionally jumping from heights or alternatively hitting myself (I now understand this was self-harm). Part of my rationale was the hope that someone would discover me and perhaps rescue me or make me safe. I only stopped because of the physical reprisals dished out when I was finally discovered by those in charge.

The only thing I could control was my silence and unwillingness to co-operate when someone was trying to positively engage (Hadn't I already learned that confidentiality was just a word that wasn't applied to me). It was called defiance, even "work of the devil" by those in charge and usually, because of my action, violence ensued, but I was okay with that, as I still believed I 'owned' the control and could change the course...The innocence of child logic or perhaps wishful thinking!

On leaving the system I found that I had a self-destruct button, and I seemed hell bent, on trying all manner of substances, engaging in risky behaviour, relationships and homelessness. My value of myself didn't sit easy with me. I constantly compared myself to peers and others. I never felt as if I was 'good enough', to either be with someone, to be in their company or deserving of any positive interest. I even believed that others could see my shame and recognised that I wasn't their equal (I was quite harsh on myself).

Following a particular incident, I questioned 'What' I was doing and took the first steps to not fulfil the prophesy that others had predicted! (I'm not sure where that little voice came from but I'm glad I listened).

The reach of 'domestic violence' still continued, and impacted on the relationships I initially made as an adult, and I struggled making 'mutually equally balanced' relationships, as I sought individuals who were domineering and appeared strong. I wanted to take on a subservient role (comfortable and easy for me to negotiate, as it's what I knew best). By my mid thirties

I finally began to understand what I really needed from a relationship and more importantly 'what' a healthy relationship looked like, I was beginning to find my own sense of value!

Finding the right relationship has meant that I could 'iron out my creases' in a safe place, where I have been given space to reflect, where I can look at my experiences and use it positively to move forward and help myself and I hope others.

PAUSE TO REFLECT

Reading Paul's perspective what strikes you?

When working with parents you may have a clear understanding of, and empathy for, their difficulties. How do you keep the focus on the impact on the child?

RESPONDING TO CONCERNS IN THIS AREA: BELONGS

Throughout this resource it is clear (particularly from Paul's perspectives) that children want to belong. In fact, a sense of belonging is one of the most consistent and important issues that come out of talking to children who have grown up in contact with the care system. So, a sense of where someone belongs is important in social work practice. Joint working can also throw up questions about where responsibility for something 'belongs'.

Where there are concerns about the impact of adult behaviours and circumstances on children then working through the different stages of the acronym BELONGS can be helpful in practice:

Bring concerns to light – remain focused on the impact on children.

Ensure engagement – work to make sure that everyone understands the concerns and is working towards change.

Levels of concern – be clear about the risks to children and young people and ensure that managing these risks and ensuring the child's wellbeing is paramount in all the work undertaken.

Observe the situation – keep the situation under regular review. What impact is the social work intervention having on the outcomes for the child?

Networks – look at the networks that the family already has. How might these networks support change in the family circumstances? Or will they hinder it?

Get the right support in place to enhance these networks to ensure children are protected.

Safety first – always make sure that children and young people are kept safe.

One of the most significant challenges that social workers face in respect of this aspect of practice is working with adult services. It can feel as though there is a major conflict about where the concerns 'belong.' Is this about the adult's needs or the child's needs? Social workers (from both service backgrounds) report feeling as though the situation is being batted backwards and forwards in some kind of game. A 'think family' approach which explores the inter-relationship between an adult's needs, their parenting responsibilities and the child's needs is vital. The most important factor for everyone must be the child's welfare.

Working in the area of practice covered by this chapter can highlight some of the most significant conflicts of interest and competing demands, both in terms of working with parents and in terms of working with other professionals, but it is essential that the child's needs are paramount.

CHANTELLE

Chantelle is 14. She has been living with her grandparents since she was 2. Her mother is a drug user and is unable to look after Chantelle. Chantelle's father died about two years ago following a drug overdose. Chantelle's grandparents, Jacob and Prospera, have a Special Guardianship Order in place.

Jacob had a stroke six months ago. He has been left with a number of physical limitations and his verbal communication is now very limited. Jacob was discharged from hospital with a package of home care consisting of three care calls a day. Prospera's own health is failing and she is struggling with supporting Chantelle. Chantelle has stopped attending school. She has been reported as missing on a number of occasions. You have just taken a call on duty from the adult services home care manager. Care staff have reported that when they visited this morning Chantelle was in the house with several young people. They were shouting at Jacob when the staff arrived and Prospera was in tears. The young people left quickly. Care staff have refused to go back today as they are concerned for their own safety. The care manager says children's services "have to fix this".

What do you do?

Hannah Shead – CEO of Trevi House, been in post since 2011. Hannah has been in the addiction field since 2000 and has experience in both the statutory and voluntary sector.

Hannah is particularly passionate about women's issues; in January 2018, Trevi House opened Plymouth's first Women's Centre, which has recently received funding from the Ministry of Justice to move into larger premises and support more women.

Website www.trevihouse.org
Twitter @HannahFShead
Facebook @TreviHouse93.

Trevi House is a mother and child rehab that was opened in 1993.

We were opened in response to unmet need; three local practitioners had identified that there were no facilities offering residential rehabilitation from drugs and alcohol that enabled mothers to be accompanied by their children.

Based in Plymouth, we work with families from throughout the whole of the UK; a placement at Trevi House is between 12-24 weeks. Our therapeutic programme focuses upon parenting, domestic abuse and addressing the issues underlying the addiction. We offer both group and 1-2-1 therapy, with care plans tailored to the individual and unique needs of each family.

We offer detox from methadone, buprenorphine and diazepam. 95% of women successfully complete their detox, a statistic that we are proud of and attribute to motivational power offered when a mother and child are kept together.

We work with up to 20 families a year, providing a range of interventions for both the mother and the child. Whilst mum is in therapy, her child can be cared for on site in our specialist Ofsted registered nursery. We carry out a Thrive assessment with each child to help us understand and support any unmet emotional needs.

We work with families across the spectrum of children's social care involvement. Some children are on a Child in Need. Others are on an interim care order; It is not uncommon for a placement at Trevi to be the last option before permanent removal.

Our goal at Trevi is to avoid separation of mother and child, both in the short term whilst mum undertakes her recovery, and longer term as women learn to live drug and alcohol free and to keep their children safe.

Children up to the age of 9 can come to Trevi with their mum. We have forged strong partnerships with a local school, thus minimising disruptions to a child's education. In the case of newborn babies, we aim to admit into placement the mother and child together directly from the hospital or where possible, during pregnancy. This enables us to support the infant attachment process during those early critical days. We have a midwife on the team who is able to support with establishing and maintaining breastfeeding. We have a team who are able to support new mums to find their feet as they care for their baby.

We are working with a highly vulnerable group who need an enhanced level of support. Attempts to make changes accessing community services have failed due to the complexity of the women's needs.

Providing a safe, nurturing and trauma informed environment is key. At Trevi we work hard to provide a space that is safe and trauma informed. We have a saying, "we come to work in your home". Visitors all remark that Trevi is a homely environment, it does not feel like an institution. We recognise that the little things are often the big things, for example a welcome card and toiletries in a room for a woman and her child upon arrival.

All staff participate in trauma informed training which enables us to reflect upon our practice and see the world through the lens of a traumatised woman. When presented with challenging behaviour, rather than saying, "What is wrong with you?" we begin to ask, "What happened to you?"

We try to hold in mind the fear that accompanies most of our residents, fear of losing their baby. Distrust of professionals and 'the system'. Many women have had negative experiences of professionals both in childhood and adulthood. We have to work hard to build their trust, it will not be given to us easily. We are transparent with women, reflecting our concerns as well as the positives that we see. We try to manage the challenges that sometimes arise when simultaneously empowering and supporting a woman and safeguarding a child; we are able to be open with women about that tension and try to make them part of the solution.

We try to demonstrate in our practice that we have a genuine respect for the women we support; they are included in all new staff recruitments and if they raise any concerns, we seek to respond with openness.

A high proportion of the women that we work with are survivors of both childhood sexual violence and domestic abuse.

Most of the women who we support have had at least one previous child removed. They are families trapped in a desperate and traumatic cycle of repeat pregnancy and removal.

In cases of recurrent proceedings, 60% of care proceedings are issued within 4 weeks of birth (Broadhurst et al 2017). Whilst there undoubtedly are occasions where separation is necessary, we believe that it is important to explore opportunities for babies to be given the chance to remain in the care of their mother from birth whilst decisions are made regarding their longer-term care.

We have seen too many times that when a mother no longer has her child in her care, subsequent attempts to cease using drugs fail. We have seen many times that upon removal of her baby, a mother immediately reunites with an abusive and controlling partner. We understand how those external factors eat away at self-esteem and self-belief, two key ingredients for achieving change.

We have learnt over the years, that fear is a significant interrupter of motivation and undermines a woman's potential to achieve change. We have observed that when women are scared and feel powerless, when they believe that they are going to have their baby removed from their care, they behave in ways that are counterproductive to achieving change. They take drugs to block out the pain. They don't attend key meetings or access the support on offer. At Trevi we support mothers to learn to work in partnership with professionals. To build relationships of trust and respect.

We all know that parenthood is a tough job! A 2012 study by the Essential Parent Company showed that around 80% of new parents felt both anxious and completely unprepared with the practical skills they need to look after their new baby. For the mothers who we work with, this 'normal' anxiety is compounded by the stressors of care proceedings, alongside the many other challenges that they are seeking to overcome, for example substance misuse, domestic violence, unresolved childhood trauma and their own experiences of being parented.

Key to our approach, is the value that we place upon keeping a child and mother together. Whilst not every child will leave Trevi House in their mother's care, we want to create the best possible conditions for safe enough parenting to flourish. The relationship between mother and child is able to develop in an environment that is more nurturing and supportive than, for example a contact centre.

Between 60-70% of children will leave Trevi House still in the care of their mother. We can confidently say that for many of these cases, if mother and child were living separately in the community whilst proceedings were underway, they would not have achieved reunification.

To find out more about Trevi House or to make a referral, please contact our admission team on 01752 255 758.

"7 Months before coming to Trevi (January 2012) I relapsed on drugs and alcohol I was 6 months pregnant with my 5th child, my drug and alcohol use was out of control I was scared to ask for help in case social services used it against me. As none of my other 4 children lived with me I didn't want my 5th to go into care as well.

But 9 weeks into my relapse I admitted to professionals I'd been drinking and using. My drugs worker booked me into a detox centre where I went on to a waiting list. I waited 6 weeks and then was given my date to go in. I was 8 and a half months pregnant when I went in, 4 days into my detox I went into labour. I gave birth to a beautiful baby boy. The moment I saw him I knew everything was going to be alright. I had to make sure of it. My son was relying on me.

I completed my detox and then went to a dry house; my son went into foster care at this time, whilst there I worked on my substance misuse and parenting completing courses in the community for about 3 months. When this finished, I asked my social worker about going to a mother and baby unit. She agreed and I came to Trevi House with my son.

I was nervous and anxious and excited to be able to have the opportunity to be with my son something I thought would never had happened. Thanks to Trevi this was possible. I came to Trevi a very angry person but, since I have been here and worked through my issues, I am a different person. I am a better mum and I now believe in myself again. It's also made me become a more caring and understanding person. I now know that I am a nice person and I deserve to be loved and without Trevi I know I wouldn't be the person I am today. I have a future now that's full of excitement and a new journey has begun for me and my son. I really do owe Trevi my life.

The next part of my journey is for me and my son to move into our new flat and make it our home. We'll take each day as it comes but the future I want for me and my son is a lot brighter now."

PAUSE TO REFLECT

What services can you draw on to work with children and families when supporting them in relation to adult factors?

Emergency services	*Routine services*

Where are there gaps in services?

How might you address these gaps?

WHERE AM I NOW?

Revisit the start of the chapter. Look again at the KSS standard. Then consider the following questions:

What has surprised me in working through this chapter?

What three things would I highlight as key learning?

What do I still need to do in working towards being fully confident with this KSS statement?

What single next step should I take in working towards an improvement in my practice?

Chapter 5

ABUSE AND NEGLECT OF CHILDREN

This chapter sits right in the middle of this resource, in the same way that this statement sits right in the centre of the Knowledge and Skills Statement. It is an unfortunate fact that the abuse and neglect of children is at the core of social work with children and their families, the very purpose of what we do being about keeping children safe from abuse and neglect. To do this we need to draw on each of the other statements. So for example, a social worker must be able to create a relationship and communicate effectively with children; they need to be able to undertake a clear assessment of the child's needs; where there are concerns of abuse and neglect then the court process may be activated; all of this will involve understanding and analysis and an ability to work within the context of the organisation.

THE KSS REQUIRES PRACTITIONERS TO:

Exchange information with partner agencies about children and adults where there is concern about the safety and welfare of children. Triangulate evidence to ensure robust conclusions are drawn. Recognise harm and the risk indicators of different forms of harm to children relating to sexual, physical, emotional abuse and neglect. Take into account the long-term effects of cumulative harm, particularly in relation to early indicators of neglect.

Consider the possibility of child sexual exploitation, grooming (on and offline), female genital mutilation and enforced marriage and the range of adult behaviours which pose a risk to children, recognising too the potential for children to be perpetrators of abuse.

Lead the investigation of allegations of significant harm to children in consultation with other professionals and practice supervisors. Draw one's own conclusions about the likelihood of, for example, sexual abuse or non-accidental injury having occurred and the extent to which any injury is consistent with the explanation offered. Commission a second professional opinion and take legal advice where necessary.

Take a look at the standard above in detail. Highlight key phrases and anything that jumps out at you. Then take some time to reflect on the statement.

- *What are your immediate thoughts?*
- *What might you want to discuss and clarify?*
- *How will you clarify meanings?*
- *Who will you discuss it with?*

GETTING FEEDBACK ON PRACTICE

Who can give me feedback on my practice in this area?

How will I get the feedback?

Make sure to keep a record of any feedback you receive.

INITIAL SELF-ASSESSMENT

What do I already do well?

How do I know? (What's my evidence?)

What do I need to work on?

How will I work on this?

GLOSSARY OF TERMS

The following definitions of different forms of abuse are taken (mostly) from Working Together to Safeguard Children (2018). The final definition is taken from the NSPCC (2018).

ABUSE	A form of maltreatment of a child. Somebody may abuse or neglect a child by inflicting harm, or by failing to act to prevent harm. Children may be abused in a family or in an institutional or community setting by those known to them or, more rarely, by others. Abuse can take place wholly online, or technology may be used to facilitate offline abuse. Children may be abused by an adult or adults, or another child or children.
PHYSICAL ABUSE	A form of abuse which may involve hitting, shaking, throwing, poisoning, burning or scalding, drowning, suffocating or otherwise causing physical harm to a child. Physical harm may also be caused when a parent or carer fabricates the symptoms of, or deliberately induces, illness in a child.
EMOTIONAL ABUSE	The persistent emotional maltreatment of a child such as to cause severe and persistent adverse effects on the child's emotional development. It may involve conveying to a child that they are worthless or unloved, inadequate, or valued only insofar as they meet the needs of another person. It may include not giving the child opportunities to express their views, deliberately silencing them or 'making fun' of what they say or how they communicate. It may feature age or developmentally inappropriate expectations being imposed on children. These may include interactions that are beyond a child's developmental capability, as well as overprotection and limitation of exploration and learning, or preventing the child participating in normal social interaction. It may involve seeing or hearing the ill-treatment of another. It may involve serious bullying (including cyber bullying), causing children frequently to feel frightened or in danger, or the exploitation or corruption of children. Some level of emotional abuse is involved in all types of maltreatment of a child, though it may occur alone.
SEXUAL ABUSE	Involves forcing or enticing a child or young person to take part in sexual activities, not necessarily involving a high level of violence, whether or not the child is aware of what is happening. The activities may involve physical contact, including assault by penetration (for example, rape or oral sex) or non-penetrative acts such as masturbation, kissing, rubbing and touching outside of clothing. They may also include non-contact activities, such as involving children in looking at, or in the production of, sexual images, watching sexual activities, encouraging children to behave in sexually inappropriate ways, or grooming a child in preparation for abuse. Sexual abuse can take place online, and technology can be used to facilitate offline abuse. Sexual abuse is not solely perpetrated by adult males. Women can also commit acts of sexual abuse, as can other children.
CHILD SEXUAL EXPLOITATION	Child sexual exploitation is a form of child sexual abuse. It occurs where an individual or group takes advantage of an imbalance of power to coerce, manipulate or deceive a child or young person under the age of 18 into sexual activity (a) in exchange for something the victim needs or wants, and/or (b) for the financial advantage or increased status of the perpetrator or facilitator. The victim may have been sexually exploited even if the sexual activity appears consensual. Child sexual exploitation does not always involve physical contact; it can also occur through the use of technology.

NEGLECT	The persistent failure to meet a child's basic physical and/or psychological needs, likely to result in the serious impairment of the child's health or development. Neglect may occur during pregnancy as a result of maternal substance abuse. Once a child is born, neglect may involve a parent or carer failing to: a. provide adequate food, clothing and shelter (including exclusion from home or abandonment) b. protect a child from physical and emotional harm or danger c. ensure adequate supervision (including the use of inadequate caregivers) d. ensure access to appropriate medical care or treatment It may also include neglect of, or unresponsiveness to, a child's basic emotional needs.
EXTREMISM	Extremism goes beyond terrorism and includes people who target the vulnerable – including the young – by seeking to sow division between communities on the basis of race, faith or denomination; justify discrimination towards women and girls; persuade others that minorities are inferior; or argue against the primacy of democracy and the rule of law in our society.
COUNTY LINES	As set out in the Serious Violence Strategy, published by the Home Office, a term used to describe gangs and organised criminal networks involved in exporting illegal drugs into one or more importing areas within the UK, using dedicated mobile phone lines or other form of 'deal line'. They are likely to exploit children and vulnerable adults to move and store the drugs and money, and they will often use coercion, intimidation, violence (including sexual violence) and weapons.
CHILD CRIMINAL EXPLOITATION	As set out in the Serious Violence Strategy, published by the Home Office, where an individual or group takes advantage of an imbalance of power to coerce, control, manipulate or deceive a child or young person under the age of 18 into any criminal activity (a) in exchange for something the victim needs or wants, and/or (b) for the financial or other advantage of the perpetrator or facilitator and/or (c) through violence or the threat of violence. The victim may have been criminally exploited even if the activity appears consensual. Child criminal exploitation does not always involve physical contact; it can also occur through the use of technology.
ONLINE ABUSE AND HARM (Definition taken from NSPCC 2018)	Online abuse is abuse that is facilitated using internet-connected technology. It may take place through social media, online games or other channels of digital communication. Children can also be re-victimised if evidence of their abuse is recorded or uploaded online. Technology can facilitate a number of illegal abusive behaviours including, but not limited to: harassment; stalking; threatening behaviour; child sexual abuse material; inciting a child to sexual activity; sexual exploitation; grooming; sexual communication with a child; and, causing a child to view images or watch videos of a sexual act. Using technology to facilitate any of the above activities is online abuse. Alongside those illegal activities that are perpetrated online and constitute abuse, children may also be exposed to online harms, such as inappropriate behaviours or content online. For instance, children may be bullied online by their peers or they might, either accidentally or intentionally, view content which is intended for adults. Both online abuse and exposure to unsuitable content or behaviour can have a long-lasting impact on the wellbeing of children and young people.

WHAT'S MISSING?

The title here is purposeful!

Looking at the Glossary on the last two pages, you may have felt that some forms of abuse and neglect were missing. What didn't you see? I added in a definition taken from the NSPCC in relation to online abuse since I felt that was a real omission, but there are many things that are missing from the list.

Having been in social work for almost 30 years, I am conscious about how knowledge and understanding has changed considerably. There are some situations and people that you work with which remain with you throughout your professional careers. One of the most vivid recollections from my very early career lies around my work with a young woman, who I will call Jodie. I had worked with Jodie for a few months and I felt that we had a good working relationship. There were a number of issues for Jodie living at home and as she moved into local authority care I remember driving her to the residential service about an hour away from her home. I visited her a couple of times over the next week and very quickly our relationship changed. Jodie refused to see me and was often out of the service setting when she knew I was visiting. Over the next few weeks Jodie was seen getting into taxis, she went missing for days at a time and returned to the service simply to shower and change, leaving again when any staff tried to have conversations with her. Reading this story now any social workers will recognise the key signs of child trafficking and sexual exploitation. At the time, I was really concerned and had various discussions about Jodie with residential staff and my manager. I was told that Jodie had made a 'lifestyle choice' and that she was now a child prostitute. I was advised to prioritise my time differently and not to spend so much time on trying to engage with Jodie ("I know it's difficult - but it's best to just give up on her. Move on to others that you can make a difference for.") Even writing that now angers and upsets me. At the time, there was little or no language that I could draw on to help me to challenge the dominant discourse within the organisation. I challenged at every level I could. As a result, I was told that I had a training need and was sent on a training course entitled Child Prostitution. I recall how uncomfortable I felt about the fact that I had been involved in supporting Jodie to move into local authority care which had now chosen to label her in such a way. Shortly after this I left the post, largely because I felt so uncomfortable in the role.

Now, it is impossible for us to look at stories of young people like Jodie and not understand that she was being abused, trafficked and exploited. However, less than 30years ago social workers had no framework for understanding this. It was not part of either the public or professional consciousness. It is important to recognise what knowledge is missing and how this might impact on our work.

Going back further even issues of child sexual abuse were not clear in social work practice. Indeed in 1982, Judith Herman picked up that the issue of childhood sexual abuse "has been repeatedly unearthed in the past hundred years, and just as repeatedly buried... The information was simply too threatening to be maintained in public consciousness" (Herman 1982:7). Even following Judith Herman's work in the early 1980s it could be argued that knowledge about child sexual abuse was buried again. Press coverage about Jimmy Saville and Operation Yewtree illustrates very clearly the way that knowledge about child abuse and societal values around the safeguarding of children have changed significantly in the recent past.

So what is "being buried" or is missing from our understanding just now? Issues of Female Genital Mutilation and breast ironing are becoming clearer in our understanding, as are issues of a belief in evil spirit possession. The prevalence of institutional abuse, the fabrication of illness, the impact of bullying for example are all areas where we are becoming more aware. It is vital that you keep your knowledge under review and that wherever you feel a child is not safe you keep them at the very centre of your practice, exploring appropriate responses in conjunction with colleagues. What is missing must be kept under review, but who is missing should never be an issue – the child and their voice must never be missing from our practice.

PAUSE TO REFLECT

What is missing from the glossary of terms on pages 158-159?

How do you ensure that you keep up to date with current thinking and awareness in relation to the abuse and neglect of children?

Have there been any situations where you have felt that there were risks to a child, which were not clear and which people did not seem to recognise in terms of abuse and neglect? What did you do? What might you do differently in the future?

CONTEXTUAL SAFEGUARDING

Contextual Safeguarding has been developed by Carlene Firmin at the University of Bedfordshire. It is a fairly new concept but has gained widespread recognition. It is now included in Working Together to Safeguard Children (2018). It is an approach which is designed to be used with young people and organisations. It is based on understanding, and responding to, young peoples' experiences of significant harm beyond their families. It recognises that the different relationships which young people form in their communities (both real and virtual) can feature violence and abuse. Parents and carers have little influence over these contexts, and young peoples' experiences of extra-familial abuse can, in fact, undermine parent-child relationships. (Firmin 2017).

Contextual safeguarding demonstrates the importance of the social worker connecting the I and the E (a core theme which runs through this resource). In a young person's world, what goes on in their external environment can impact on what goes on in their internal world, and the two can compound each other.

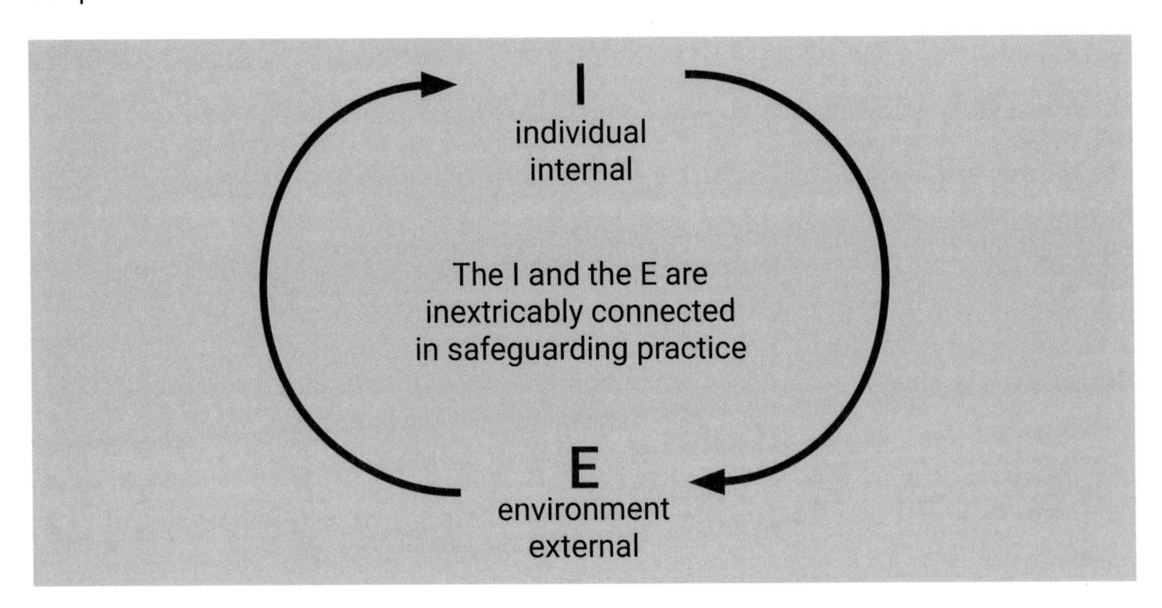

According to Firmin (2019) a contextual safeguarding approach seeks to create a response to extra-familial forms of abuse that can:

- Target the contexts in which that abuse occurs, from assessment through to intervention.
- Frame practice to address extra-familial risk through the lens of child welfare, as opposed to crime reduction or community safety.
- Utilise partnerships between children's services and agencies who have a reach into extra-familial contexts (such as transport providers, retailers, youth workers, residents' associations, parks and recreation services, schools and so on).
- Measure success with reference to the nature of the context in which harm has been occurring, rather than solely focusing on any behaviour changes displayed by young people who were at risk in those contexts.

According to Firmin (2019) a contextual safeguarding approach is made up of two tiers:

The first tier involves acknowledging context more explicitly in all work with children and families. This could include talking with parents about the context in which they are trying to parent their child and engaging young people in activities where they can explore their feelings of safety in public, as well as private, spaces. Rather than just 'safety planning' with a young person, and therefore focusing on the actions they can take, practitioners might also do 'safety mapping' with a young person to put their decisions in context. They can help them to identify safe adults or community guardians they could reach out to when feeling vulnerable in their local neighbourhood.

At the second tier, work is undertaken to create resources and approaches for assessing and intervening with peer groups, schools and public spaces identified as ones in which young people have experienced abuse. This ranges from thinking about how to conduct observations in neighbourhoods, through to creating processes to refer contexts into safeguarding hubs, and holding context conferences, in place of child protection conferences, to build plans for contexts that have been assessed. This is about looking beyond the I to the E – not just considering safeguarding responses to an individual child, but also to an environment.

There are a number of trials around contextual safeguarding at present, and methods and resources are likely to emerge from these. It is important, however, to recognise that contextual safeguarding is all about context and therefore resources are likely to be context and community specific. That said, there is a wide range of helpful material available online, particularly from the Contextual Safeguarding Network (https://www.contextualsafeguarding.org.uk/en/about/the-contextual-safeguarding-network)

PAUSE TO REFLECT

What do you know about contextual safeguarding?

How might it be useful to you in your practice?

The expectation that childhood should be happy, carefree and fun isn't unrealistic, but unfortunately for some children this isn't their norm. Growing up in the 'care system' during the 60s and 70s, I, and countless others I shared the space with, were shaped, marked and defined by violence, abuse and the neglect experienced there.

How did this happen? Surely children in institutions would be looked after and cared for, wouldn't they?

Sadly, safeguarding and the welfare of children didn't feel like the driver then. The children growing up were often overlooked and subjected to unprecedented acts of violence and abuse from various sources, both internally and externally due to their vulnerability, little advocacy and certainly a lack of systems in place to keep them safe.

The term abuse and neglect conjures up all sorts of negativity, hardship, pain, hurt and feelings of helplessness for me. These are the memories and unseen scars that marked my childhood within institutional care. Looking back, I replay aspects of my childhood and take from it that no repeats of this existence should happen again, certainly never to any child who I have responsibility for.

Definitions of abuse and neglect often 'muddy' each other's waters. The crossover of both of these isn't lost on me and probably reflects most of my growing up.

As a child, abuse and neglect came in many guises and equally from many sources. Physical and sexual abuse were prevalent and unfortunately for me I escaped neither. The acts themselves are and were horrific, but they eventually pass as the hurt experienced was physical and momentary. The mental and emotional hurt coupled with the feelings of shame become the beast within and certainly fuelled my self-belief regarding my own worth. Combine this with no one taking responsibility and children like me become lost, we become emotional vacuums or time bombs, awaiting to explode.

Feelings were so important for me as well as some sort of belief in justice (I'm not sure where that came from!) Unfortunately, I learned that being a child in care meant I wasn't allowed them (feelings) and no one was looking after 'how I felt'. The emotional hurt I understood, left me believing that I didn't matter, that I couldn't be loved and everything that happened was because I deserved it. This also meant I lost my willingness to speak and impacted on my ability to trust 'big people' as my experiences had already taught me that when I spoke, I would be rewarded with a punch or something far worse.

Events continued which only increased my sensitivity to movement and my surroundings (I still subconsciously 'clock' my exits wherever I go!) I became increasingly aware and able to detect or respond to slight changes or signals regarding the emotional states of others, their movements and their moods in order to survive where I was growing up, the only change or relief came about eventually, when those that were hurting me and those that should have been responsible, were moved on. It didn't stop all the abuse, but it lightened the load, and for me that was enough.

So how did the various abuse and neglect impact on me? To be told almost on a daily basis that you don't count or wasn't wanted eventually took its toll on me. I began believing the words and expression used towards me. I actually believed no one could care for me or wanted to, and even if someone remotely expressed an interest I reacted in a destructive and distrustful manner believing I didn't deserve that level of interest. I challenged people by being overly compliant in complete silence or without expression. I struggled or refused to hold eye contact. To look someone in the eye created fear for me, it felt as if I was challenging them and I understood from experience that this only resulted in me receiving some sort of physical chastisement. This legacy followed me through most of my adult life. I found it difficult to accept touch, often flinching and mistrusting of people's intentions and because I had learned silence I struggled to express my thoughts especially if they differed from others.

Wearing three hats (Care experienced, an adopter, a fostering family) I hope gives me some understanding of some of the young children we have looked after. Most have come from households experiencing varying degrees of abuse and neglect. Initially they show signs of watchfulness and are hyper alert to their new surroundings, whilst others have come to us closed and shut down and very unresponsive.

We get asked how do we help the children 'turn around' their behaviours? There isn't a magic formula! Time, patience and consistency help. Operating always at the child's pace. Positiveness, even in the smallest of ways, as for some children, it may be unrecognisable to have received praise!......The reward of witnessing a child smile and 'look' pleased with themselves is priceless! The satisfaction of watching a child gain an understanding that the world can be a kind place where they won't be hurt is perhaps the greatest joy.

One child who came to stay with us could barely take their eyes off the floor and had very limited vocabulary, they flinched if I approached them and assumed the fetal position if I moved my hands towards their head. We could only assume that some sort of violence had been experienced as there was very little known regarding the type of abuse, either witnessed or experienced by them. At night time this child slept rigid, stiff like a board, unable to relax as if they were preparing themselves for some sort of altercation!

For the next three months, I spent a lot of time on my knees in order to effectively reduce my height and be on their level. I established 'walking' routines, where we explored the village we lived in, keeping the same routes, talking about the same things, before introducing new interests. The aim, of course, was to create a safe routine that they understood and could learn to relax in.

One day about three months in, the child asked if they could have a hug on my lap. Of course, I obliged, and they sat upright unsure what to do. They asked if they could have a nice hug (they had noticed that we, as a family hug each other, and our other children often used the phrase 'that was a nice hug'). They leaned into me and for 45 minutes we sat like this. (I was desperate for a wee and had decided that if the worse comes to the worse I'd have to wet myself, as this child needed this hug.) Throughout this time, they stroked my hands and eventually said to me "Babu (Their name for me), your hands soft". "Not all men's have soft hands, I like soft hands".

These words meant so much to me and I cried later on, to hear this little child find words to say he felt safe and knowing that they understood that not all men will hurt them was a real game changer.

The real change in this child was seeing their development and understanding of the world accelerate. Using picture cards, we were able to play and talk about what we thought was happening in the picture, what someone might be feeling etc. Their ability to name feelings increased as did their level of empathy and we were fortunate to see the 'waking' of the child they were meant to be.

I still get to see this little person (well not so little now). They love stroking my head, face and hands and still tell me I've got soft hands...How good is that!

Siobhan Pyburn is the founder of the Beam Project.

The Beam Project offers training workshops based on lived experience of child sexual abuse. Siobhan has written for several publications including Care Knowledge and the Journal of Family Health, and is currently completing an MSc in Safeguarding in an International Context. You can connect with her on twitter at @beam_project

'Why didn't you just tell someone?' Some factors you may not have considered.

'You've got your father wrapped around your little finger.' My step mother loved to remind me. It was my third Monday off school in as many weeks, and they were as likely to question it as my step mum was to look under the bonnet of why I always seemed to 'get my own way' at home. There is an expectation that fathers dote on their little girls, but mine was neither warm nor paternally-inclined. It seems he wasn't much interested in my education, either. He was an Irish mechanic who met and targeted my Indian mum at just the right moment of vulnerability (the wrong moment): as she was fleeing to the UK to get away from her violent husband, with their five year old son in tow. She later told me that she thought my dad would protect her.

No one knew that he was sexually abusing me behind closed doors, in return for food, gifts or days off school. Looking back, I don't think I tolerated things like waking up to find his hand up my pyjama top, or how he would get me to touch him in the bath because he told me I was his nurse for the perceived 'payoff' of the gift; he didn't pay attention to me unless there was the option of abuse. He was so cold towards us, his children, the rest of the time. My brother had it worse; at least I got fed and was never beaten for not being able to complete mathematical problems way beyond my age range until the blood stained the chest of drawers, where no one would bother to clean it off and our mum just pretending it didn't happen. I wanted to feel like I had a normal father who loved me in a normal way. He used to tell me he loved me 'in every way'.

It went without saying that I would not tell anyone. After all, I felt I'd got myself into this situation. If only I hadn't asked for fish 'n' chips so often, then it never would have happened, right? I met my first boyfriend at school when I was 13, and that compounded everything. I knew that if he found out he would dump me, and that was simply not an option. I needed him to be my passport away from home. All I had to do was marry him as soon as we were old enough, then I could get away. However, his presence in my life brought my terrible home situation to a boiling point, until one day during the Christmas holidays in 2005, I disclosed to my mum when my father wasn't around. She asked me why I was doing this to her.

Next thing I know, the police are there, I'm making a statement, then recording a video interview a few days after, and I'm never seeing my father again, except across the hallway of the court antechamber a year and a half later, of course. And at the sentencing, which I had to battle my family to attend. They thought it would make the judge let him off easy if they could see that I wasn't too traumatised to show up. Can't argue with that, I suppose. Now I'm 27 and devote most of my time to running workshops for frontline practitioners based on my (and others') lived experiences. I want all the children who are where I was to feel able to tell someone. But without a trusting environment with adults who take an invested interest, I'm not sure how likely the little Siobhans out there are to just come out and say it.

So what can you do? Firstly, understand the full picture of why little Siobhan isn't telling you. Most people understand that it has something to do with shame. Aside from things like abuser threats, blaming the child and convincing the child that they're complicit, I want to use my limited word count to bring up a few factors which either are not understood, or are too uncomfortable to say out loud, but which could be the main barrier to the little Siobhan in your life telling you (given the stats about the prevalence of abuse, I'm going to assume that she or he is definitely present in your place of work).

The first is that victims sometimes have a sexual response to the abuse. There. I said it. Children need to understand that the human body is designed to respond to touch, and that this isn't the same as consent. Imagine being the girl who calls herself 'slut' thinking that her body betrayed her, or the boy who got an erection during abuse and now feels sick to his stomach about it, and is sure that you will be too, if he tells you. If children had a grasp of normal bodily functions and consent issues, then that might help them to feel less ashamed and therefore more likely to speak out. So I hope this will form some part of the government's agenda for sex and relationship education.

Another barrier is the desire to protect the abuser. My father would threaten to commit suicide if I talked, and whilst you may think that wouldn't matter to me, I still looked up to him as my dad and would even feel sorry for him that I put him in this difficult situation. Can you imagine? I hope you can only imagine. The number of messages I receive from professionals with lived experience who hear me talk is intense. But I'm grateful to have the opportunity to open up a dialogue about this. I didn't want another thing to feel guilty about, and I didn't want him to die because of me, so I kept quiet.

A third not-often-talked-about factor is the phenomena of what I call 'exceptional thinking'. I've been publicly sharing my story for over a decade, and for half that time, whilst I was sending out the message that abuse is never the child's fault, I still felt that my own experience was my fault. I thought I was the exception to the rule. It's all very well to speak and write articles and contribute to a social work training resource, but if you knew the *full story*, then you would realise that it really was my fault, after all. That's how I used to think, even after the abuse had ended and my life was moving forward. The reason for this exceptional thinking, aside from being a normal symptom of abuse itself, will vary from person to person. It could be a gesture or a snippet of conversation the person remembers having with the abuser which proves, in the privacy of their own mind, that they are the exception. It'll be something that they might not boil down to for years afterwards. Even in therapy, one box may remain unopened. This is why an ongoing process of storytelling, of getting it all out there, all of it – is so important.

At the crux of why I used to blame myself was the fact that, the very first time I was abused, I asked for it. I had realised that the space between my legs felt tingly and weird when touched and so, one day, I told my father something like 'it feels funny when you touch me here!' and guided his hand to my genitals. That was it. How could anyone say it wasn't my fault? From speaking to parents since, I realise now that so many children have a moment like that, or even many moments like that, where they invite an adult to touch them or run around naked or whatever. It doesn't make it their fault. It doesn't make it mine. I wanted to share this as an example of how sensitive the issues are when you are the victim and speaking out seems like a terrifying prospect.

To encourage a child to speak out, you need to demonstrate awareness of these issues in your conversations with them, and you can do it without asking leading questions. Let's say you've noticed a change in behaviour and want to explore if there's something underneath it. You might start by asking open-ended questions about how they feel, how things are going at home, if there's anything on their mind. Then, you can reassure them by letting them know that they're not in trouble, perhaps referring to the behaviour you've noticed. Let them know that there's nothing they can tell you which would make you look at them funny. Finally, you can show pre-emptive understanding by encouraging them to tell you anything on their mind, even if they feel they can't, shouldn't, or it's a secret. At this point, you could be referring to anything – cheating on an exam, shoplifting, other troubles at home – it doesn't have to be abuse, and so you are not leading them. You're just letting them know that you are sincerely interested in their wellbeing. This is what I believe would have helped me to tell someone, although I'm not blaming myself for not doing so.

The emotional barriers against disclosure are strong and often caught up in the child's self-image and understanding of their sexuality. Your job is to be present, to notice strange behaviour and to have those difficult conversations. Above all, believe the things children tell you, and don't be so afraid of saying the wrong thing that you end up saying nothing at all.

Siobhan offers some suggestions to encourage children to speak out about abuse. To what extent do the children you work with have the opportunity to speak out?

Working Together to Safeguard Children (2018:10) explains that children have said that they need:

Vigilance: to have adults notice when things are troubling them

Understanding and action: to understand what is happening; to be heard and understood; and to have that understanding acted upon

Stability: to be able to develop an ongoing stable relationship of trust with those helping them

Respect: to be treated with the expectation that they are competent rather than not

Information and engagement: to be informed about and involved in procedures, decisions, concerns and plans

Explanation: to be informed of the outcome of assessments and decisions and reasons when their views have not had a positive response

Support: to be provided with support in their own right as well as a member of their family

Advocacy: to be provided with advocacy to assist them in putting forward their views

Protection: to be protected against all forms of abuse and discrimination and the right to special protection and help if a refugee

PAUSE TO REFLECT

How often do you revisit this list of things children have said they want?

What more could you do to make sure that the children you work with feel that they have these things in place?

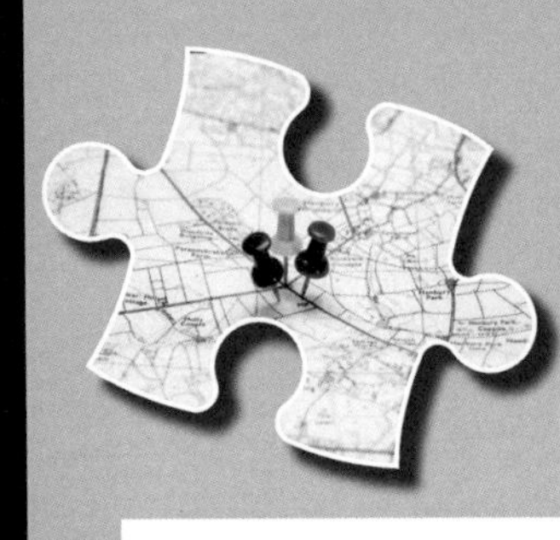

WHERE AM I NOW?

Revisit the start of the chapter. Look again at the KSS standard. Then consider the following questions:

What has surprised me in working through this chapter?

What three things would I highlight as key learning?

What do I still need to do in working towards being fully confident with this KSS statement?

What single next step should I take in working towards an improvement in my practice?

Chapter 6

CHILD AND FAMILY ASSESSMENT

Assessment is a key part of your everyday practice and you may be at a stage of 'unconscious competence' at this point of your career in relation to a child and family assessment (you might be on auto-pilot). Revisiting your understanding and practice in this area is vitally important. Assessment is a key part of a child's journey and so this chapter will use the analogy of a journey throughout in order to enable you to take a step back and look at your assessment practice in a different way. This should enable you to reflect on your strengths and areas for development in relation to this standard.

THE KSS REQUIRES PRACTITIONERS TO:

Carry out in-depth and ongoing family assessment of social need and risk to children, with particular emphasis on parental capacity and capability to change. Use professional curiosity and authority while maintaining a position of partnership, involving all key family members, including fathers. Acknowledge any conflict between parental and children's interests, prioritising the protection of children as set out in legislation.

Use child observation skills, genograms, ecomaps, chronologies and other evidence based tools ensuring active child and family participation in the process. Incorporate the contributions that other professional disciplines make to social work assessments.

Hold an empathic position about difficult social circumstances experienced by children and families, taking account of the relationship between poverty and social deprivation, and the effect of stress on family functioning, providing help and support. Take into account individual child and family history and how this might affect the ability of adults and children to engage with services.

Recognise and address behaviour that may indicate resistance to change, ambivalent or selective cooperation with services, and recognise when there is a need for immediate action, and what other steps can be taken to protect children.

Take a look at the standard above in detail. Highlight key phrases and anything that jumps out at you. Then take some time to reflect on the statement.

- *What are your immediate thoughts?*
- *What might you want to discuss and clarify?*
- *How will you clarify meanings?*
- *Who will you discuss it with?*

GETTING FEEDBACK ON PRACTICE

Who can give me feedback on my practice in this area?	*How will I get the feedback?*

Make sure to keep a record of any feedback you receive.

INITIAL SELF-ASSESSMENT

What do I already do well?

How do I know? (What's my evidence?)

What do I need to work on?

How will I work on this?

ASSESSMENT: REVISITING THE BASICS

Child and family assessment is the bread and butter of social work and so you will already have a range of skills, drawing on a variety of tools and methods in your practice. As always though it can be helpful to revisit the basics to reflect on your practice wisdom and how it has developed.

Traditional views of assessment usually focus on process, either in terms of exploring the assessment process or the assessment as part of the social work process.

THE ASSESSMENT PROCESS

In considering the assessment process, Milner and O'Byrne presented a five stage model of assessment (2009); which is still very useful ten years on:

Preparation. Preparing for an assessment is incredibly important. This might include deciding who to see, what the purpose of the assessment is, what information will be needed etc. In fact, it can be useful to develop a brief assessment plan before beginning the assessment. This can provide a framework for the practitioner - helping to clarify what they will be doing. In many ways this is about reflecting *for* action.

Data collection. This is the stage where the social worker gathers the necessary information. A good assessment plan will help guide this stage although as the assessment unfolds more information may be sought.

Weighing up the data. At this point the social worker weighs up the information to reach an answer to the key question 'is there a problem and is it serious?'

Analysing the data. The information is interpreted so that the social worker is able to gain a fuller understanding. Ideas for intervention can be developed.

Utilising the data. This stage is used to finalise judgements. The data will be used to evidence judgements and recommendations for intervention.

Whilst this is a very basic process framework, it can be helpful to use this to reflect on assessments. Slowing things down is there a particular stage which you often miss out or skip through quickly?

This basic stage model of assessment is reflected in Working Together, which describes the purpose of assessment as:

- To gather information about a child and family.
- To analyse their needs and/or the nature and level of any risk and harm being suffered by the child.
- To decide whether the child is a child in need (section 17) or is suffering or is likely to suffer significant harm (section 47).
- To provide support to address those needs to improve the child's outcomes and welfare and where necessary to make them safe.

ASSESSMENT AS PART OF A SOCIAL WORK PROCESS

Traditionally assessment is presented as the start of an overall process in social work. This was described by Taylor and Devine (1993) as the 'basic helping cycle', illustrated in the following:

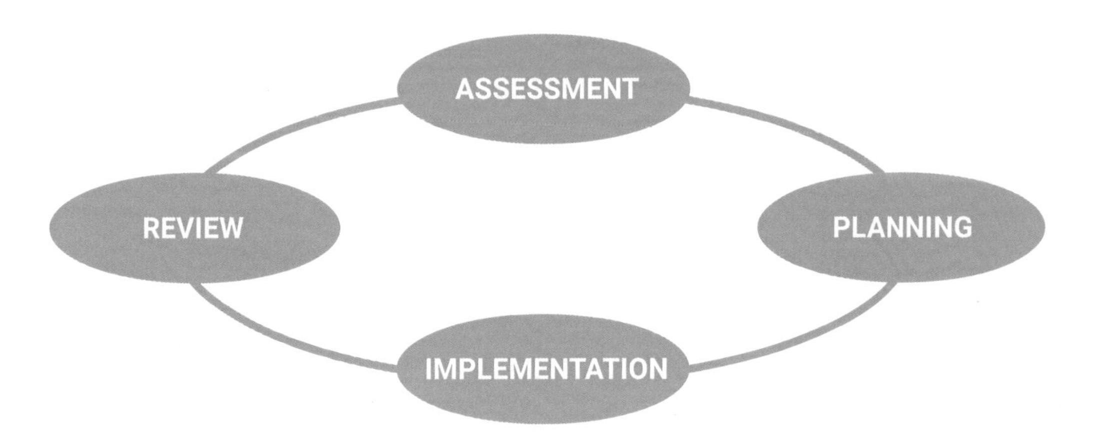

PAUSE TO REFLECT

Looking back at some of these basics, how has your understanding of assessment changed since your initial training?

ASSESSMENT: MODELS, METHODS AND FRAMEWORKS

Chapter 7 explores the difference between models and methods when exploring the use of theory in practice. At this point you may find it interesting to take a quick look at pages 211 and 212 to clarify the difference between a model and a method. Essentially a model covers how a social worker goes about doing something – so a model of assessment suggests how the social worker will go about undertaking the assessment. A method is basically a specific tool or technique used in practice. In terms of assessment there are a range of contemporary models and out of these a range of methods and tools can be utilised.

Frameworks are essentially about structures. Sometimes organisations talk about developing practice frameworks. This really refers to the structures underpinning practice in their organisation, which might include a range of different assessment models and methods. The assessment framework essentially provides a structure against which social workers should be undertaking a child and family assessment.

PAUSE TO REFLECT

What is the main model influencing your assessments?

Specifically what methods do you use as part of your assessment?

Robert Russell is the Signs of Safety Implementation Manager for Coventry. Here he shares how Signs of Safety has been introduced in Coventry.

Coventry is the second largest city in the West Midlands with a population of around 345,00. There are 50 first languages spoken within Coventry, such as Polish, Punjabi, Urdu, Romanian, and Bengali. Throughout its history, Coventry has been famous for its silk, wool, and more recently its car industry. Famous landmarks include the Lady Godiva statue in Broadgate, and the new and old cathedrals. In 2018, Coventry was delighted to be named the 'City of Culture 2021' which will bring great attention to the city and provide an economic boost.

Between 2012 and 2013, children's social care in Coventry went through a period of transition. There was a high turnover of social care staff, low staff morale, and a workforce which was quite averse to managing risk. This resulted in a high number of children subject to Child Protection plans spiking at 886 in 2014. In 2014, Ofsted found Coventry Children's Social Care 'inadequate' following an inspection.

In 2015, there was a significant change in Senior Leadership within Coventry children's social care, and a new drive to improve the outcomes for children through strong leadership, good practice and building workforce stability. One of the initial gaps identified within children's social care, was the lack of an identified Practice Framework. As such, it was agreed that Coventry would introduce 'Signs of Safety' into children's social care, by means of buying in trainers and up-skilling a number of Practice Leads. By 2017, evaluations suggested children, young people, families and professionals felt that Signs of Safety was making a difference in the way child protection conferences were being facilitated, alongside positive outcomes from families subject to Early Help services.

The implementation and embedding of Signs of Safety across multi-agency children's services in Coventry has resulted in a positive change for children's social care practitioners. Coventry Signs of Safety training has focussed on some Key Disciplines. These are:

- Building positive working relationships with families and professionals.
- Identifying Family Networks at the beginning of any intervention.
- Making assessments clear, smart and understandable for families.
- Ensuring children's voices are heard.
- Creating Safety Planning by drawing on family networks.
- Working with children to ensure they understand what is happening within their families.

By focussing on these key disciplines, there has been a shift of culture in how children's social care practitioners are engaging with families, building working relationships and ensuring children's voices are heard. In addition, families feel they are empowered, understand what is being written and take ownership of the plans in place for them. Staff are more confident in managing risk, by identifying family networks and building safety plans for children. Furthermore, workforce morale has improved, staff turnover has reduced significantly, and there is a motivation and commitment throughout multi-agency children's services to improve outcomes for children. In 2017, Ofsted rated Coventry as 'requires improvement to be good'. The number of children subject to Child Protection plans has reduced to 373 (May 2019).

Coventry children's social care are still on their journey to 'getting to good' and recognise there is still work to be done. However, by introducing, and embedding Signs of Safety in their practice, there is a recognised practice framework which supports the development, enhances practice and builds confidence throughout the workforce.

SHARE: HELPING DEVELOP EMPATHY IN ASSESSMENT

SHARE was initially developed as a model of assessment for social workers (Maclean, Finch and Tedam 2018), although as it has developed it is used in a range of ways. The use of the word SHARE for the model is important because it promotes the importance of taking a partnership approach with children and families and it reminds us of the importance of information sharing in gathering the information necessary to do a good assessment. However, the word in itself stands for the five separate, but interconnected, components of evidence in an assessment.

So a social worker needs to think about:

Seeing
Hearing
Action
Reading
Evaluation

These components do not need to be covered in any particular order. So for example, when a social worker receives a referral they read it and immediately begin to evaluate the information they have in the referral. This helps them to think about what information is missing and they may begin to develop a hypothesis even at this stage about what they think is happening. When they see the child though and hear their voice they may well change their initial evaluation.

The most important aspect of SHARE is that it recognises that everyone has a different 'share' – so two social workers might go to see the same family, but they come away with a different view. This might be based on the fact that they have read something different or they have heard from a different person. However, it is not just different professionals who will have a different 'share.' A parent may well have a very different 'share' to the social worker, and a child might have a different 'share' still. So in an assessment a social worker will want to think about their 'share' in the following way:

Seeing	Who have they seen? Who with? What have they seen? What haven't they seen? How might they draw on their observations in the assessment? What might they have lost sight of?
Hearing	What have they heard? Who from? Whose voice have they privileged? Why? Who do they still need to hear from?
Action	What action have they taken? What impact has this had? What have others done?
Reading	What have they read that they may be able to draw on in their assessment? This might include research, theory, legislation, assessments from others or case notes and chronologies.
Evaluation	How are they evaluating all the evidence? Is any of the evidence conflicting? (for example in there a conflict between what they have seen and what they have heard?)

The social worker's 'share' becomes SHARED when they draw on the 'share' to reach a defensible decision.

It is important though to maintain an empathic position during the assessment and SHARE can really help with this. So the social worker thinks through the service user's share:

Seeing	What does the parent see in the social worker? How do you know how they see you?
Hearing	What does the parent hear? Is your communication full of jargon? Are you clear about your expectations?
Action	What action might they take as a result of the rest of their 'share'? Drawing on how they see you, what they hear from you, how they feel when they read your assessment and how they evaluate the social work experience will influence their future action.
Reading	Do you encourage the parent to read your ongoing notes? When they read your assessment what will their response be?
Evaluation	How will the parent evaluate the social work experience? How do you know?

SHARE can also be used to explore the child's world:

Seeing	What does the child see? How do you know? How might you be able to see the child's world through their eyes?
Hearing	What does the child hear? Who from? How do they interpret that? What has the child heard about a social worker seeing them? How might that impact on what they tell you? How does the language that you use make the child feel about themselves?
Action	What action might they take? Why? How can you involve them actively in the assessment? (What can they do?)
Reading	If this child reads your assessment when they are an adult what will this mean to them? Will it show that they mattered?
Evaluation	How does the child interpret their world? What does what they see and hear mean to them? Are they left with any questions? Who will answer those?

ANNIE'S ADVICE

Assessment: (noun) the act of judging or deciding the amount, value, quality, or importance of something, or the judgment or decision that is made.

Social worker: "I'm not here to judge..."

You can see where I'm going with this can't you.

Social workers: It's okay to be judgemental. In fact, it's more than okay. It's your job. It doesn't do much for a working relationship between a family and worker if that worker claims to be non-judgemental (or is "not here to judge"), and then big-fat-makes-a-judgement-on-our-family-anyway.

So, let's go right back to the start.

What does an assessment mean to a family? Well, here's an analogy for you.

If you've ever toyed with the idea of getting a cleaner (because there's just not enough hours in the day), or you've actually gone ahead and got one (I'm not there yet because I'm too much of a skinflint), I'm willing to bet you did what many people do. You cleaned before the cleaner got there.

You're employing someone to clean your home for you, why would anyone clean it then first?

"Assessment" and "judgement" is why.

I can remember having a social worker come into my home with a clipboard and sit on my sofa to undertake a "Child and Family Assessment". Among the rich and varied questions I was asked were:

"How often do you wash your towels?"

And

"How often do you wash your bed sheets?"

Well, Moira, how often do you wash yours?!

I didn't know "the answer" to these questions, and I found myself second-guessing what the correct answers could be. The honest truth is I wash my bath towels after each use (sorry, environment), and I generally wash my family's bedding on a Saturday morning. But what if that was too much? Or not enough? And what was on that clipboard anyway?

In all seriousness, this is just the tip of the iceberg. Faced with an assessment by a social worker on your own family and therefore, by default, your ability to parent your children, you either go on the defensive (see Moira, above), or you over-compensate ("new bed sheets each day darling, like the Beckhams"), or you just talk and talk and talk, hoping that somewhere is the "right" answer.

So, how do you as a practitioner deal with this dynamic? How do you get the best out of the families you are working with? Here are some of my ideas on the subject:

I've been the subject of more assessments than I care to recall. Single, CAF, S17, S47, pre-birth, rehabilitation home, psychological, psychiatric. I've had them all. Every single one made me feel sick with nerves and on almost every one of them, I've felt like the outcome has been decided before Moira has got her clipboard out. Families pick up on this; it matters.

1. The little things aren't little

I say this quite a lot. In fact, if you read this whole book, I'm willing to bet I've said it in almost every chapter I've written in.

In the context of assessments, start at the beginning. Where is the assessment going to take place? Does it need to be undertaken in the cold and clinical offices of the local authority? Or can it be done in the home of the family you're assessing? I've had both experiences, and I know which one I prefer. In their own homes, families feel safer, more confident, more in control and more able to assert themselves (which may or may not be a good thing!). But consider the point of an assessment. This shouldn't be a 'tick-box exercise'.

This should be about a conversation, a dialogue in which you, as a worker, can be curious and probe a little. How are you going to get the best out of your families in these circumstances? By doing it on their territory.

Of course, sometimes there may be safeguarding risks to you, and you must always be mindful of this. If you think you may be at risk, the assessment needs to be held in a more controlled environment, and the reason for this explained to the family. Neither parent, nor practitioner should feel at risk.

So, location is important. It's a little thing, but it also really isn't.

2. **Timing**
   Working around the family in terms of where the assessment should take place is going to help build a relationship. What will help further is considering the individual family needs and, again, trying to work around this. So, for example, if you need to speak to mum and dad for the assessment, it's probably better if you do it when the children are at school. But mum and/or dad may work full-time or may have other caring responsibilities. So, what can you do, as a worker, to help to create an environment where parents are not having to rush from work, or try to look after a toddler whilst answering questions about laundry or some-such? The key here is being helpful.

3. **Go with an open mind**
   I know mums who have had five/six/seven children removed almost immediately after birth and subsequently adopted and are currently pregnant with another baby. It would be a fair assumption to make that a mum in this position wouldn't be able to keep another baby and so, as a worker, you start to predict which way 'the case' will go. But what that doesn't allow for is the capacity a parent has to change. If you go into an assessment with this attitude, you might not be able to see the subtle changes that are taking place. You might not be able to see that this parent has recognised your worries and wants – maybe for the first time – to do something about them. An open mind is a must.

4. **Read the paperwork but reserve your judgement**
   I've had social workers come into my home and earnestly tell me they haven't read any of my paperwork because they want to "hear it from me". I found this really quite unhelpful – though I recognise that other parents will feel differently. At some point, that worker is going to read the paperwork and I for one would far rather it was before they came to see me. Partially because it means I don't have to recount every facet of my life, and partially because it give me an opportunity to "answer" what has been written about me. What the paperwork also does is gives an idea of a parent's previous experience with social workers, positive and negative. By reading the paperwork beforehand, the worker can then acknowledge the more negative experiences a parent may feel they have had. This acknowledgement will go some way to building a relationship with the assessing worker.

   The final point to note on paperwork is that it is often written at that time, in that context. As in my previous point, parents do possess within them a capacity to change and so historic records only tell you part of the story. And that parent might be in a very different place now.

So, read by all means, but save your judgement until you have all of the information.

5. **Probing and the elephant in the room**

For clarity; I'm not suggesting any living elephant should be probed whether it be in the room or not. But you're there to do a piece of work, and it's important you explain to families why you're asking the questions you are, as you're going along. Let's face it, it's not exactly a comfortable situation all-round. It's too easy to allow your own discomfort to stop you from being really clear, honest and transparent about why you're there. Be confident in your practice (and if you don't feel it, fake it 'til you make it), and your questioning. Because sometimes there will be difficult questions to answer that will cause pain, and shame and anger. You need to hold that pain that parents are feeling and stay with it. Reflect back to families their feelings so they know they have been heard and you "get it". Keep probing where you can, keep being curious and giving parents the space to keep talking. But also – and most importantly, know when to stop. If a parent is showing real distress, stop the session and make sure the parent has some support, physically and emotionally. Yes, timescales are important, but a family's well-being is more so.

6. **Identifying...and over-identifying**

Whilst it is imperative that a good working relationship is built between the family and their social worker, it is also imperative that that relationship is carefully managed. I have spent time with many parents through the work that I do and have often met with parents (either physically or virtually) who are in the thrust of assessments in relation to care proceedings. I am quiet, and listen to their story, taking time to reflect as they are talking and identify for myself the worries that the social worker may have. Very often, I will be able to identify with many of the feelings these parents are experiencing; fear, mistrust, pain, loss and anger. On odd occasions, I have really "gelled" with a family. I've found them easy to engage with, and I've felt they were willing to listen to my advice and guidance around changes they may need to make to keep their children safe in their care. This is where I need to use my own supervision and my own ability to reflect, to consistently keep this question at the forefront of my mind:

"What is the risk to the child/ren?"

I need to keep bringing it back to being about the children, and their own lived experiences, rather than it being all about the parents and their feelings. This, I've discovered, is a common theme within social work too. Sometimes workers have told me that they have "over-identified" with a family, and they've sometimes prioritised what the parents want above what is best for the children. This isn't a criticism of their practice you understand, it's something I've done myself. But it is something to be mindful of.

7. **"Disguised compliance"**

Okay, I said it. I used the term. I'm sorry – forgive me. But being overly, and underly (that's a word, right?) compliant is something to watch out for.

I'm not going to lie; I have been the overly compliant parent. I told lies during the assessment process about how well I was coping and that my relationship was fine. I've cleaned furiously before the assessing worker arrived and maintained an air of Mary Poppins throughout their visits with my children. Why did I behave in this way? Fear, mainly. I was aware of the power dynamic and that this social worker could conclude I was not a "good enough" parent and swiftly remove my children. When your family is threatened by the State you become a lioness. You will do anything it takes to make them go away.

So, how do you spot a parent who is being particularly compliant? You look for the umbrella and spoonful of sugar, of course.

On a serious note, it's about creating a safe enough environment for that parent to feel that they can disclose what's really going on. That could be to do with some of the points I've raised already; location and timing. It could be about assessing parents separately or making sure each parent has a supporter with them (either another professional they feel safe with, or a friend or relative). You need to try to move toward the parent to help find out what they need to make them feel safe. It won't be helpful to say, "I'm not here to take your kids away". Because you don't know that, and that might be exactly what happens (and when it does, hell hath no fury like a parent scorned). It will be helpful to tell the parent that you want to help them to keep their family safe, and you want to listen to what they think would be helpful to do just that.

There are reams of (scathing) information about there about "disguised compliance", so I shall not labour the point. But I hope I've helped you to think about it within the context of assessments.

8. **Think about the purpose of your assessment**

Again, a blindingly obvious point of mine (I'm really good at these). But I mean this in the wider sense of the word. Clearly you are going to undertake a pre-birth assessment to decide what support or intervention the unborn baby and their family require to keep this baby safe. But, actually, what are you really doing there?

Are you "evidence gathering" because the outcome seems obvious, or perhaps because you are looking at this through a risk averse lens?

Are you asking questions you already know the answer to simply to tick a box?

Are you asking closed questions so that you can meet the demands of timescales?

Are you demonstrating belief in this family and their ability to parent this child?

Are you starting with the foundation that all children should stay with their birth families where it is safe for them to do so? And if you are, how do you show the family that this is the standpoint from which the assessment will be conducted?

The ultimate purpose of any assessment by a social worker is around risk, and it is right that it should be so. You must never, ever be blind to risk.

But what of trust? And what of hope? What about positive risk taking? Or thinking about the strengths the family has and how you as a worker can build upon them. And what about thinking creatively about the local authority's role? If there's a gap, which part of the local authority could help to fill it? If we begin with the ethos of working with parents right from the assessment stage, supporting them to work through their issues and safely parenting their children, then my firm belief is you stand a better chance of not only long-term engagement, but also less risk of escalation.

I hope these pointers have been helpful when considering child and family assessments. This is a crucial part of your role, but it is also a crucial part of the family's future and so it's important to do whatever you must to get it right.

ASSESSMENT METHODS AND TOOLS

Social workers can draw on a range of assessment methods and tools in their assessments. These tools are not an assessment in their own right and are not analytical. However, what they provide is a clear, succinct way of presenting information to enable analysis as part of a wider assessment.

GENOGRAMS AND ECOMAPS

Genograms and ecomaps are both visual representation tools designed by social worker Dr Ann Hartman. Whilst genograms address family relationships ecomaps explore systems more widely.

GENOGRAMS

A genogram is basically a specific way of drawing up a family tree to represent a family system, structure and history. Genograms can be particularly helpful in situations where there is significant complexity in the make-up and development of a family. They are widely used and there is clarity about how they should be drawn up. They should always be included in assessments.

ECOMAPS

Ecomaps are sometimes referred to as ecograms. Essentially, they map a child's support networks. They come out of an ecological or systemic approach. An ecomap should show a child's social and personal relationships and their relationship with their environment or the different systems impacting on their lives.

The idea of the ecomap is to highlight connections between a child, their family and their ecological environment. Identifying the connections should include highlighting the strength of connections and can also demonstrate the energy flowing in and out of a family; the reciprocity of relationships and access to resources/networks.

Ecomap styles vary but generally they consist of circles (representing the different people/ systems) and lines (demonstrating the relationships between systems). Often arrows are added to demonstrate the flow of energy between relationships. Whilst there is a very standardised understanding of what the different symbols on a genogram mean, there are a range of ways of doing ecomaps, so each one must have a key so that a reader will understand the map.

The child should always be placed in the centre of the ecomap and generally other relationships will be placed in circles around the child.

It is important that relationships between the different players or systems on the map are demonstrated. So, a line should be used to connect the child with each part of the map. The line will be different to show different kinds of relationship. The following lines are often used:

- - - - tenuous insecure connection

——— secure close connection

/\/\/\/ a stressful connection

——X—— a broken connection

Some people go further than simply connecting the child to the different systems on the map, by showing the quality of relationships between different people on the map. This can be helpful since it could show, for example, whether the child's network of support is strong or whether the child is surrounded by conflict.

Ecomaps should not just show the quality of relationships but should also indicate the flow of energy. If the energy to create a connection is all moving in one direction, then it is likely that this will not create a long-term meaningful connection for that child or family. Generally, arrows are used to demonstrate the flow of energy.

Whilst there are a number of templates and a range of ecomap software, it is generally preferable to undertake the ecomap with a child or their family, since it is partly reliant on an understanding of the quality of connection and the flow of energy, which can only really be clarified in discussion. To facilitate the discussion about an ecomap photos can be used. With children it can be helpful to use buttons, the child picks which button represents each person going on their ecomap. This can lead to some really useful discussions about why each button was selected.

PAUSE TO REFLECT

What difficulties do you experience in using genograms and ecomaps?

How do you address these difficulties?

Can you reflect on a time when you found using either a genogram or ecomap particularly helpful in an assessment. What was helpful? How might you draw on this in other assessments?

CHRONOLOGIES

The word chronology comes from the Greek Chronos which means time. Whilst 'ology' is basically about studying. So, the word chronology can be taken to mean the studying of dates and times to find meaning. A chronology is basically a list of significant events in date order. It enables us to study events and can help to identify emerging patterns, highlighting potential concerns. Basically, a chronology means that current concerns can be viewed in light of past concerns. It brings together hindsight and insight to create foresight.

A chronology should:

- Identify significant incidents and events for the child and family.
- Record organisational intervention and action taken.
- Be a working tool – a chronology is not an end in itself, it must be kept up to date.
- Be accurate.
- Contain sufficient detail to understand the event so that patterns can be seen but not be too detailed that it is difficult to plough through.
- Be flexible: the detail recorded may increase in line with risk increasing.
- Be reviewed and analysed regularly.
- Be utilised as a key tool in an analytical assessment.

There are of course, different types of chronologies. So, the chronology required in a court will be different to the chronology perhaps held on file. Sometimes a chronology will be done for a single child and sometimes for a sibling group. Sometimes there will be a single agency chronology and sometimes a multi-agency or integrated chronology. A multi-agency/integrated chronology brings together chronologies created by different agencies and presents them coherently. It is particularly important that multi agency/integrated chronologies include the source and date of the information, with a record of the justification for why information was shared. Integrated chronologies often give a fuller picture of what is happening for a child or family.

I've never understood it when a social worker says "I've done my assessment, now I have to do a chronology" – how can you write the one without the other? For me, the chronology is the start, and heart, of a good assessment. (Dyke 2018 online)

PAUSE TO REFLECT

How do you develop and use a chronology as the start and the heart of your assessments?

ASSESSMENT CHECKLISTS

There is an increasing use of checklist tools in assessments. These are very often based on an understanding of risk indicators and generally include some kind of fact based (tick box) screening tool, often combined with an individual analysis of the situation.

In research undertaken for the Centre of Expertise for Child Sexual Abuse, Brown et al (2017) undertook an overview of the tools and checklists used in assessments around child sexual exploitation. They found that across England and Wales there were between 9 and 28 different assessment tools and checklists used. These were very varied:

> **"In particular, we found that the risk indicators being used varied considerably across the large number of tools in operation. An examination of 10 tools identified 110 different indicators, with each tool having a different combination of these." (page 9).**

The report recommends that:

> **"The purpose and use of any tool/checklist or assessment should be clear to all professionals involved in the process (including those developing it) – for example, is the tool/checklist designed/used to screen a large number of individuals and identify those most at risk, or to complete a comprehensive assessment? Tools should be used for the purposes for which they have been developed." (page 7).**

PAUSE TO REFLECT

What checklists do you use as part of your assessments?

How do you 'select' the checklists you use?

Chapter 6

JOURNEY MAPPING

Journey mapping is increasingly being utilised in exploring the progress that student social workers are making through placement and on into their ASYE experiences (Maclean 2018). This method can also be used with children and their families to good effect. Journey maps can be developed at the start of intervention, helping families to plan what they need to do and to develop strategies should they face obstacles along the way, or they can be developed towards the end of involvement to help review progress towards goals.

Gary Jones is a social worker and practice educator based in Newcastle, he is currently supporting student social worker, Sharon Belisle.

We used 'Journey Mapping' as a tool in supervision to be a visual representation of the journey Sharon had been on during her placement to help explore the progress that she had made. The map was then used as a talking point for the session. Sharon described the process of completing, viewing, sharing and discussing the journey map as paramount in helping her to recognise achievements and challenges that she had encountered, promoting both confidence and self-esteem in her own ability.

We considered if a similar resource could be used collaboratively with families, to enable them to have a visual representation of their involvement and 'journey' working with Children's Social Care. We thought about one family who found it particularly difficult to recognise the positive changes they had made and how much progress they had achieved. The family regularly described 'going around in circles' and they were overly focussed on anything negative which had occurred. They were clearly 'stuck', whereas professionals recognised significant changes that the family had made.

We thought that the Journey Map would be an excellent visual way of engaging them and really encouraging them to think about the journey the family had been on. The planning of the session involved a pre-drawn road with a variety of road signs that could be used to symbolise different points and experiences in their journey from the start of Children's Social Care involvement, to now and then looking to the future.

When starting the session, the parents were initially a little apprehensive but with a little conversation and encouragement were eager to undertake the activity. Picking the different road signs encouraged the parents to discuss with each other the different points in their journey, how this felt for them and how it impacted on the wider family. This was real progress for them and gave them the space and opportunity to think about the whole family as well as each child individually. Having something visual to represent a challenge seemed to give them the permission and confidence to share their feelings about what happened, even if their experiences differed.

As the session went on, the parents really began to notice the journey they had been on and how difficult things had been for them, but how much progress they had all made and they were able to reflect on the strategies they had used to be able to make those changes. This really encouraged a shift in their thinking. Their confidence in themselves became really visible in their engagement with the activity and how positive they became. When going on to discuss their future, the parents became much more motivated, acknowledging what the challenges may be, but then drawing on their previous experiences of overcoming challenges to explore how they would overcome them.

Following the session, the parents fed back to several professionals how valuable they had found it, how engaging it was and how effective it had been in encouraging them to see the progress they had made. They felt it helped them identify how strong they are as a family and made them feel positive and motivated about what they will be able to achieve in the future.

As the practitioner leading the session, Sharon reflected that undertaking the activity felt collaborative and engaging. Hearing the family reflect on their experiences and how much they have valued social work support was really rewarding.

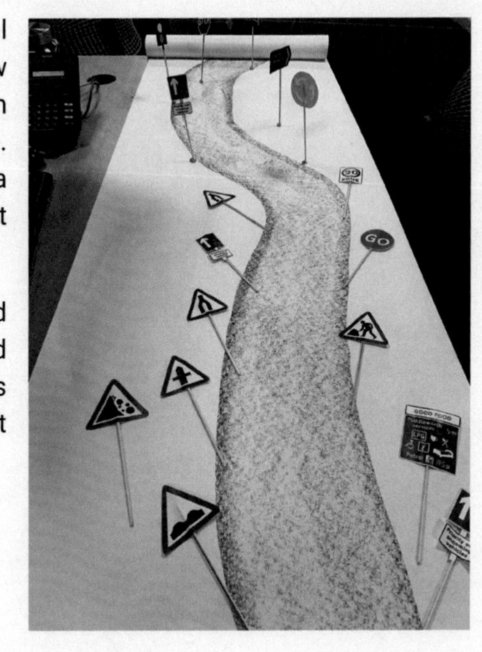

PAUSE TO REFLECT

How might you be able to use the journey mapping method in your work with children and families?

THE SOCIAL WORKER'S CAR

The main reflective space reported by social workers is the car (Maclean, Finch and Tedam 2018). Social workers talk about reflecting extensively in the car after a visit which then clearly impacts on how they might analyse the information they have gathered. Thinking about assessment and linking this to a social worker reflecting in the car, it might be helpful to think about the components of the car):

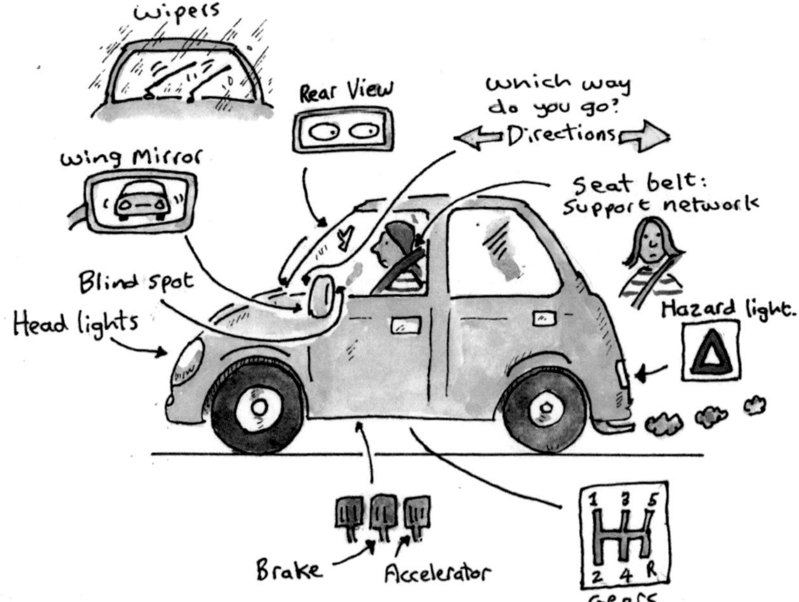

Windscreen: What can you see ahead? How might you be able to use the wipers to change what you see and clear your view?

Rear view mirror: If you look back perhaps at what is behind the child and their family or to what has happened in the past, does it help clarify things?

Wing mirrors: Are you clear about environmental issues? What is going on for the child in their environment?

Mirror, signal, manoeuvre: Have you prepared effectively? Are you keeping the basics in mind?

Blind spot: What can't you see? How are you addressing that?

Accelerator: What is powering the car? Is there sufficient motivation to move things forward for this child?

Brake: What is stopping this child having a positive journey? What is stopping you from taking action?

Speedometer: Are things moving to timescales? Are things going too quickly or too slowly for this child?

Headlights: Are you shining a light on things that may not be clear to others?

Indicators: Are you clear about the direction of travel for this child? Has that been communicated clearly to others?

Hazard warning lights: Have you checked the risks and talked these through with others?

Petrol gauge: What is fuelling the car? Is there sufficient energy to move things forward?

Oil indicator: Is the engine well oiled? This could relate to the child's support system.

Gears: What needs changing? Is there a process that you should go through to create the gear change?

Exhaust: What are you leaving behind you?

Sat nav: What is directing the way? Are you just taking a route you know well? Have you read a map? Are you using the sat nav? Who programmed it?

Who is in the driving seat? Are they wearing their seatbelt? Are they a safe driver?

What seat is the child in? Are they safe?

PAUSE TO REFLECT

How might you add to the car-based questions? Think about what else is in your car and how that might be used to prompt your thinking about a child's circumstances...

UNDERSTANDING A CHILD'S JOURNEY THROUGH ASSESSMENT

Journeys are used as a common analogy in a range of ways, both inside and outside of social work. People talk about their life journey; we discuss a child's journey through social work systems; we also discuss journeys in terms of learning and professional development. A range of words associated with journeys are used in social work when we talk about pathways and signposting for example. The KSS standards also contain a range of words associated with journeying. Using a journey analogy can be very helpful when undertaking assessments and reviews with children and families.

It is helpful to think about a journey in terms of the child and family assessment process. Whilst the last two pages looked at the components of a car, these pages consider the views that you might have from that car journey and your wider journey. These may enable you to take a step back from your busy day to day practice to think about assessments in a different way.

When we go on a journey everyone starts at a different point. Children, of course, each have a unique start point for their journey. In many ways an assessment helps you and the family to consider the starting point for the child and their family.

©Shutterstock/Brian A Jackson

Process driven practice is like giving a social worker or a family a map and then checking whether they read the map to get to an end destination. The problem with this is that everyone has a unique journey towards their ongoing destinations. No one can give you a map. You need to work with a child and family to understand where they are now and to clarify where they need (and want) to be. A unique map then needs to be developed for each child because in any journey everyone has a different starting point, everyone will face different barriers and everyone will be using different transportation. Unique routes for each child and family need to be mapped and reviewed.

Suitcases are things that you pack and then drag along behind you on journey. Children and their families are just that – children! They are not cases to be dragged along behind you on a journey. The assessment process is about understanding where a child is and exploring with them and their family where they need to be (What does a good outcome look like for this family?) it is not about dragging them along behind you. A child is a child, never a case!

©Shutterstock/ Nutlegal Photographer

You need to involve all the services currently supporting the family in an assessment. Different professionals will have different views and can add to the full picture. It is important, however, not to see an assessment simply as a prelude to service delivery. Services might be helpful for a child and their family, but an assessment must never be approached from the basis of, "What services should I be putting in?" although it can be helpful to think about "What can I signpost this family towards?"

There will be a stage at which you need to think about analysing the information that you have in order to reach a decision, rather than continuing to gather more and more information. I have heard social workers say, "I am still gathering information" when asked about the conclusion they have reached. Yes, we need to gather information, but there is a point at which the information gathered must be analysed to create a decision and to enable the child to move forward. The analysis will include consideration of what information is missing. Make sure you stop, look and listen along the assessment journey.

It is important to ensure that things do not go round and round for a child. There is a need to support families to create change and in many ways this photograph could represent the cycle of change in itself. It provides a crossing point where a practitioner may pause for a while to consider where a parent is in terms of a readiness to make change.

Is the direction the family needs to take in creating that change clear to them? Do they know which way to go? Might you need to help them plan their route?

You might face a range of diversions along the way. Maybe some of the roads that you hoped the family would travel are closed off to them. Are they clear about how to continue on the journey? There is always an alternative route. Often the diversion means the journey takes a little longer and you might need to adapt the map to account for it, but sometimes travelling the new, usually unfamiliar roads can open up a range of options and you can learn new routes for the future.

Endings are important and they should be planned for from the very beginning of intervention. Be clear with a family about the outcome of the assessment. If there is no need for further intervention be sure to say goodbye properly. Children involved with social care services (especially those who are looked after) often have many different people travelling their journey with them at different times. To help children to build resilience we need to be clear about our involvement in their lives, clarifying endings and the reasons for these. Are you always clear about endings? This photograph, whilst illustrating the importance of goodbyes may not be the most appropriate in terms of the other part of the sign. We don't really want to see families again soon, because we want them to function effectively as a family without the need for social work support.

ALL ABOARD!

Of course, journeys are not just limited to cars. Train journeys provide a range of different views. Thinking about a train journey in more detail can also be helpful. In many ways assessments are about tracking what is happening for a child and their family. As the assessment progresses what is your train of thought?

There are gaps everywhere in social work. For example, there might be gaps in the information we have, gaps in the way that we might see something and the way that a parent sees it, or gaps in our knowledge and understanding. There could be a range of gaps in a child's life.

The best way to address the various gaps is to think GAP:

Goals: Always start with the end in mind. What are the goals for this child? What goals do they have and what goals do their family members have?

Action: What actions do the family need to take to work towards these goals? Are they clear about this? How do you know? Are they taking the necessary action?

Practice: What do you need to do to bridge the gap between goals and action in a child's life?

The power cables above the railway tracks can act as a remainder about the importance of power in the child and family assessment process. Where does the power lie? How are you using your power and authority? What difficulties are there in relation to power in this child's life?

The assessment process should be two way in terms of the provision of information. The assessment is not simply about gathering information, it is also about sharing appropriate information with a family. The old phrase 'information is power' can ring very true in social work – in two ways. Often parents hold 'informational power' (Seabury, Seabury and Garvin 2011) in that they know their family story. Social workers can hold key information, for example about early help and services that might support a child and their family. Information should be exchanged, such that the assessment operates not simply as a gathering of information, but also as a support helping the child and their family. Early help and the assessment of need are closely related, as is identified in Working Together to Safeguard Children (2018). To what extent do you take the exchange of information and the need for early help into account in your assessment practice?

The Knowledge and Skills statement refers to the need to "apply twin and triple track planning to minimise chances of drift or delay, being alert to the effectiveness or otherwise of current support plans." This photo demonstrates that where a social worker has a single train of thought in relation to planning for children, this causes significant problems when the track runs out or a barrier is placed in the way. Do you always apply multiple track planning?

PAUSE TO REFLECT

Take a look at the following photographs. How might they link to child and family assessment?

WORKING WITH FATHERS

Whilst there are clearly some exceptions, the involvement of a father in a child's life is positive in a range of ways:

> A considerable knowledge base has built up that reveals the overall protective and positive effect of father involvement on social, educational, behavioural, and psychological outcomes – throughout infancy, childhood, adolescence and adulthood.
> (Panter-Brick, 2014: 1188 in Clapton 2017)

However, studies repeatedly show that child protection work tends to focus on mothers, involving fathers only on the edges of practice, with fathers being described as 'invisible' (Strega et al, 2008) or 'shadows' (Ewart-Boyle et al, 2015).

In an audit of six local authorities, Osborn (2014) reported that fathers were invited to child protection conferences only 55% of the time, and in a study of child protection case files, Baynes and Holland (2012) found fathers were contacted by social workers prior to the child protection meeting in only 25 out of 40 files. In this study it is interesting to note that fathers who lived with their children were more likely to be invited to meetings, but less likely to attend, whilst fathers living separately to their children were less likely to be invited, but more likely to attend.

If we apply the What? Why? How? framework to the idea of working with fathers, we know what is happening – we are largely failing to engage with fathers during the child and family assessment process and in the child protection system. Exploring why this is the case can help us to develop strategies to more effectively engage with fathers.

WHAT ARE THE BARRIERS AND HOW CAN THESE BE OVERCOME?

There are a range of barriers to social workers engaging fully with fathers, including:

Stereotyping - Page et al (2008) in their review of UK services for fathers undertaken on behalf of the Department of Children, Schools and Families, found that very traditional stereotypical views about fathers were still prevalent, particularly in safeguarding teams and in looked after children services.

Wider services - many children's services overlook the importance of father involvement. Clapton (2017) explains that "Fathers as 'bystanders' remains a recurrent theme" in health and education services. This ambivalence towards fathers can spread throughout the family support system.

Fathers not identified - a number of studies indicate that fathers are not identified on referrals or in case files. For example Roskill (2011) found that there was no information recorded about fathers in 20% of the cases in her study of child protection, with the figure standing higher still at 31% for the fathers of looked after children.

What other barriers are there to working with fathers?

In a review of the research in this area Clapton (2017) highlights the following strategies as helping to bring fathers "on board" in the child protection process.

- Have expectations that a father's details are included on referrals. Seek information actively when it is not included.
- Do it from the start: The earlier fathers can be engaged the better.
- Gender-differentiation is often necessary. If you want to involve all parents then fathers might need to be targeted specifically.
- Consider the timing of any meetings or other services to enable the attendance of fathers who are at work.
- Communicate with both parents as standard practice.
- Arguably 'men like facts.' Helping a father see the 'evidence' of a problem such as sharing information and assessment results may encourage him to take part in services.
- Working with non-statutory agencies can provide alternative locations for provision and facilitate engagement with fathers who might be unwilling to engage with local authority services.
- Be prepared to hang in there with fathers; male ego and pride can get in the way of asking for help.

In Australia, Sandstrom et al (2015) made specific recommendations about identifying fathers and male carers, including:

- Being explicit with mothers about the importance of speaking to the father and including him in the process, while also ensuring that she would not be put at risk.
- Speaking separately to the father rather than gathering information solely through the mother.
- Arranging separate home visits where necessary, to explain the relevance of his involvement with the child, communicating a willingness to include him in decisions.

In practice, a range of strategies are used to engage fathers:

- Some organisations have developed 'father champions' who will challenge workers to think about the involvement of fathers.
- Fathers advocacy schemes are not common, but a number are working well in different services.
- There needs to be a recognition that every father is different. Young dads, dads with learning disabilities, dads in prison, dads who are working will all need different strategies to ensure that they are fully involved in the child and family assessment process.

What do you do to ensure that you identify and work with fathers effectively?

In my mid to late thirties I became aware that I could access my 'file' and decided with a degree of trepidation that this was the right thing for me to do!

My working career up to then had already given me the opportunity of writing assessments for my staff and for clients on a regular basis but I hadn't quite prepared myself for my own!

My file has two main components. The first an assessment of my birth family circumstances and the rationale why 'care' would be the best place for me to be and secondly, assessments that charter my time in care, highlighting me the child. (I will add that this is the mid 60s and 70s and diligence wasn't often overseen or enforced!)

Now, admittedly, my file covers 18 years of 'being in care' is only about 1cm so it may give an indication that not a lot was written about me and, to be fair, you'd be quite right. However what is written gave no consideration to the possibilities that I may read it as an adult. The language used and assumptions made at best give little hope for me and at worst imply that I will go the expected way of all children who grow up in care...a park bench or prison, quite a grim prediction!

Details of assessments ask very little, and areas noted that should be of concern don't appear to have been followed up. Scant information relating to birth family is contradictory and 'jumps out'. No attempt to clarify or quantify information has taken place and the 'authors' involved write with the appearance of not being aware of previous information or not caring enough to ask!

Regarding me the child, the language is negative and highlights very little in the way of potential. Reading it gave me the impression that I was of little relevance, just part of 'someone's' job! On reading the assessments I can see serious concerns regarding my health and wellbeing, but no follow up is recorded.

To read about me when I was an adult and see that I was deemed *"backward"* *"a child of little note or worth"* shook me somewhat. It felt like the author of these notes had little, if any, regard for me or my feelings and it is extremely sad and worrying that no follow up was attempted. It felt like my whole childhood had been a 'fait accompli'. Had I read it without being secure in myself, I could have found it quite damaging. If anything, it made me angry, that I was seen as a child of such little value!

So that's what a poor child assessment looked like back in my day. Has it changed? Yes, but there is still room for improvement. I believe that the social workers who 'author' assessments are better placed and have a better understanding of children and more realistic expectation of the 'family' and what it should 'look like'. There now appears, to be some sort of checking system in place, which hopefully keeps authors better focused, ensuring content is factual whilst written in a more child focused way.

The 'real' thing 'authors' need to consider, is the language they use, they must remember that one day this assessment/file could be read. Perhaps they need to 'wear the other shoe' and write with a degree of empathy and hold the thought 'Would I want to read this about me, written in this way'?

As children sometimes move around the 'system', so does their paperwork, and the authors of their developing biography change regularly. The need to have ownership of files should still exist, as well as the need to remain mindful that the information is 'precious' to the subject (Child) and should be written with some of the following as guidelines:

- What if that information was about me?
- Would I want someone to be careful and considerate with it?
- Would I want the information to be correct, true without any assumptions?
- Does it look like I had mattered and been considered when it was written?
- Would I want someone to be respectful about my private me?
- Would I want it full of 'jargon' or 'acronyms' that highlight my differences, making me feel negative about myself?
- Would I want information in a chronological order?

(My own file was in no order, handed to me in a 'disarray' and left for me to place in order. It left me feeling that the organisation still held me in contempt ..Shocking!)

So, what would work better? At least what would improve the relationship, and therefore the assessment, to demonstrate that the author has a better understanding of the child/family they are working with? It isn't rocket science. 'Getting to know you' surely is the most vital part of assessment. Be creative. Let the child see a little of your personal you. The child will understand (get) that you have come to see them, that you are interested in them, and that they are important to you.

It helps create and build trust so that when difficult conversations are needed or appropriate, a sound relationship has already been built. If a file needs to appear, explain what it is and why (even young children can grasp this). Tell those involved what is being written down and why, and where appropriate, ask if they would like to read or agree it. Younger children may want to draw a picture! Why not? ...When they look back, they can see that they were involved with the assessments and not just part of a process, where someone writes details that they may have no memory of...It's just a thought!

What might you change about your practice based on Paul's perspective?

POVERTY INFORMED PRACTICE

The statement that this chapter relates to identifies poverty as a specific factor where social workers need to "hold an empathic position about difficult social circumstances" and take "account of the relationship between poverty and social deprivation, and the effect of stress on family functioning". This is very clearly stated. Poverty informed practice is being discussed more regularly in contemporary social work. For example, Research in Practice has just launched a new briefing paper on neglect in the context of poverty and austerity, whilst the British Association of Social Workers have been doing a great deal of work on anti-poverty practice.

As discussed in Chapter 4 poverty is a significant factor impacting on the lives of children and families. It is important that social workers do not lose sight of this.

It can be helpful to use SHARE in relation to poverty awareness. For example, the social worker should think about whether they have recognised the impact of poverty on the child and their family. Poverty is currently so pervasive in the lives of the children social workers work with, that often practitioners become immune to it. 'Poverty-blindness' can occur. Equally it is important to think about the family's 'share'. I have seen social workers who wear a great deal of expensive jewellery or carry an expensive designer handbag. When a parent sees that what impact might it have?

PAUSE TO REFLECT

Think about an assessment you are currently completing, or one you have recently completed. Reflect on your work with that child and family. How have you taken account of the relationship between poverty and social deprivation, and the effect of stress on family functioning?

Matthew Purves is a school-based social worker employed in Stockport's Enhanced Integration Programme. He is currently working towards NAAS.

Before I moved into the world of children and families social work I was employed by the local authority as a family support worker. Those formative years were 'the best of times and the worst of times.' My manager afforded me a level of freedom that gave me time and space to form strong working relationships with people in the community - I felt I was on the family's side and making a difference. Sadly, the worst of times became apparent later when, after moving into a locality social work team, I learned that some of the children of the families I'd worked with so closely had been taken into care. Knowing the parents and the adversity they'd overcome, I was deeply upset and spent time critically reflecting on my own practice questioning what I could have done differently. This involved a return to academic reading and struggles with impostor syndrome. However, it wasn't until I encountered stories of parents who had experience of children's social care intervention that I began to take notice of the elephant in the room: Poverty.

Whichever way you define poverty, social and economic deprivation looms large over many of the families we work with. It has become so every-day that it can be easily overlooked, especially its association with family functioning. The media and politicians would have us believe that people are entirely responsible for their own lives and that the so-called toxic trio of drugs, domestic abuse and mental health problems are more often than not due to bad personal choices. There is a tendency to individualise difficulties; to pathologise or problematise those who are suffering, and it is politically expedient to do so. Blame is shifted away from the State via a 21st century revival of the early modern narrative that those in poverty are feckless and undeserving.

In 2016 The Joseph Rowntree Foundation published "*The relationship between poverty, child abuse and neglect: an evidence review*". I recommend that you read it. The associations between poverty, child abuse and neglect are made cogently. Poverty matters because, like other social determinants, it has a huge bearing on how children and their families function. When I look back at the family support I offered some years ago, I was embroiled in the complexity of micro-level needs; tackling the macro-level grip of social deprivation was eclipsed by visits to the GP, food banks, fuel payments, house moves, etc.. but arguably these were merely sticking plasters. The unforgiving stress of poverty continued unabated - as did the family arguments, depression, anxiety and temporary escapism via cannabis and alcohol.

What can be done differently? I don't have all the answers but here are some suggestions. Raise the profile of poverty as a social determinant and tell the story in assessments, in supervision, in child protection meetings and with service leaders. Challenge the use of section 17 funds and argue stalwartly that the local authority should buy the cooker, the fridge, the instrument, the laptop - whatever it takes to give families capacity. Connect with community groups who can support a family through deprivation and crisis. Create a directory of agencies that can work alongside people and that offer emotional support and material help. Above all, I've learned that neat, SMART social work plans that recommend a GP visit won't necessarily fix a mental health problem, nor will a drugs worker fix addiction or a parenting course resolve domestic conflict. Social problems require social solutions and that's a cause worth fighting for"

CONFLICTING INTERESTS / COMPETING DEMANDS: CREATING COMPLEXITY

In social work there are almost always competing demands and conflicts of interests and the same is true in families, so social work with children and families has these in abundance! These conflicts and competing demands lead to significant complexity and this complexity often causes difficulties in social work assessment.

Complexity theory is a recent idea, taken from scientific fields. It originally comes out of experimental mathematics and chaos theory. Ideas around complexity theory are still developing in science but essentially complexity theory seeks to understand, predict and control complex situations.

Complexity theory starts from the basic premise that complexity in itself is difficult to define. Something can be complicated but not complex. Rick Hood (2018) uses a car engine analogy to explain the difference between complex and complicated. A car engine is complicated – it has many moving parts and is largely determined by the laws of science and engineering. However, the engine is not complex - each separate part does not make its own decisions, it does not change its feelings on a daily basis, it does not form new relationships outside of the engine, it does not adapt, it does not find new ways of functioning when the car won't start one morning. Once a mechanic learns how to fix a car their role is fairly standard with each breakdown because the car engine behaves in a fairly predictable way. Social work, however, is much more than complicated – it is complex.

The ideas behind complexity theory are very complex in themselves and are therefore difficult to summarise. However, they do offer some points of interest for a social worker undertaking an assessment. This basic idea is:

- Traditional linear thinking about relationships or connections are based on the idea that A will lead to B.
- Chaos theory (in science) would say that relationships or connections between things are random - such that A could lead to anything.
- Complexity theory would say that A could lead to B or possibly to C, maybe even D. Whether A leads to B or to C will depend on small initial variations in A. Ultimately the theory is that consequences are not random, but neither are they simply linear and predictable.

Working with complexity requires an understanding about interconnections and an ability to put the pieces of the jigsaw together to create a clear picture. The use of complexity theory in social work is very new but there are a number of links to systemic thinking in practice.

The assessment documentation and the requirements for different assessments to address different things (parenting assessments, risk assessments, impact assessments...) are complicated, but what makes child and family assessment so complex is that each child and family we work with is unique. They bring with them a range of competing demands, and there are likely to be some conflicts of interests. We may have some information but other information may be hidden from our view. The relationships between people may be complex as may the relationships between aspects of the child's life.

Most of us will recognise that there are some assessments that are more complex than others, indeed that there are some aspects of work which are more complex than others. In 1973, Rittel and Webber referred to 'wicked problems' in social work, which could be characterised as:

- Having no definitive formulation.
- Relating to multiple issues.
- Being significantly conflictual – with conflicts of interest, conflicts of opinion, conflicts of values.
- Lacking clarity about the end point goal.
- Being uniquely configured, such that 'solutions' which worked in other situations may not be helpful.

(adapted from Hood et al 2016)

Good social work finds the simplicity in the complexity. The simplicity is that the child's needs and welfare are always paramount. The child must always be at the very centre of the assessment process. Whilst that in itself sounds simple, there is significant complexity in ensuring that the needs and views of the child are central to the assessment.

PAUSE TO REFLECT

Think about the most complex assessment you have been involved in. What was it that made this so complex?

How did you ensure that the child's views and needs were central to that assessment?

What might you be able to learn from this to take into other complex situations?

CONFIRMATION BIAS

Chapter 7 considers the importance of analysis and decision making, so this chapter will not cover the detail of analysing the information gathered in an assessment. However, the issue of conformation bias sits very specifically here since this has such a significant impact on the assessment process. Confirmation bias does not just impact on how information is analysed but also on how information is gathered. Confirmation bias is the phrase used to describe the tendency to:

- Seek information which will support your hypothesis.
- Place more value on information which confirms your thinking.
- Largely ignore information which challenges your hypothesis.
- Interpret information in such a way that it evidences your claims.
- Recall information which backs up your hypothesis.

Featherston et al (2018) found that confirmation bias had a significant impact on social work decision making across a range of sectors. This research identified that considerable work was needed within the profession to look at how best to prevent bias impacting on decision making and, therefore, outcomes for children.

Confirmation bias is a cognitive (thought) process which changes the way you seek, view and use information because of your own bias or prejudgements. The following diagram illustrates this well.

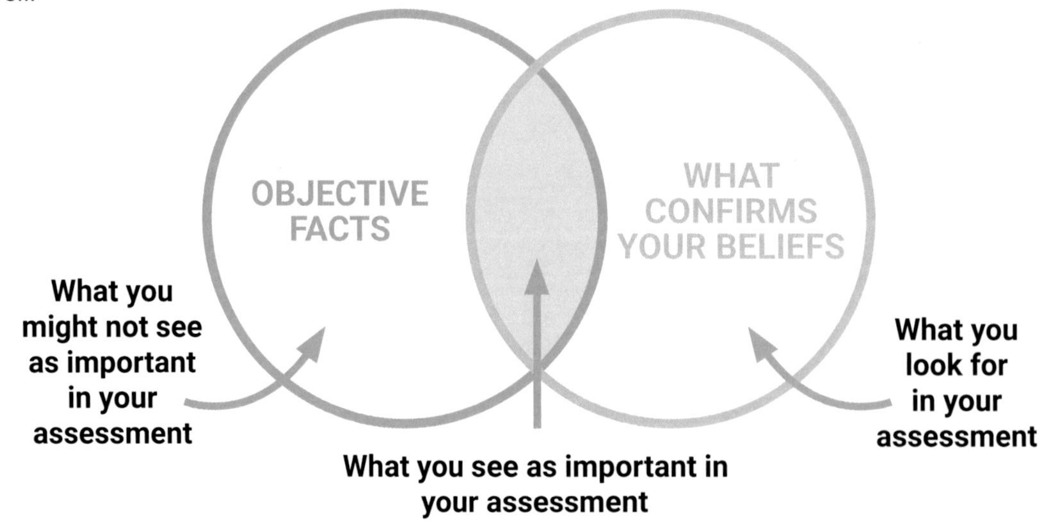

Understanding confirmation bias is a starting point, but it is not enough to mitigate against the impact that the bias may have on the information that you seek and how you view this. Thinking the situation through from a different standpoint can be helpful here. If you start with a different hypothesis, will the information you have take on a different meaning? How can you check this out?

ATTRIBUTIONAL BIAS

Whilst confirmation bias impacts on how we gather and analyse information, attributional bias impacts on who we view as responsible. We gather information that something has happened – who do we hold responsible? Where should we attribute this behaviour? Who is to blame? The basic idea is that we 'blame' our own negative behaviour on external factors whilst we 'blame' negative behaviour in other people on them (it's their fault). We do the opposite for positives. So if we achieve something or behave in a positive way then that's totally down to us. If someone else does it then it's luck or external factors (they had help).

Drawing on the journey in a car that we have been on in this chapter, think about when you arrive at a roundabout in your car. If you get in the wrong lane you think to yourself, "this is a really badly signposted roundabout!" However, if you are in the right lane and someone else is in the wrong lane you think to yourself, "they are a really bad driver. They can't even get themselves in the right lane!" Where someone is similar to us, we are more likely to be able to externalise their behaviour. So if I am in the right lane of the roundabout and I see a middle aged woman in an old banger of a car I am likely to think, "poor woman, this roundabout is really badly signposted I must let her in." On the other hand if I am in the right lane and next to me is a young man in a brand new BMW with special alloy wheels, I am likely to think "he thinks he owns the road. If he thinks he's getting in front of me he's got another thing coming!" Please don't judge my driving! I am just trying to illustrate the point.

When gathering information it is easy to make judgements about why something happened drawing on attributional bias. However, social workers who try to maintain a person in environment perspective, draw on both internal and external factors, recognising that sometimes we get in the wrong lane of the roundabout because we are not concentrating, sometimes it's because the roundabout is really badly signposted and sometimes it's because the sat nav didn't tell us in time. So when analysing the information gathered as part of an assessment, it is important to consider the fullest range of reasons why something may have occurred.

PAUSE TO REFLECT

What strategies do you use to mitigate the impact of confirmation and attributional bias in your assessment?

WHERE AM I NOW?

Revisit the start of the chapter. Look again at the KSS standard. Then consider the following questions:

What has surprised me in working through this chapter?

What three things would I highlight as key learning?

What do I still need to do in working towards being fully confident with this KSS statement?

What single next step should I take in working towards an improvement in my practice?

Chapter 7

ANALYSIS, DECISION MAKING, PLANNING AND REVIEW

Analysis and decision making lie at the very heart of social work practice and as such the themes covered in this chapter connect to each of the other chapters in a range of ways. This chapter will help you to explore the meaning and importance of analysis in social work. The chapter is structured around a decision-making tree for social work, which draws on the role of theory, research, expertise and evidence in decision making. Working through this chapter will prompt you to think about how you reach decisions in your practice and how you keep these under regular review.

THE KSS REQUIRES PRACTITIONERS TO:

Establish the seriousness that different risks present and any harm already suffered by a child, balanced with family strengths and potential solutions. Set out the best options for resolving difficulties facing the family and each child, considering the risk of future harm and its consequences and the likelihood of successful change.

Prioritise children's need for emotional warmth, stability and sense of belonging, particularly those in public care, as well as identity development, health and education, ensuring active participation and positive engagement of the child and family. Test multiple hypotheses about what is happening in families and to children, using evidence and professional judgement to reach timely conclusions. Challenge any prevailing professional conclusions in the light of new evidence or practice reflection.

Make realistic child centred plans within a review timeline, which will manage and reduce identified risks and meet the needs of the child. Ensure sufficient multi-disciplinary input into the process at all stages. Apply twin and triple track planning to minimise chances of drift or delay, being alert to the effectiveness or otherwise of current support plans.

Take a look at the standard above in detail. Highlight key phrases and anything that jumps out at you. Then take some time to reflect on the statement.

- *What are your immediate thoughts?*
- *What might you want to discuss and clarify?*
- *How will you clarify meanings?*
- *Who will you discuss it with?*

GETTING FEEDBACK ON PRACTICE

Who can give me feedback on my practice in this area?	*How will I get the feedback?*

Make sure to keep a record of any feedback you receive.

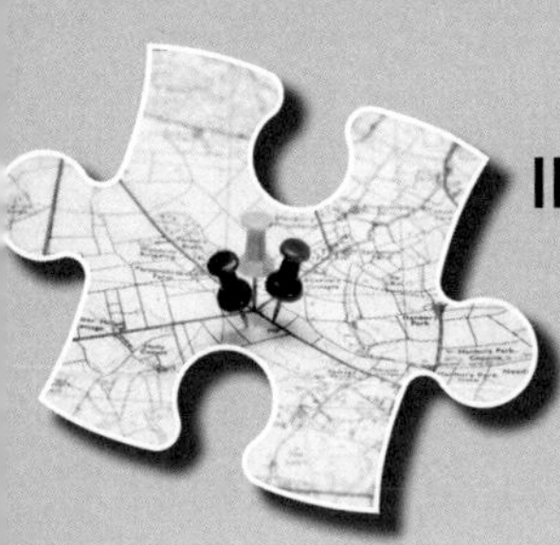

INITIAL SELF-ASSESSMENT

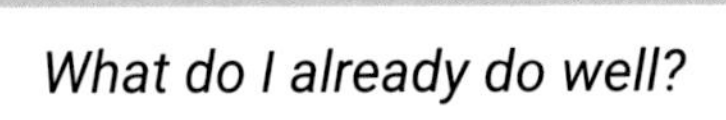

What do I already do well?

How do I know? (What's my evidence?)

What do I need to work on?

How will I work on this?

How will I assess my process?

ANALYSIS IN SOCIAL WORK PRACTICE

The word analysis comes from the Ancient Greek word análusis which literally taken means 'a breaking up.' Dictionary definitions of analysis generally build on this idea. For example, the Oxford dictionary definition of analysis is "detailed examination of the elements or structure of something to improve understanding."

In many ways analysis is like taking a jigsaw puzzle to pieces to examine each piece in more detail. The initial picture may be confusing but taking it to pieces can help to restructure our understanding.

In social work analysis is often taken forward into synthesis. The dictionary definition of synthesis is "the combination of components or elements to form a connected whole".

Synthesis is about putting the pieces of the puzzle back together to form a fuller picture. The puzzle may be put back together in different way, giving us a new perspective and ideas for action.

When we talk about analysis in social work, we generally use the word to mean a combination of analysis and synthesis, because in practice analysis goes beyond simply presenting information to exploring what this information means and how it can be used.

Essentially good social work is about understanding the whole in light of the parts and this holistic understanding only comes about through professional analysis where the parts are looked at separately, then connected and can be considered such that the whole can be viewed from an informed perspective. Critical analysis goes further, bringing in a consideration of where the information has come from and why you have been given this information.

Brown, Moore and Turney (2012) report on a Research in Practice Development Group, which developed a set of principles to support social workers to create more analytical assessments. These principles, referred to as Anchor principles, can support social workers to think beyond the simple presentation of information to develop an analytical understanding of the information.

The principles guide a practitioner through the following five questions:

- What is the assessment for?
- What is the story?
- What does the story mean?
- What needs to happen?
- How will we know we are making progress?

These anchoring questions can help a social worker to break down the social work process into component parts, so enabling a more analytical approach. Wilkins and Boahen (2013:11) explain that a social worker needs to develop an analytical mindset:

> **"By an analytical mindset, we mean an approach to practice that is repeatedly questioning the information you have, asking what information might be missing and why it might be important, actively hypothesising and considering different interpretations of the same information (without speculating too widely or too wildly). In other words, an analytical mindset is about taking an overall approach to practice and as such, it affects how one writes assessments, interacts with service users and colleagues but especially how one thinks."**

Summarising analysis in the following way can be helpful:

Accuracy – it is important to ensure that all of the information you have is accurate.

New – always be open to new information changing the picture.

Acknowledge – acknowledge any missing or conflicting information.

Look – look carefully at each piece of information and its interconnections with other information.

You – be clear on how *you* see things. Your perspective, your role etc will change the way that you interpret information. Everyone sees things in different ways, so your sense of self is vitally important in being analytical.

Scepticism – take a healthily sceptical approach, question the information you have. Why do I have that information? Where did it come from? This should lead you onto:

Investment - consider who has vested interests in the way that information is interpreted and who has an investment in the decision making process.

Synthesis – when the information has been considered in parts then it must be looked at in terms of the whole picture.

PAUSE TO REFLECT

What does analysis mean to you?

DECISION TREES

Decision trees are a specific tool used to support decision making. They are generally based on mathematical algorithms and are widely used in science and industry. Decision trees are very mathematical in design, usually drawing on a range of graphs and calculations to support decision making. This often puts social workers off, although maths and science have a great deal to offer the profession in terms of thinking through complex decision making. Increasingly, algorithms and decision trees are being trialled across social work with children and families in a range of different ways (McIntyre and Pegg 2018) with a number of local authorities using algorithmic profiling to make initial identifications of children at risk. Whilst initial media coverage of the use of predictive data systems resulted in significant concerns within the profession, (expressed through letters to the press and social media posts), analytics are widely used in contemporary society and the use of such systems is likely to increase. Social workers need to be clear about how they use a more individualised nuanced decision-making model, whilst drawing on what data is able to offer. The development of a decision-making tree specific to social work can be helpful here.

THE SOCIAL WORK DECISION TREE

In many ways the components of the social work tree are acknowledged within the KSS. In reaching decisions, social workers should draw on:

T *theory*

R *research*

E *evidence*

E *expertise*

Reaching analytical, ethical decisions calls for social workers to draw on each of the branches of the tree, requiring practitioners to critically understand the difference between theory, research, evidence and expertise or, in other words, each branch of the decision-making tree. The following pages will offer some clarity around the distinctions between each.

THEORY

Theory is vitally important in social work but its use in practice is not always well understood by practitioners. Certainly, there is a distinct lack of clarity between theories, models, methods and approaches in the social work community (Maclean, Finch and Tedam 2018). Very often they are all lumped together in teaching, or in the literature, under the heading social work theory. In some ways whether something is a theory, a model, a method or an approach is merely semantics, but actually, understanding the differences can be really helpful in aiding social workers to be more theory-informed in their practice.

In science, a theory is said to:

1. Describe (*What is happening?*)
2. Explain (*Why is it happening?*)
3. Predict (*What is likely to happen next?*)
4. Control and bring about change (*How can I change what will happen, to produce a different outcome?*)

In many ways, this can be directly applied to the social work role, although it is preferable to change the final phrase from 'control and bring about change' to 'intervene and bring about change'. Very often in contemporary social work practice there is an element of control to the social work role, but the phrase 'intervene and bring about change' often sits more comfortably and recognises that wherever possible social work intervention should be based on working in partnership with people.

With this change to the final phrase, these four points could be used to describe the social work role: in an assessment, a social worker seeks to describe what is happening for a child and attempts to explain why the situation came about, they then look to the likelihood of future harm, predicting what might happen next. This initial process culminates in a social worker planning with the family group what can be done to bring about change. As such, these four points are often used to argue that a social worker is always using theory in their practice even if they are not able to confidently name it (sometimes the use of theory is unconscious).

In fact, these four points are particularly helpful in clarifying the difference, in social work, between a theory and a model. Essentially a theory helps us to do the first three points. It helps us to describe, explain and predict. It does not tell us however, how to intervene and bring about change – theory informs our intervention, but it does not structure it. A model on the other hand does not help us to describe, explain or predict but it does help us to intervene and bring about change. In short, a theory informs our 'thinking' and a model informs our 'doing.'

So, for example, attachment is a theory. Attachment helps us to look at a child's (or an adult's) behaviour and explain where this may have come from, it also helps us to consider the likely impact of this behaviour on their future relationships. It does not, however, provide us with a clear intervention strategy. Whereas, something like task centred practice is a model – this does not help us when we go to see a family, to look at what is happening, why it is happening or what might happen next. It does, though, suggest a useful way of intervening to bring about change in a given situation.

Methods and models are often confused, but they are separate concepts. A method is a specific tool, or a particular technique used in practice. Methods are always drawn out of models, such that the method can be seen as a way of putting a particular model into practice. Where a social worker is using a particular method in practice it doesn't mean that they are using the whole model, but they should know where that method comes from. As an example, the three houses direct work tool is a method of direct work. It comes from the model signs of safety.

An approach brings together theories, models and methods – an approach is a way to describe our overall way of working. If a theory is about thinking and a model is about doing, then an approach is about 'being.' Our approach describes the way we like to go about something. Social workers develop their own approach to practice over time. Some employers adopt a particular approach to practice and the social worker may find it difficult if this is not complementary to their own approach. Some approaches work well together, but others clash.

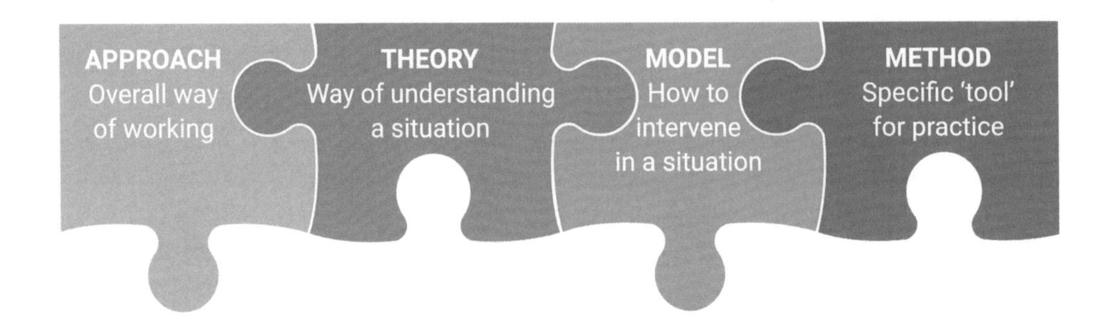

Social workers can lack confidence in explaining their practice in a theory-informed way. Take the use of the three houses direct work tool, which is a commonly used tool in social work practice. The following diagram illustrates how three houses as a method is drawn out of a model (signs of safety) and in this situation signs of safety is being used as part of a solution focused approach. It could equally be used as part of a strengths based approach or a systemic approach. A variety of theories could be being used to understand what is happening – so this box has been left generic.

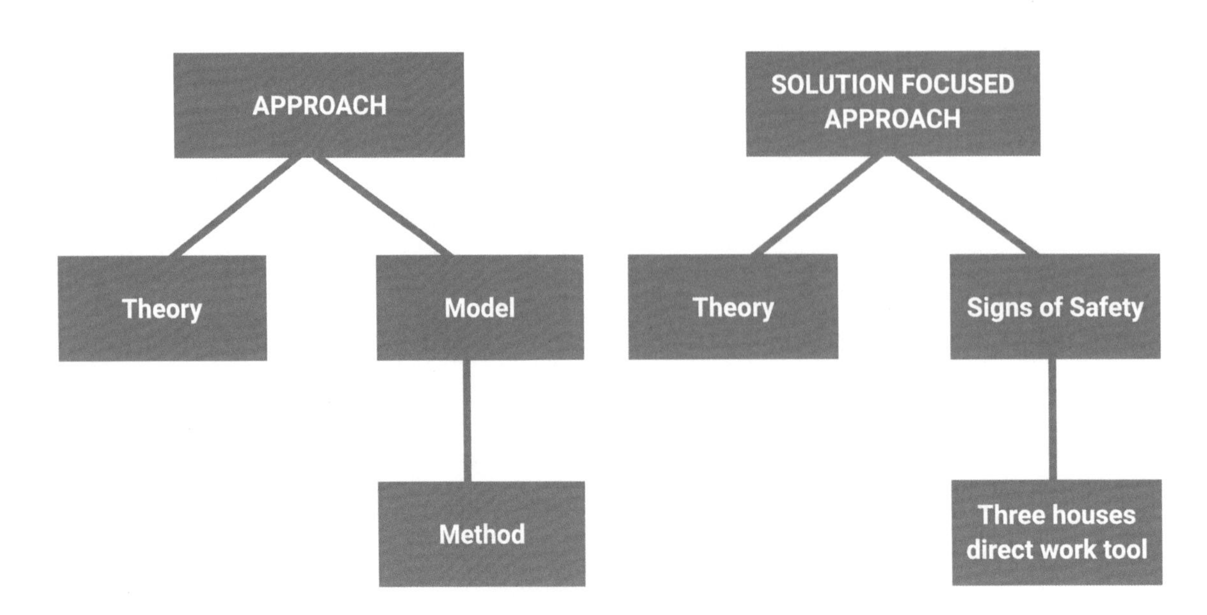

USING THE HEAD, HEART, HANDS FRAMEWORK TO UNDERSTAND THEORY IN SOCIAL WORK

Another way of looking at the relationship between theories, models, methods and approaches is to return to the head, heart, hands framework explored in Chapter 1.

Head

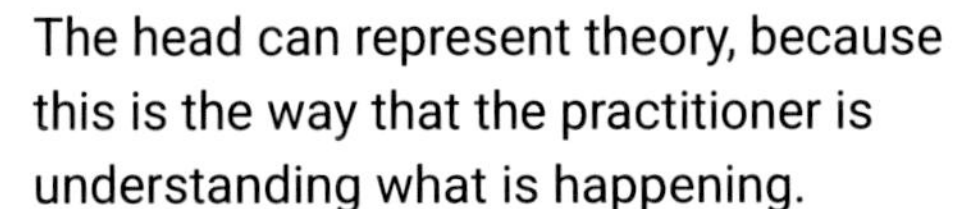

The head can represent theory, because this is the way that the practitioner is understanding what is happening.

Heart

The heart represents the worker's overall approach to practice.

Hands

The hands represent the model used, because this is all about what the practitioner actually does in the situation.

The method can be represented by a tool placed in the hands.

The tool demonstrates that this is about the use of a specific skill or intervention.

THEORY AS THE FOOD FOR SOCIAL WORK PRACTICE

It can be helpful to think about theory as the food of social work practice (Maclean 2016). Theory helps to provide the essential nutrients and sustenance that is required for effective social work practice. Using a food analogy can also help in developing a clearer understanding about how theory, models, methods and approaches work together.

Think of an approach as the kind of food you like to eat. Do you like Indian, Chinese, Mediterranean, traditional English, fast food, comfort food, healthy food? Do you follow a particular kind of diet – vegan, vegetarian, gluten free? This is like your approach to practice.

Now, think of a model as a curry. You can get a curry in a Chinese restaurant, an Indian, a Thai, a Caribbean, you can get curry sauce in a chip shop, you can even get little pots of curry sauce in fast food places. They are all curry – but they are completely different. If the model you use in practice is a curry, then it will have a very different taste depending on whether it is being used as part of one approach or another. So as a practitioner you really need to understand the approach that you take to practice. The approach you take will be a combination of your own cooking and the favoured food of your employer.

The approach that you take to practice will flavour everything that you do.

In science a theory is seen as helping to:	In practice, social workers seek to:	So, in practice social workers use:
Describe	Understand what is happening	Theories to describe what is happening and why it came about.
Explain	Consider why this situation has come about	Theories to predict what might happen next.
Predict	Explore what might happen next	Theories to guide thinking.
Control a situation and create change	Intervene to bring about improved outcomes	A model to structure the intervention. Methods to put the model into practice.

Theory-informed practice means a social worker can identify their overall approach to practice, the theory/theories which inform their thinking, the model which they are using to intervene and the specific methods they are using in the particular practice situation.

The fact is that reflection and theory provides more than simply "food for thought". They it provide the essential nutrients that enhance, inform and validate for social work practice...

Theory also reflects the complexity and diversity of social work practice

PAUSE TO REFLECT

Try thinking through a piece of work that you are involved in.

What theory are you drawing on to understand what is happening?

What model are you using to intervene?

What methods are you using in your practice?

How is your overall approach flavouring your work?

RESEARCH

Within the social work decision making tree the use of research has two branches:

- Drawing on research evidence
- Using research skills in practice

DRAWING ON RESEARCH EVIDENCE

Using research to inform practice is helpful for social workers. Research findings are particularly helpful in understanding:

- Likely outcomes in situations
- What works in practice
- Risk indicators
- Likelihood of successful change

However, it is important to take a critical, questioning approach to research. Where is the research from? What methods were used? What was the motive? Who funded it? Who carried it out? How near to practice is it? Each of these will have an impact on how valid and useful the research is. Perhaps most importantly a practitioner needs to look at:

WHY am I using this research?

Sometimes people seek out research and evidence to confirm their perspective, often ignoring information which might challenge their findings and would therefore cause them to revise their assessment or plan. Practitioners who practice in this way could be called verificationists.

Where practitioners are drawing on research simply to verify their thoughts, this often spreads so that all of the branches of the tree become compromised. For example, practitioners may ignore evidence which does not fit with their hypothesis. This is potentially dangerous. It is vital that social workers always remain open to change their perspective as the branches of the tree grow in different directions. There is an old African proverb, "When the roots are deep, there is no reason to fear the wind." If the hypothesis is correct, then it will be firm enough to have all evidence fully considered.

It is important to have access to a range of research and to be clear about the validity of this research. Many local authorities provide access to resources like Research in Practice which brings together research and practitioner expertise to build evidence informed practice.

Some employers provide social workers with specific offcuts of research that will be helpful in their practice. A number of organisations have been established to support the further development of research in social work with children and families, for example the What Works Centre for Children's Social Care looks at supporting practitioners and social work leaders to access the best evidence. CASCADE (Childrens Social Care Research and Development Centre), which is based at Cardiff University, provides overviews of research which are accessible for practitioners.

PAUSE TO REFLECT

Where do I access research evidence?

When have I made good use of research evidence?

How was it helpful?

How might I make better use of research evidence in my practice?

USING RESEARCH SKILLS IN ASSESSMENT AND ANALYSIS

Social work students are often required to undertake some sort of research project as part of their qualifying programme. The teaching to support this generally includes research methodology. This approach to teaching research skills can limit social workers' understanding of the use of research skills in practice. Books about the use of research skills in practice focus on how to undertake an academic research project or assignment. However, research skills can be very helpful in social work practice itself and most certainly social workers can draw on a range of research skills in their assessments and wider practice.

There are a range of references in the KSS to research skills and methods. For example:

- The use of best evidence is referred to in standards 1 and 2.
- Using observation is referred to in standards 3 and 6.
- Triangulating evidence is referred to in standard 5.
- The use of evidence based tools is referred to in standard 6.
- The testing of hypotheses is referred to in standard 7 and standard 9.
- Standard 9 refers to a range of research skills and methods, such as the testing of hypotheses, drawing on the best evidence from research and exploring the potential for bias.

Quite clearly then, social work practice calls upon a range of research skills. In many ways social workers are researchers in the community. When a social worker carries out an assessment, they may for example be researching the child's world or researching the quality of parenting. Child and family assessment processes and methods are essentially drawn from research techniques and the research process.

The joint statement of the seven research councils in the UK (UK Research Councils undated) is effectively the equivalent of the knowledge and skills statement for researchers. It outlines skills under the seven broad headings of:

a) Research skills and techniques

b) Research environment

c) Research management

d) Personal effectiveness

e) Communication skills

f) Networking and team working

g) Career management

The skills detailed within these broad headings bear a remarkable similarity to the key skills required in social work practice. Many of the skills could be considered as good generic professional skills, such as: self-awareness; flexibility; original, independent and creative thinking; clarity around boundaries; ethical approach and the use of information technology.

There are, however, a range of specific skills often used in practice by researchers which can be drawn on by social workers in assessment and analysis. Some of the most relevant, and those which are referred to in both the research council standards and the knowledge and skills statement for social workers are clearly interconnected and will be covered in the next few pages:

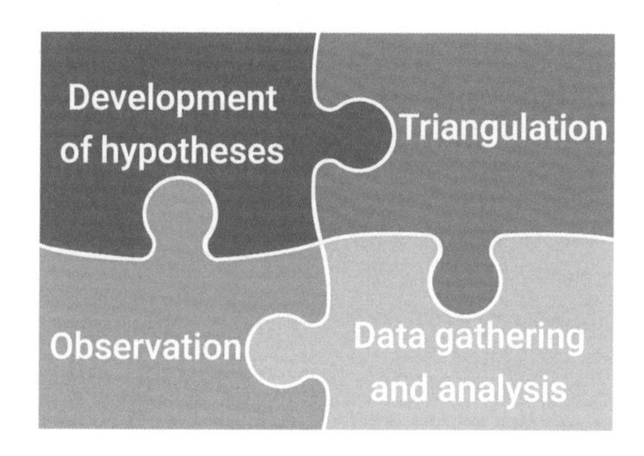

DEVELOPMENT OF HYPOTHESES

Understanding what a hypothesis is can be helpful in considering how and why social workers should develop multiple hypotheses in their work. The word hypothesis comes from Greek:

hupo meaning under

thesis meaning placing

A hypothesis can therefore be seen as the underpinning of our decision making. Definitions of the word generally indicate that a hypothesis is a suggested explanation for a situation or phenomenon. The Oxford Dictionary helpfully demonstrates the fact that a hypothesis is the starting point for further investigation.

"a supposition or proposed explanation made on the basis of limited evidence as a starting point for further investigation."

(Oxford Dictionary online 2019)

Effectively the hypothesis that a social worker develops can be seen as the roots of the decision making tree. The hypothesis is what the social worker thinks is happening. They then need to look at each branch of the tree to decide whether their hypothesis is correct. As they look to each branch of the tree drawing out theory, research, evidence and expertise they may realise that their hypothesis is incorrect, the roots of the tree do not hold up the branches and the hypothesis should be changed based on the way the tree has grown.

ROSIE

Rosie is 2 years old. She is brought to the hospital minor injuries clinic by her mother. She has broken her right arm. Rosie's mother says she has no idea how the injury occurred. She picked Rosie up from nursery and noted that she was holding her arm in a strange way and she wasn't picking anything up with her right arm, despite being normally right handed. The nurse notes that Rosie has a black front tooth and a number of bruises of different shapes and shades across her body. Rosie is back at the same minor injuries unit two days later. Her other arm is broken. Rosie's mum is asked how this injury occurred; she says she has no idea and starts crying.

What might be happening here?

There are many potential hypotheses in Rosie's situation. She may be being physically abused by her mother, or by another person in her life. Was she at nursery when both injuries occurred? Is this about negligent or abusive care in the nursery environment? Rosie may have a medical condition which is causing the injuries. Rosie may simply have been very unlucky in that she may have had two accidents very close together – is she being adequately supervised at home? Maybe the nursery refused to have Rosie whilst her arm was in a cast and her mother left her at home alone whilst she went to work. There could be a range of things going on.

This is what the development of a hypothesis is all about. Social workers develop an idea about what they think is happening in any given situation. What is important is:

- Being clear about where the hypothesis came from. What is the idea based on? Why did you think this and not something else?
- Being open to changing the idea, but being equally clear about why the idea has changed
- Being open to defending the thought process

I have used this particular example here to illustrate the importance of being open minded. I know this situation, because I was that mum. My youngest daughter Rosie had just started walking (the lateness of her walking had been explored in an appointment with a paediatrician who said she was just taking things slowly). She fell over a great deal and generally landed face first on the floor. I picked her up from nursery one day; she seemed her usual cheerful self, but her arm looked misshapen and I noticed that she didn't pick things up in that hand. I took her to the local hospital where she laughed when being examined so they said she was fine and sent me away. I took her to the minor injuries unit the next morning where they agreed to do an x-ray and found that her arm was indeed broken. I stayed home with her rather than her going to nursery the next day. Towards the end of the day I noticed that her other arm looked misshapen and it was also broken. I cried when asked how she had done it, because I was so upset and I had no idea what was happening.

As a social worker hearing this story, I would be really concerned about a potential safeguarding issue.

I totally expected that an investigation would take place. Instead a letter was sent from our GP requesting that Rosie be seen by another paediatrician. The letter started by listing her injures, it then said, "Both parents are social workers so there are no safeguarding concerns". This story is now 17 years old and Rosie has given her permission for me to talk about it. It took two years for Rosie to be given a diagnosis which explained the injuries she had and the delays in her physical development. If that outrageously biased statement about her parents being social workers hadn't been made, what might the professional hypothesis have been?

I know that this experience has certainly enabled me to recognise that, whatever we think as an immediate response, there could be other things going on in any situation and we must always keep our hypothesis open to change. It has also enhanced my understanding of professional bias and the potential impact of this.

PAUSE TO REFLECT

Think about a child that you are working with at the moment, where you feel that something is happening that you are not sure about it.

Develop a number of hypotheses. So, try to come up with at least 5 explanations of why this might be happening.

What knowledge have you based these hypotheses on? Think about the whole tree - so draw on what theory, research, evidence and expertise you have used to develop the hypothesis.

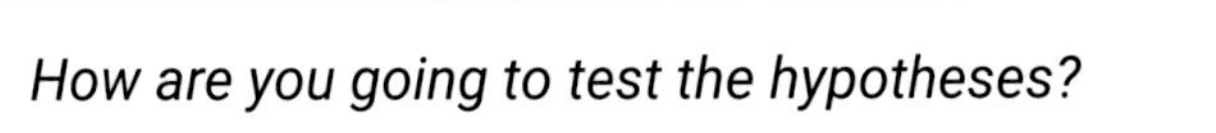

How are you going to test the hypotheses?

How will you reach a conclusion?

TRIANGULATION

Triangulation has a range of different meanings in different contexts. In research triangulation is about validating data by cross referencing the data from more than two sources (hence the triangle). Essentially it is about checking a hypothesis by seeking evidence from a variety of sources. According to Carvalho and White (1997) triangulation goes further than validation in that it:

- Offers a deepening and widening of understanding, especially in complex situations
- Produces innovation by providing a range of interpretations
- Enriches evidence
- Prevents the potential for bias
- Can confirm, refute or explain evidence

Triangulation originates in navigation, where it describes the process of determining the location of a particular point by taking measurements from other points. It is an essential aspect of creating maps. On page 5 we explored the way that a reflexive approach can be understood by considering maps. Good social work practice supports a family to identify where they are now and to understand clearly where they need to be. Developing a map to help the family to travel the unique journey that takes them from their starting point to the identified destination is an important aspect of a social worker's role. Triangulation clearly helps in supporting this map development.

Observation
What has the practitioner seen?

Feedback
What conversations has the social worker had? What are others saying about the situation?

Product evidence
In social work, product evidence would largely be seen as documentation. So, this corner of the triangle would be about drawing on records, chronologies etc.

Good social work practice connects the evidence drawn from each corner of the triangle and the analysis, then considers the interconnectivity. For example, what is observed may contradict feedback of the evidence or the product evidence might suggest one thing whilst feedback evidence indicates something else. Digging deeper and exploring each corner of the triangle really helps with this analysis.

It is good practice in any assessment to triangulate the evidence. Social work students have triangulated assessments of their practice:

- Practice educators observe students in practice with service users.
- Practice educators will obtain a range of feedback, for example from service users, from colleagues and from other professionals.
- Practice educators will read and review the documentation kept by the student and they will read the student's assignments and reflections.

Of course, the NAAS triangulates assessment of social work practitioners. As you put together the pieces of accreditation you will be assessed using observation, feedback and product strategies.

PAUSE TO REFLECT

What difficulties do I experience with triangulating evidence?

How might I be able to draw on triangulated evidence more consistently?

OBSERVATION IN SOCIAL WORK

Drawing on observation in social work is vitally important, as Claudia's contribution to Chapter 1 demonstrates. Observation is pretty much about watching. Watching is essentially a natural human activity that requires little thought or analysis. However, in research, assessment and social work this 'natural activity' needs to be carefully considered.

The origins of direct observation lie in research, where direct observation is a method used within qualitative research. Quantitative research gathers data in numerical form, whereas qualitative research gathers more descriptive data. Qualitative research is commonly used in the social sciences where the researcher seeks to understand the 'how and why' of aspects of human behaviour rather than simply the 'what'. Qualitative approaches to research draw on a variety of methods, including participant observation and direct observation.

Participant observation requires the researcher to become an active participant in the activity or culture being observed. This method usually requires weeks or months in order for the researcher to be accepted as part of the culture, enabling accurate findings to emerge.

Direct Observation differs from participant observation in that the researcher is not part of the event taking place. The researcher is able to adopt a detached view of the event although this in itself can potentially impact on the findings of such research as the researcher is likely to influence the interaction being observed.

In social work we are more likely to refer to formal and informal observation. Sometimes we might observe a child by becoming involved in an activity with them, but because we are not a long term 'natural' part of that child's world, the observation would still be regarded in research terms as a form of direct observation.

Ruch (2017:7) defines observation as "*watching carefully the way something happens or the way someone does something*". Here, the word carefully demonstrates the consideration that needs to be given to what is seen and the way that this is analysed. In social work when we refer to drawing on observation, we are looking at not just what was seen, but how we interpreted what was seen.

There is a quotation which connects each of the following pitfalls and is incredibly relevant for both observation and social work. The quote is difficult to attribute but probably has roots in old Jewish law.

"We don't see things as they are, we see them as we are."

Bias has a huge impact on our observations, even though this is often unconscious. The bias that we have will impact on what we decide we need to observe and on how we see things when we observe something. Essentially, each of the pitfalls in observation covered on the following page is either based on an individual's bias or provides a basis for bias. Attempting to be more conscious about bias can be particularly helpful for social workers. Why does one social worker see something in a different way to another social worker? The more conscious we are about this the more effective our analysis will be.

POTENTIAL PITFALLS IN OBSERVATION

Drawing on your observations in assessment and decision making is important, but it is vital to be aware of some of the dangers in observation. For example:

The Hawthorne effect: This term was coined following a study carried out in the 1930s at the Hawthorne Works, an electrical engineering company near Chicago (Rothlisberger and Dickson 1939). The study attempted to assess whether workers productivity was influenced by light levels in the workplace. A number of years later, researchers recognised that the data generated from the study suggested that productivity increased while the research was being carried out and slumped when it had been concluded. The conclusion being that individuals modify their behaviour simply as a reaction to being observed. This clearly has relevance to social work practice in that children, parents and families are very conscious of a social worker's observations and so they may well behave in different ways, whilst you are with them.

The halo/horns effect: This effect involves a practitioner inferring positives (halo) on the basis of previous experiences or findings, or indeed inferring negatives (horns). So, because a parent has demonstrated effective parenting before, a social worker might look for all the positives in any further observations. Equally they may look for all the negatives in any observations, perhaps failing to see the positives. Clearly the Halo effect links into what is often called the 'rule of optimism'. Dingwall et al (1983) used this phrase to describe the tendency for social workers to ascribe positive views about parents, leading to inaction in situations where there was abuse and neglect.

Similar to me: This involves judging a person favourably on the basis that they are like you, or that they have done something in a similar way to you, or conversely, judging someone negatively because they are different to you, or have done something differently to you. It is really about bias. That is why understanding your social GGRRAAACCEEESSS (see Chapter 1) is important in terms of all social work practice.

Inferring or generalising: Practitioners can infer something based on partial observation evidence. So, for example working on the basis that because someone can do A they must be able to do B, C and D. It is vitally important when drawing on observational evidence that a practitioner only draws on what they have actually seen.

Contrast effects: This arises when one person is compared to another by an observer. The inferior performance may then be deemed as not good enough no matter how it stands in relation to the criteria they are being assessed against. This can happen in many situations in social work where practitioners may compare the circumstances of one family against another – as opposed to looking at specific assessment criteria.

Unconscious bias: Whilst bias can impact on analysis and decision making in a range of ways, it is perhaps in observation that bias can have the most obvious effect. Most of the pitfalls above are either based *on* or provide a base *for* bias.

PAUSE TO REFLECT

What does observation in social work mean to me?

How often do I draw on my observation skills?

How could I further improve:

a. My observation skills?

b. My use of observation in practice?

DATA COLLECTION AND ANALYSIS

In research, collecting data might relate to gathering a wide range of information using a variety of research methods and techniques. In social work, data collection is about gathering a wide range of relevant information about a child and their family circumstances. The sources of information are best considered by thinking through triangulation, as covered on the last few pages. Information can come from observation, feedback or product evidence. When collecting data, the three stages of plan, do and review are particularly helpful. So:

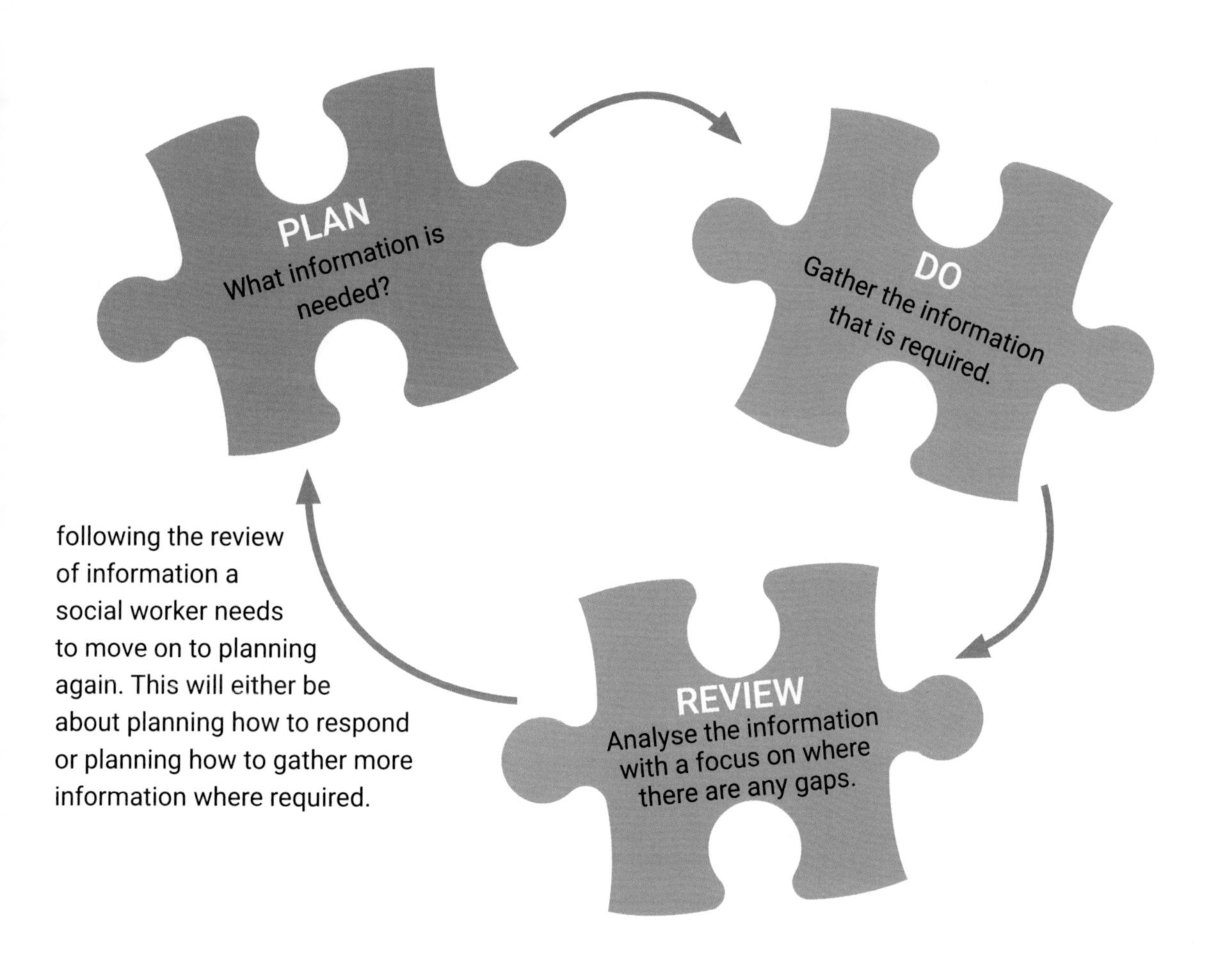

Learning the lessons from serious incidents which have taken place over a number of years tells us that social workers are generally good at gathering information, but they may not always effectively analyse that information. However, analysing the information that we have is perhaps the most important stage of good social work practice.

Analysing information means looking carefully at the information and the connections between it. It is about drawing on each branch of the decision tree. So what might theory offer in developing an understanding of the information? What research might be helpful? And so on. It is this in part which links analysis and decision making.

EXPERTISE

Fook, Ryan and Hawkins (2000: 4) identified that *"the study of expertise and expert practice is highly controversial... professions can be criticised for dominance over and disempowerment of the constituency they are ostensibly servicing."* The very notion of expertise can be disempowering – who is the expert? Why are they an expert? The expertise branch of the decision tree recognises this and draws on expertise in a partnership based manner.

Dictionary definitions of expertise refer to significant knowledge or specific advanced level skills acquired through training or study. Increasingly, in practice there is a recognition that people can become experts through experience and not simply through training and study. In social work there has long been a view that service users are the experts about their own situations. Increasingly there is a recognition that people with lived experiences of systems can add a great deal to the evidence base we draw on, so the voice of the care experienced community is increasingly being listened to.

In many ways each stakeholder in any situation has expertise in their position. So, for example a social worker may have some expertise in the systems that support families, a health visitor may hold expertise about child development, health and wellbeing, a teacher may have expertise in the educational context, the family has expertise about their circumstances, and children have expertise about their experiences.

So, drawing on expertise as part of the decision tree calls for the practitioner to consult widely with all those who hold expertise in the situation. It also calls for the practitioner to draw on their own experience or practice wisdom. Perhaps most importantly it requires the social worker to be attuned to the power dynamics – who is the 'expert' and why?

This resource draws significantly on the expertise of Annie and Paul who have lived experiences, others with lived experiences have also contributed to the resource. An argument could be made that rather than expertise, the final branch of the decision tree should be experience. However, it is important to recognise that each person's experiences may be very different and how each person understands their experiences will differ. Herein lies expertise, each person with experience (whether that be professional experience or lived experience) can only be an expert on their own situation. The individual expertise in any given situation must be considered as just that – individual and unique to any given situation.

In addition to drawing on the expertise of others practitioners should draw on their own expertise in decision making. Hood (2018: 46) identifies that

> **"expert practitioners are more likely to have an intuitive grasp of situations, adopt a holistic approach, perceive underlying issues, and find creative solutions to problems. In contrast, novice practitioners tend to be more reliant on rules and protocols, tend to consider only individual aspects of a complex situation, and are reluctant to use their discretion."**

Professional expertise then means drawing on each branch of the decision tree – theory, research, evidence and a range of expertise and then connecting each branch to be clear about the roots beneath the tree. Was the original hypothesis accurate or is there something else beneath the surface?

PAUSE TO REFLECT

Think about a family that you are currently involved with:

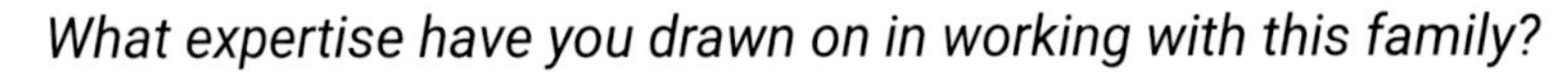

What expertise have you drawn on in working with this family?

Why this expertise?

How has this helped you in your work with the family?

In what ways could you improve your use of expertise in other work?

EVIDENCE

Sometimes practitioners think of 'evidence' as the information they draw from research findings. However, drawing on thinking about the whole TREE – research and evidence are separate branches. So, whilst research findings are very important in terms of social work decision making, evidence is really about a specific situation: What is known? How do you know it?

Triangulating evidence is vital, as this chapter has explored. The SHARE model (Maclean, Finch and Tedam 2018) for social work can be used to consider what constitutes evidence in any given situation, supporting the development of triangulated evidence. SHARE is based around the five separate but interconnecting components of seeing, hearing, action, reading and evaluation.

Using SHARE, evidence can be drawn from:

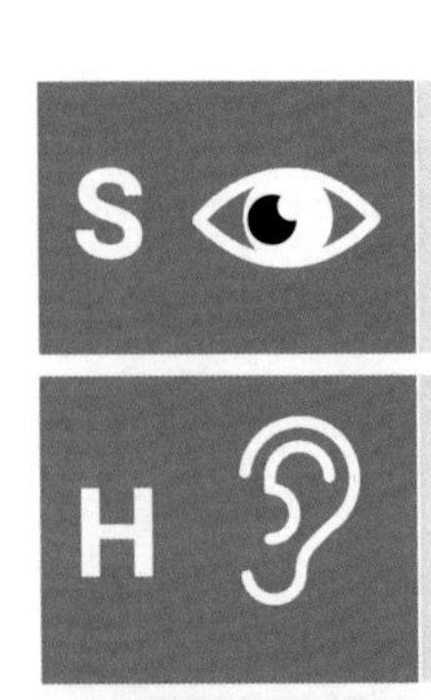

S — SEEING

What have you seen? And what haven't you seen?

H — HEARING

What have you heard? (From the child, the family, others involved? From other professionals?)

A — ACTION

What actions have you taken to make sure that you have the full range of evidence?

R — READING

What have you read? (Have you read the previous case notes, the chronology or perhaps some research or theory which you may be able to draw evidence from?)

E — EVALUATION

How do you evaluate the evidence? How does it connect? Are there any parts of the evidence which contradict other parts?

Your SHARE becomes SHARED when you reach a decision based on connecting and analysing the evidence drawn from the five components of SHARE.

PAUSE TO REFLECT

Think about a specific child or young person you are working with at the moment where you need to reach a decision. Then work through SHARE as follows:

S

What have you seen?
What haven't you seen?
What might you have lost sight of?
How would you describe your vision in terms of this situation?
What would a good outcome look like?

What have you heard?
From who?
What haven't you heard?
Whose voice is the most influential? Why?
Have you fully heard all the key stakeholders?

A

What have you done?
What impact has it had?
What have others done?
What impact has that had?
What hasn't been done?

What have you read?
Previous case notes?
Other professional reports?
Research?
Theory?
Legislation?

How are you evaluating all of this?
What is important? What isn't?
How do you feel? What impact does that have?
What's worked well? What hasn't?
What are the facts? How do you know?

What decision have you reached?
Why?
How do you need to take that forward?
When will you review the impact?

Towards the end of 2017 I tried to express a verse I'd written using a mixed media of paint and luggage labels on canvas, as my way of creating a visual message. In a nutshell I created my own life story of a childhood spent in care with this one piece of work. I never expected it to provoke the reaction or discussion that followed once it was displayed....I need you to hang in there for a moment and let's try and explore this chapter from another angle, hopefully it will make sense!

Being creative isn't something we should shy away from, instead lets actually embrace it! I believe we're all creative one way or another. We have to be, in order to live the lives we do. So, taking this as our base line we could say that art in all its forms can be used as a way to promote discussion, to open up views, to consider our own and other's perspectives, and that's why it's so subjective and personal.

When we look at a picture or listen to a poem we see or hear something different to the next person. So, here's the challenge or at least starting point, STOP reading any further... but before you put this book down, I'd like you to flick through the pages and take a moment to look at some of the pictures and re-read some of the words. Take your time and really think about what it is you're looking at or reading. What do you see? Perhaps jot a few notes down and ask yourself... Is what you see influenced by your learned theory or perhaps, you see something that reflects your own personal life experience. Do the same with the verse. Think about the words used. What message is it I can hear? This very simple exercise is called analysis. Give yourself some time to consider what and why you're doing this.

Welcome back. How did you find it?

So, here's a little bit more of my story...Like most moments in my life writing and now painting led to other things, and before I knew it I'd immersed myself into the spheres of visual and creative art, creating an explosion of pieces that reflected the emotions and stories I wrote relating to my childhood in the care system.

Now here's the rub for me. I like the fact that my art is my creative way of using something to inform, contradict or support what others may think when they stand look or listen to what's evolving in front of them.

You may like it, maybe not. That's your perspective!

It's your analysis, your take, so to speak.

This view alone, may influence what you do next. Do you commit? Do you get involved? Do you ignore? Do you invest? Does it fit in with your ideas, your ideals, your values or your beliefs? What are you going to do about it?

All are areas of interest that you can explore or follow, but how about you swap art for people, young people, children etc? What if you're viewing a situation as it unfolds? How do you feel now? Uncomfortable, confident, challenged, uncertain, out of our depth? How might you be viewing this family? Their circumstances, their situation, themselves? How do you bring balance or clarity to a situation?

Like pieces of art we view, we may choose to ignore or look away but either way we will process what we see or hear and attempt to make some sort of sense of it.

Should we also be asking ourselves, what is it I don't see? What does it mean? How I am I going to deal with (Plan, assess etc) this? What aspect of this picture or situation speaks to me?

Taking a 'gallery' approach, I have been fortunate to exhibit and during these occasions it has been interesting to observe and have conversations with people viewing my work. Some of the pieces displayed effectively say 'What you see, is what you get'.

It is honest in its delivery and isn't open to interpretation. Other pieces are perhaps a little more subtle and lend themselves for the viewer to decide or explore what they see. Conversations held have demonstrated to me that people view the images on show, based on their own personal perspective and sometimes experience. It has led some to ask questions about what they actually see and offer an explanation regarding their interpretation or what may lie behind the picture, whilst some will try to articulate what they think my intentions were.

It has allowed lively debate about these experiences, how they may have felt or in fact feel. It has also opened up discussion with regards to how things could be done differently, perhaps reconsidering small changes like a change in language or approach.

For some, it has allowed them to talk about their own experiences for the first time. One such lady aged approximately 60 spoke with me telling me how a certain piece of my art reflected her childhood growing up in care. She stated she has never spoken of this time with any of her family. She returned with family members over the next few days. I watched them speak with their mother and at times wept and hugged her. They spoke with me, explaining what they understood when looking at these pieces of art and what the impact must have been for their mother. The lady concerned told me it gave her peace, she no longer needs to hide this part of her life and now feels a sense of pride for achieving what she had since becoming an adult...a humbling moment in time.

For others, it has enabled them to process what they see and form a conclusion, even a plan to carry forward that will ensure repeats of events mustn't happen again.

Some social workers stated the experience has made them re-evaluate the language they use and has helped them to reflect on their own approaches when dealing with young people growing up in care...That for me is analysis in motion.

REFLEXIVITY IN ANALYSIS, DECISION MAKING, PLANNING AND REVIEW

Connecting everything covered in this chapter so far with a clear focus on the use of self is vital. As part of our work together, Paul and I have been developing some ideas around professional analysis drawing on the use of visual and art-based techniques. A study in America used observing art to help develop the clinical observation skills of nursing students. The study found that those who attended the arts programme, developed better clinical observation diagnosis skills and improved analysis (Pellico et al, 2005).

In this resource we have drawn on a number of picture-based techniques. We have included:

- Photographs
- Diagrams/Infographics
- Illustrations drawn by Harry Venning
- Art work by Paul

Paul has encouraged you to take a look at some of the pages in this resource, revisiting pictures and words. Specifically, here, I am going to ask you to look at the front page of each chapter. Why did we choose the photograph we did? How does it link to the content of the KSS statement and indeed to the chapter content? Jot down your own thoughts about each chapter front page on the following table.

Chapter	How would you describe the photograph?	Why did we choose this image?
Development as a child and family practitioner		
1. Relationships and effective direct work		
2. Communication		
3. Child Development		
4. Adult mental ill health, substance misuse, domestic abuse, physical ill health and disability		
5. Abuse and neglect of children		

6. Child and family assessment		
7. Analysis, decision-making, planning and review		
8. The law and the family and youth justice systems		
9. The role of supervision		
10. Organisational context		

As you look at the table above what connects the images and your thoughts?

Did you see this before working through each chapter front page?

The activities in this chapter encourage you to make some connections drawing on material you have already been using.

Connected practice requires social workers to look at the parts, to connect each part to reach a whole, but then to see the individual parts in the light of the whole. This is really where analysis lies.

There were some very specific reasons that we chose the different photographic images for each chapter page and we spent some time together doing this. What you see and why you think we used each particular image could well be very different to our reasoning. So for example, we chose the barriers which had been blown over for the communication chapter because understanding and overcoming barriers is key to communication. We chose the waterfall with the rainbow for Chapter 4 because rainbows represent hope and there is always hope for change in relation to the issues covered in Chapter 4. We chose the photo on the front of this chapter because it is a flower, so it has links to a decision making tree, but mainly because it represents the fact that each hypothesis can spread as a seed and sometimes analysis blows away something into the wind. All of the photographs (except that on the front page of Chapter 5) are things that you might see along a journey. Very often social workers describe their key reflective space as their car. Each of the photographs shows a view from a car. This describes our reasoning. However, each photograph could be read in a very different way and herein lies analysis. Each individual will see something different in the image, in just the same way that different social workers will see the same situation in a different way. Analysis helps to explain our thought process and our decision making. The key is ensuring that this goes beyond individual thoughts and insights and so there are a range of frameworks designed to help social workers ensure that their analysis and decision making is transparent and which can help to address individual bias.

PAUSE TO REFLECT

What frameworks do you use to help clarify your analysis?

What are the most significant barriers you face in terms of analysis and decision making?

ANALYSING WHAT YOU HAVE SEEN

As we draw this chapter to a conclusion, we want you to take an analytical approach. Each of the branches of the decision making tree has been covered and the role of the creative arts in helping to develop analytical skills has been touched on. At this point let's go back to the beginning of the chapter where we explored the fact that analysis and synthesis should be combined in terms of breaking down information into separate parts and then putting these parts together again to see the picture in a new way. Now that you have taken a look at the front pages of each chapter of this resource look again at the very front page of the whole resource. You have probably looked at it a number of times.

What have you seen when you looked at the image on the front page previously?

What do you see now?

Why?

Paul and I have shown this picture to a number of social workers at different times. We have specifically shown it to them at different stages when they have been listening to different things. Perhaps as a result the responses we have had to the question, 'What do you see?' have been varied. Social workers have said that they see:

- A caring adult putting the pieces of a child together, giving a piece of themselves to make the child feel complete.
- A social worker giving a piece of themselves to the child – helping them to form their identity adding a piece to their puzzle.
- A shadow of my former self. My younger self giving me a piece of myself, who I wanted to be when I was younger.

- Opportunity in the picture which could make all the difference. You have to give of yourself at those times.
- Love between the two. Giving of parental praise.
- A mother giving every piece of herself to her child (bit by bit) with some pieces getting lost over time.
- A puzzle being completed.
- A white woman – maybe a teacher – giving knowledge / information to a child. The child may be of BAME background. To me it shows an adult giving knowledge to fill the child up as if she is missing things. Therefore, although it looks caring, it also has power all over it.
- An adult threatening a child.
- Sadness – a child has been removed from their parent and they cannot be fully complete afterwards. They have left their heart with their parent.
- A child with many pieces – some missing but the professional gives them that one piece that fixes everything back together.
- At first, I thought the adult was picking up the pieces for the child – then I thought that maybe the child was picking up the pieces for the adult. I now think that the adult is giving a piece of their heart to fill the missing piece in the child's mind.

As Paul and I have explored this together we realised that what the person had just heard significantly impacted on what they saw. So, for example, after a keynote presentation on the importance of professional kindness and the role of love in social work many people referred to seeing love or seeing a heart. After training on power then people saw a misuse of power. Some of what people saw could be directly linked to what they had heard. Other things that people saw seem to be based on their own experiences and other comments puzzle us significantly. We do not know how a person saw what they saw. We have now asked in excess of 100 people and the most significant thing that I see has not been commented on by anyone else. After Paul heard me talk about how I see reflexivity as hanging on the X and this connecting to the complexity of social work, he also saw what I had seen – the jigsaw puzzle in the centre of the image, held by both the adult and the child is shaped as an X. In fact, Paul hadn't seen this previously and he didn't paint it in this way, but to me this piece was all about reflexivity.

Why do people see different things in the same piece?

What I understand about art is this, it's a way of expressing how we feel. There isn't a right or wrong image. It is the creator's message that says what they see or feel. How others interpret it, is largely based on their own life experiences and ideas at that time. So, to me art, is another way of communicating.

Siobhan and I have had many conversations, discussing all sorts of ideas and life events. In essence our conversations have become the building blocks of our friendship and perhaps more importantly I have discovered a different perspective of social work and of those that practice it...Who'd have thought?

During one such conversation I relayed a specific incident with my social worker where I had disclosed reluctantly to them the things happening to me, becoming very distressed and tearful. I'd desperately hoped for an arm around me, a hug or to be told "I'll make it better". Instead I was told that I needed to be good and then bad things wouldn't happen! What I heard, understood and felt in that moment, was that I didn't matter, and no one cared...It's a lot to take on board when you are barely 5... It was also the catalyst for my 'stone throwing' at anyone or thing that represented social work...My style of communication!

As Siobhan and I spoke, an image started to take form in my minds-eye, as I pictured the broken me putting myself together but this time with the help of my social worker, it's the message I really wanted to hear and feel.

The 'jigsaw' pieces represent the 'puzzlement' of me and how I saw myself. Joined together, it shows me dressed in something unique and special, which is how I wanted to be seen whilst allowing me to make sense of my situation.

The jigsaw piece inside the social worker represents 'them'. It's a piece of them that I wanted to be given. Their piece fits into my mind so that I can understand they believe in me and I'm important to them, and the piece we are both touching is 'our' relationship piece, the piece we share.

Basically, we all need to feel that we matter to someone. Being in care can isolate that feeling of 'not being up to much', it can be a lonely space. Loss and separation occurs on a regular basis, but when you understand someone is in 'your' corner, because they WANT to be, really is the difference in your feeling of self-worth.

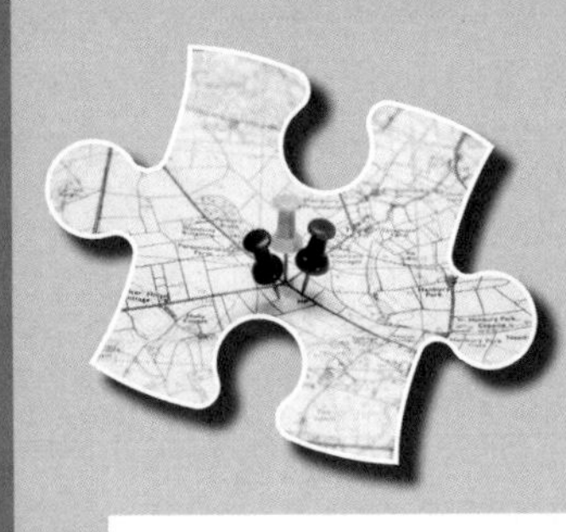

WHERE AM I NOW?

Revisit the start of the chapter. Look again at the KSS standard. Then consider the following questions:

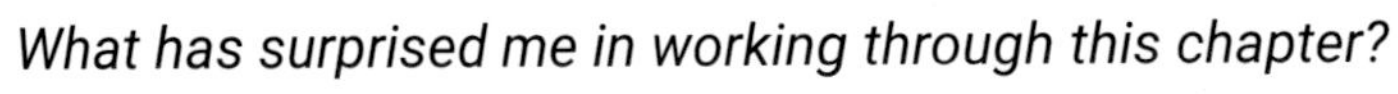

What has surprised me in working through this chapter?

What three things would I highlight as key learning?

What do I still need to do in working towards being fully confident with this KSS statement?

What single next step should I take in working towards an improvement in my practice?

Chapter 8

THE LAW AND THE FAMILY AND YOUTH JUSTICE

The relationship between the law and social work is an interesting one. Of course, social workers are a key part of the family and youth justice systems and the law surrounds and guides practice. Good social work practice and the law are inherently connected, and all of the areas covered in other parts of the knowledge and skills statement must be undertaken with a clear understanding of the legal framework. For example, a key part of decision making and analysis is the use of the law. Working through this chapter you will reflect on the perspectives of a legal representative and a parent who has experienced the family court system. This should help you to consider the law and the justice systems in the round.

THE KSS REQUIRES PRACTITIONERS TO:

Navigate the family and youth justice systems in England using legal powers and duties to support families, to protect children and to look after children in the public care system, including the regulatory frameworks that support the full range of permanence options. Participate in decisions about whether to make an application to the family court, the order to be applied for, and the preparation and presentation of evidence.

Seek advice and second opinion as required in relation to the wide range of legal issues which frequently face children and families involved with statutory services including immigration, housing, welfare benefits, mental health and learning disability assessment, education and support for children with learning difficulties.

Use the law, regulatory and statutory guidance to inform practice decisions. Take into account the complex relationship between professional ethics, the application of the law and the impact of social policy on both.

Take a look at the standard above in detail. Highlight key phrases and anything that jumps out at you. Then take some time to reflect on the statement.

- *What are your immediate thoughts?*
- *What might you want to discuss and clarify?*
- *How will you clarify meanings?*
- *Who will you discuss it with?*

GETTING FEEDBACK ON PRACTICE

Who can give me feedback on my practice in this area?	*How will I get the feedback?*

Make sure to keep a record of any feedback you receive.

INITIAL SELF-ASSESSMENT

What do I already do well?

How do I know? (What's my evidence?)

What do I need to work on?

How will I work on this?

LAYERING LEGISLATION

It is worth firstly clarifying what is meant by legislation. There are a variety of layers to legislation, as illustrated in the following diagram:

The triangle does not represent the quantity of each layer. If it did the shape would be the other way around, since there is a great deal more case law than relevant Acts of Parliament.

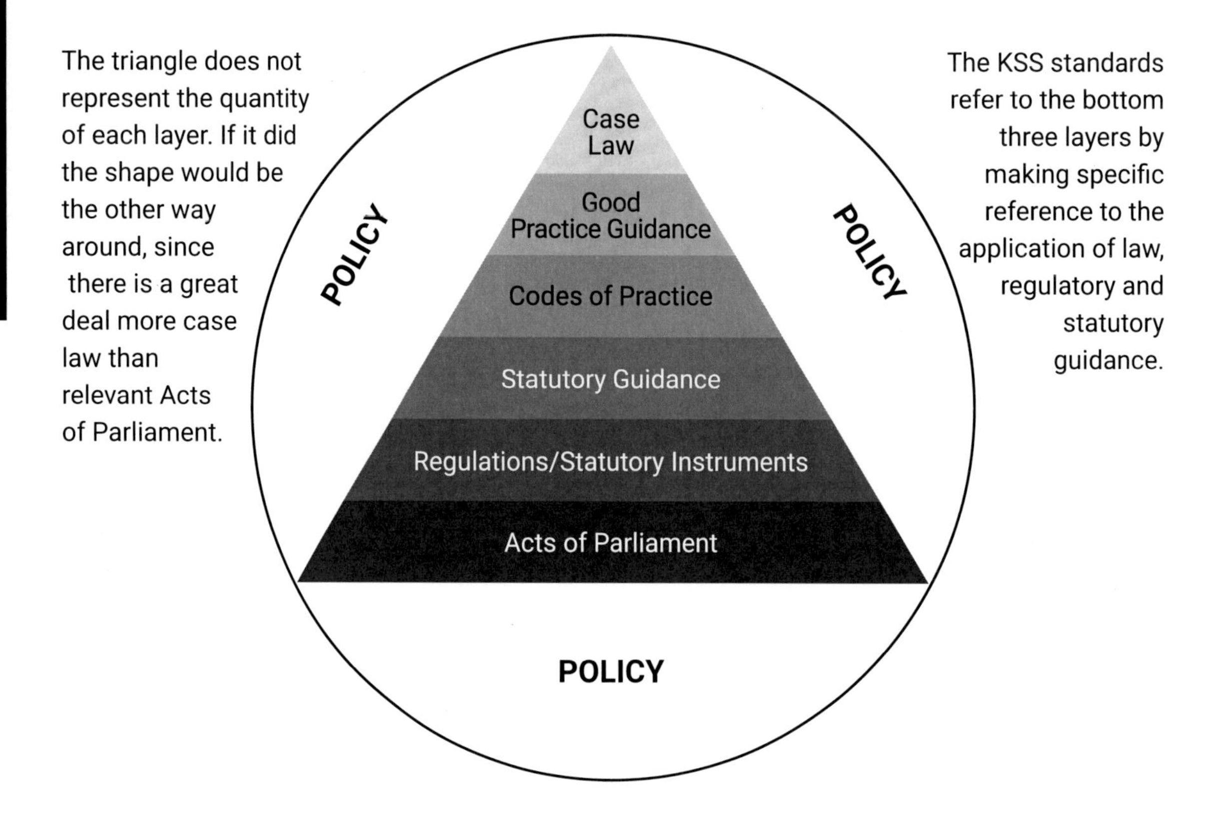

The KSS standards refer to the bottom three layers by making specific reference to the application of law, regulatory and statutory guidance.

Acts of Parliament: The main Acts of Parliament impacting on social work with children and families are the Children Acts of 1989 and 2004, but there are potentially many more Acts that you will need to draw on in your practice.

Regulations/Statutory Instruments: Acts of Parliament often include a clause which gives the senior minister involved (usually the Secretary of State) the power to introduce regulations at a later date. These Regulations detail more specific law on areas covered by the Act. This is done by means of a statutory instrument which goes before Parliament, but which is not usually debated. Regulations are used extensively around health and safety.

Statutory Guidance: Major Acts of Parliament may be followed at a later date by Statutory Guidance. Statutory Guidance explains the law and clarifies expectations and is regularly reviewed and updated. Working Together to Safeguard Children is Statutory Guidance. Statutory Guidance is exactly what it says it is - Statutory - so it must be followed.

Codes of Practice: Codes of Practice are often issued to provide practice advice and guidance regarding particular Acts of Parliament. Effectively, the Code "fleshes out" legal requirements for practitioners. One example of a Code of Practice with relevance for social work with children and young people is the Mental Health Act 1983 Code of Practice. This contains a range of advice and guidance relating to practice with children and young people who have contact with mental health services.

Good Practice Guidance: The Government issues a range of good practice guidance which changes regularly. This is designed to help organisations and individual practitioners understand how to comply with the law. However, it is different to Statutory Guidance in that good practice guidance does not have to be followed. Clearly, however, it is good practice to follow it. Social workers need to be familiar with the good practice guidance relevant to their area of practice and take active steps to keep up to date with developments. Good practice guidance is not legally binding but it is viewed as authoritative.

One example of good practice guidance is Information Sharing: advice for practitioners providing safeguarding services. This is issued by the Department for Education.

Case Law: Case Law is the term used to describe the process by which the courts decide on matters of law as a result of specific cases presented to the courts. The wording in some Acts of Parliament is ambiguous, and many individual circumstances do not neatly fit in specific situations. This means that increasingly people are taking organisations to court when they feel that a particular agency has come to a decision which they disagree with and which they feel does not uphold legal requirements. Some cases result in judgements that have implications far wider than the original case.

POLICY

The diagram clearly shows policy as encircling all of the other forms of legislation we have covered. This is for two reasons:

- The Government publishes National Policy Guidance which essentially brings together the principles of all the forms of legislation covered and which often subsequently leads to new legislation and therefore changes in the "triangle".
- Organisational policies should reflect all of the legislation covered – changes in any area of the triangle should influence changes in organisational policy.
- Social workers need to be able to identify what is law and what is policy. They need to keep up to date with changes in legislation and policy to ensure that their practice is legal and informed by policy and procedure.

What is the single most important piece of legislation in your practice?

PAUSE TO REFLECT

Focus on a family you are working with at present. If you drew up the diagram from the previous what would you specifically be looking at in relation to each layer of the diagram to guide your work with this child and family? (So, what Acts of Parliament apply, what regulations, what statutory guidance? etc..)

SPIRIT AND LETTER

This chapter is the only chapter that does not have a particular colour running through it. We chose to leave this chapter as black and white, because many people believe that the law is black and white. However, the law has many shades of every colour. It very often does not provide a clear-cut answer and we may need to think about the distinction between the letter of the law and the spirit of the law, discussing this with lawyers to be clear about the direction of travel.

Someone might follow the letter of the law, drawing on what is written and a literal interpretation of that. However, it is important to also balance this with the spirit of the law. What is the intention of the law? Very often in recognition of this, major Acts of Parliament clarify the principles of the legislation, to be clear about the intention (or spirit) of the law. It is important to know and understand the principles and to work within them. However, understanding the principles alone is not enough. Social workers must know the spirit of the law but must balance this with knowledge about the letter of the law, and when to consult a lawyer.

PAUSE TO REFLECT

Thinking about the spirit of the law in terms of your practice, what are the most important principles of the law?

How do you decide when you need to consult a lawyer about the letter of the law?

LEGAL LITERACY

This is a phrase used often in contemporary social work. Understanding clearly what it means though requires an understanding of where the term first came from and how it is currently used.

Zariski (2014) suggests that the phrase legal literacy was initially used to describe a lawyer who was capable of reading and writing legal arguments which could then be used to contribute to the development of the body of law. However, he believes that the term is now used much more widely and that legal literacy can be seen as part of a continuum of concepts in the law. This might look something like:

LEGAL CONSCIOUSNESS (Awareness of the law)	LEGAL LITERACY	LEGAL MOBILISATION (Challenging legal processes and systems)

Just as literacy is about much more than being able to read and write, legal literacy is about much more than being able to read the law and write court documents. Legal literacy in social work involves:

- Having up to date knowledge of relevant legislation.
- Understanding legal processes and resources.
- The ability to understand and explain the language used in the legal context.
- Making critical judgements about this knowledge and understanding and being clear about the connections.
- Utilising this knowledge, understanding and critical judgment in practice bringing about change.

The very first word in this standard is "Navigate". This implies travelling with some kind of plan and purpose but learning along the way. The legal landscape that a social worker needs to navigate is complex. It is like trying to navigate your way around Spaghetti Junction with lots of diversions in place. It might feel like the signposts are constantly changing and there are potentially so many routes on offer that you may not be sure which direction to take. A legally literate practitioner has the sat nav and a few extra maps to hand. They understand the rules of the road, have an idea about the direction of travel, are able to direct others and reflect on the journey as it unfolds.

PAUSE TO REFLECT

How legally literate would you say you are? So, how do you:

Keep your knowledge up to date?

Ensure that you understand legal processes and resources?

Understand and explain the language used in the legal context?

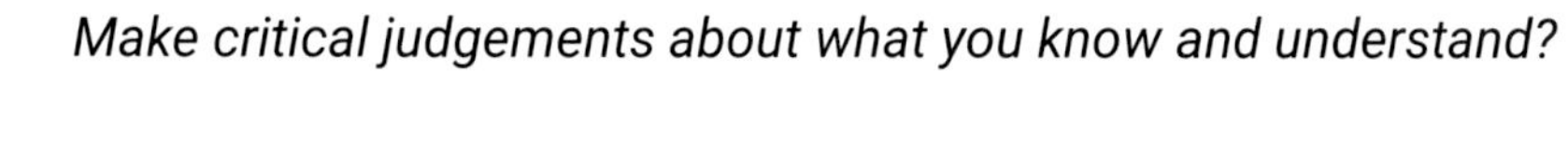

Make critical judgements about what you know and understand?

Connect all the above to use your legal literacy in practice?

THE MISUSE AND ABUSE OF SECTION 20 CHILDREN ACT 1989

The use of Section 20 of the Children Act 1989 by local authorities has been widely questioned and criticised through the legal process. In 2015, Sir Justice Munby raised major concerns about the use of section 20 in an appeal judgment (in Re N 2015) stating *"It is, in my judgment, and I use the phrase advisedly and deliberately, a misuse by the local authority of its statutory powers."*

Sir Munby highlighted four problems with the use of section 20 arrangements:

1. The failure of local authorities to obtain informed consent from parents [para 163-164]. Does the parent have capacity to consent? Does the parent understand the consequences of consenting? Is removal actually necessary? He notes that particular care should be taken in seeking consent from a mother directly after birth.

2. Care should be taken over the form of consent, which ought to be in writing, translated if necessary and ought not to be "compulsion in disguise" [para 165].

3. Far too often, s20 arrangement are allowed to continue for far too long [para 166].

4. The reluctance of local authorities to return a child to its parents immediately upon request.

Regarding the fourth point, Justice Munby was very clear:

"This means what it says. A local authority which fails to permit a parent to remove a child in circumstances within section 20(8) acts unlawfully, exposes itself to proceedings at the suit of the parent and may even be guilty of a criminal offence.

A parent in that position could bring a claim against the local authority for judicial review or, indeed, seek an immediate writ of habeas corpus against the local authority."

As a result of these concerns, Sir Munby set out new guidance for Section 20, as follows:

- Where possible, the agreement of a parent to a section 20 arrangement should be properly recorded in writing and evidenced by the parent's signature.
- The written document should be clear and precise and drafted in simple and straight-forward language that a parent can readily understand.
- The written document should spell out that the parent can "remove the child" from the local authority accommodation "at any time".
- The written document should not seek to impose any fetters of the parent's right to withdraw consent.
- Where the parent is not fluent in English, the written document should be translated into the parent's own language and the parent should sign the foreign language text, adding, in the parent's language, words to the effect that 'I have read this document and I agree to its terms.'

Sir Munby said: *"From now on, local authorities which use section 20 as a prelude to care proceedings for lengthy periods or which fail to follow the good practice I have identified, can expect to be subjected to probing questioning by the court. If the answers are not satisfactory, the local authority can expect stringent criticism and possible exposure to successful claims for damages."*

Despite Sir Munby's judgment and his statement that "*The misuse and abuse of section 20 in this context is not just a matter of bad practice. It is wrong; it is a denial of the fundamental rights of both the parent and the child; it will no longer be tolerated; and it must stop*" there have been a range of other judicial rulings which have found a misuse of Section 20.

Mr Justice Keehan made a ruling in 2018 about two unconnected children accommodated by Herefordshire Council under Section 20. He began his judgment by starting that "Their treatment by Herefordshire Council ('the local authority') represents two of the most egregious abuses of section 20 accommodation it has yet been my misfortune to encounter."

According to Mr Keehan, the children "were denied a voice in the determination of their future care. The same may be said about their parents. The boys were both denied the opportunity for clear and focussed planning about their respective futures to be undertaken and for the same to be endorsed by a court. The early issue of care proceedings would have enabled a decision to be made about their legal status and their future in a structured and time-limited manner" [para 45].

In this hearing the local authority recognised that there had been serious failings "the director noted that in 2009 it was the usual practice of this council not to initiate care proceedings where it was the social worker's perception that the parents consent to their child being looked after. This followed from a widespread misunderstanding of the 'no order principle'." [para 42].

Using the legal literacy continuum social workers working in these circumstances should have worked beyond legal literacy towards legal mobilisation to try and effect change in their local authority, challenging accepted practices.

PAUSE TO REFLECT

As a result of the concerns about the use of Section 20 there has been significant discussion and change in local authority practice.

How confident are you in your understanding and use of section 20?

How do you ensure that you are up to date in respect to case law?

Julia Hamilton has represented local authorities for 15 years exclusively in relation to Child Protection matters.

I have worked in the law for 30 years, and in child protection for approximately 15/16 years. I am a locum now and have worked at five local authorities. I have seen terrific reparative social work in my time and have also seen social workers who consider it 'too much trouble' to work alongside families. I undertake all manner of care work, advising at Legal Planning Meeting Panels, interlocutory advice, pre-proceedings, care proceedings, adoption and everything in between! I am involved in training both Child Protection detectives and legal officers/lawyers within the authorities I work with. I love what I do.

Your journey as a front line social worker will have a lot of ups and downs, it will be heart-breaking sometimes and also give you great rewards. Front line social workers are given such a hard time, in a job that is under-resourced and overstretched, I try to always be supportive and give honest, clear, pragmatic advice and have a laugh along the way.

Having worked in the law for 30 years here are 30 pieces of advice I would offer you:

PRELIMINARY

1. Know the rules around s.20 and when it is and isn't appropriate. If in doubt seek legal advice – in fact always seek legal advice even if after the fact to make sure you are on solid ground and the case is 'on the radar' as a potential need for further/ongoing advice.
2. You are a professional; when you are at court behave like one. Take ownership of your role, take notes and make notes of dates, give realistic instructions as to the timetable and check check check before you commit to a date if another team needs to do the work. Come away from court and know what went on. Do not rely on getting a note or the directions to make notes in your diary and set aside time for work. Above all don't compromise your position by agreeing too quickly for experts to be used, you are the expert in your field. Own that and be proud of it.
3. My role is to give advice on the law, to walk that journey with you and help you understand. My role is not that of your team manager or your head of service. I can't write the care plans for you or your statements, but I can give you feedback and chat with you about any areas I think need addressing.
4. Follow the evidence follow the evidence, follow the evidence: Don't pre-judge-look holistically at the case and the pros and cons, so often I am asked to advise on evidence that has a clear agenda – I won't tolerate it, and neither should you.
5. Remember your role is to get alongside parents and children and work with them not against them, often the parents are victims and need support as much as the children. Even if they are unwilling or unable to care for their children they may still need help and referrals.
6. Be clear on whether a parent is using drugs or alcohol. That, in and of itself, is not threshold; threshold must be linked to harm to the child – just because someone uses doesn't make it so.
7. Consider risk, always consider risk management – What could I do in a perfect world to make things better and what can I realistically achieve?
8. Consider risk as regards yourself. You are important and your safeguarding should be your primary concern. If you need someone to go with you to appointments do so or, better still, ask the parent/guardian/child to come into the office and meet with you.

9. Don't be too quick to rush into care proceedings. The pre-proceedings process is powerful and should be used as a last chance saloon. Everyone deserves a final chance and no parent sets out to be a bad parent. Sometimes life offers dud hands and people can be supported to change through this process and have access to preliminary legal advice.
10. Most lawyers would rather you speak to them before you undertake a change, or share information as it comes through so that we can head off any correspondence or criticism.
11. When service users become abusive and threatening finish the call politely and let your lawyer know. I have and will continue to defend social workers from abuse – parents become agitated which is normal. Threatening or abusing social workers is not part of your job. We can assist.

DRAFTING / DOCUMENTS

12. Proof-read your documents; they don't have to be perfect but lawyers are under pressure too and we don't have time to retype everything.
13. Evidence: Know what it is and what it is not. Your opinion/summary/anecdotal comments are not evidence. Evidence is from the primary source that you can use to reference harm or risk of harm. Primary source evidence is king, and part of that are your visits and interventions with the family. Make your notes as you go. Don't wait days to write up your visits onto the case management system, and scan in your handwritten notes. Obtain information in writing so that it can be filed and served – it makes your job easier in the long run.
14. When you draft your SWET and you say 'xxx report', send the report. Always send the primary source evidence (unless it is expert evidence which has already been received by legal).
15. Don't, don't, don't, don't cut and paste large chucks of reports into your final statement. This is a summary or an overview statement. The documents filed stand as evidence in their own right. If you have to cut and paste chunks, you don't understand the document or the task, so ask someone.
16. Final Care Plans should be no more than 10 pages, and final statements no more than 20. Sending something that is 57 pages means that you have not gotten to grips with the salient issues in the case and what is needed to conclude matters.
17. Speak with the Guardian and the IRO. We don't always have to follow their recommendations but if we know what they are we can consider if there are any gaps in your SWET that we need to address.
18. NEVER NEVER NEVER say you have spoken to someone or done something, that you haven't. It will be checked and will be challenged.
19. Sign documents.
20. Date documents.

COURT

21. When you are in court there is no such thing as an 'off the record' conversation. Don't have friendly chats with the lawyers or opposition barristers. They are not your friends they are there to represent their clients and may well use your conversations against you – you represent the local authority.

22. Don't joke around in the corridor or have loud laughs even if you are waiting around for the whole day. This is such a serious thing for the parents and children who attend, and they often are distressed and don't understand. They need to know we take it seriously too.
23. Wear a suit to court and not a short mini skirt or jeans (no jokes I have seen that) you are a professional you are a professional you are a professional. The suit doesn't have to be expensive. Matching trousers or a dress with a jacket is perfectly acceptable.
24. You are there to participate in the proceedings and engage with your barrister. If you have any difficulties call your lawyer if they are not in court with you. He or she will speak to the barrister on your behalf. Don't be afraid to say 'no' you have massive pressures on your time and you need to own what you can and can't achieve.
25. Know the bundle and read the evidence along the way. It won't feel like such a mammoth task when writing your final SWET at the end or giving evidence.
26. When giving evidence listen to the question, answer the question. If you don't know say so, be fair and give credit where it's due, it is not for you to try and skew the case. The evidence will fall where it will. The best interests of the child is what is of paramount consideration.
27. When giving evidence don't start from scratch, or waffle. Be fulsome in your answers but stick to the point. Don't second guess where the questions are going.
28. When giving evidence, if you have messed up or made a mistake, or missed something, or got something wrong, SAY IT. It totally takes the sting out of cross examination and means that the questions move on more quickly. If you try and fudge it, or justify your mistake, it will only make matters worse and you will be in the 'hot seat' for longer.
29. Don't take notice of tone or facial expressions. I know it's hard but some advocates are just really rude and aggressive. Don't let that put you off your stride. Remember you are one part of the case. There are others who can assist, and the local authority gets a right of response so your lawyer can redress any areas if necessary.

A FINAL PLEA

30. Children do not 'disclose' information, they share it. They tell you something or they say it, they make allegations just like everyone else. The use of the word disclosure denotes a possible bias.

    AS v TH (False Allegations of Abuse) [2016] EWHC 532 (Fam) (11 March 2016)

    At paragraph 33:

    "despite the fact that the use of the term 'disclosure' to describe a statement or allegation of abuse made by a child has been deprecated since the Cleveland Report due to it precluding the notion that the abuse might not have occurred (see para 12.34(1)), every professional who gave evidence in this case (except the Children's Guardian) used the term 'disclosure' to describe what the children had said to them)."

Disclose means 'to make known, to cause to appear, to allow to be seen'. It has the connotation of truth. Whether you believe the allegation or not, until the Court has determined it, it is an allegation not a disclosure. 'Disclosure' is a commonly used expression that has gained a cult following and I entirely understand why social workers want to use it, but don't, just don't - please resist the temptation to add a judgement to what has been told to you.

FAMILY COURT

The standards specify social workers participating in decisions about court applications. This chapter contains the thoughts of both professionals and a parent who has experienced the court process and now advocates for others. This may help you to reflect on the court experience from different perspectives. The most important thing from my perspective is to recognise that when a court application is required no one "wins." So many times I have heard social workers talking about who "won" a case in court. It is vital that this does not become part of culture and practice in teams and organisations. In itself, the law (not just family law, all law) is adversarial. A key social work skill is about drawing on empathy, applying social work values and ethics and recognising that whilst court decisions may be an important part of a child's journey, the process must be approached with care.

ANNIE'S ADVICE

We've all seen courtroom dramas on the telly. Kavanagh QC, Silk, Judge John Deed and Rumpole of the Bailey (am close to giving away my age...). We've seen the buildings and their insides regularly on the news, in soap operas (and on Netflix). It is criminal, not family court, being depicted. But, before you became a social worker and needed to go into the family court, had you ever actually been into such a building?

Well, as a mum, my first experience of going to court was as a party to care proceedings in respect of my children.

I had been vaguely aware of there being a court on Newcastle Quayside, because I'd seen some journalist fella on the local news reporting on the latest criminal trials taking place there. I knew it was a big building next to the River Tyne, but that was about it. I had no idea about the security checks, what was permitted to be taken into court, and what wasn't (although my experience of even that was inconsistent). I assumed all the legal lot wore capes like Batman and funny wigs and that the judge would always be a man in a red gown with a similar daft wig looking foreboding and serious and like he would sentence you to Life if you so much as sneezed within the court. I (hilariously naively) thought that if you had a "Hearing" at 10am, when the clock struck 10, in you'd go. I thought the media were allowed into everything and I didn't know criminal and family courts were separate (and thus fully expected to see gangsters galore upon my first visit). I didn't really know what to wear, if I was supposed to take anything, where I was supposed to sit and wait, and I had never met my barrister before and didn't know what the bugger looked like. I didn't understand why my barrister was in a separate room with the local authority barrister, the social worker, the children's guardian and their solicitor and I really didn't understand why their conversations all seemed very jovial. Firstly, this never happened on Rumpole, and secondly – wasn't my barrister supposed to be on 'my team'?

I can honestly say that my first, second, third (and probably many more) experiences of attending court were both horrifying and harrowing. They were also the best laxative I've ever known, but the least said about that, the better.

So, how does it feel to be in the position of going to the family court when legal proceedings have been initiated in respect of your children? And what can you, as a social worker do to help?

First of all, that last question is a bit of a sneaky one on my part (sorry about that). One of the most important things to remember is that when you get into the realms of the court, relationships change. To us – and I'm not speaking for all parents, but certainly all I've spent time with – you are no longer "the helper". That relationship is on hold. When we are in court, you are the person that brought us there. You are our opponent. The relationship becomes adversarial. It can't help but be so by the way the system is set up. Do you know of any other litigation where the opponents all get along in and out of court? I certainly don't.

So, how do you maintain a working relationship under these circumstances?

A good starting point is to acknowledge your part in it.

The reality is you are a cog in a much larger wheel within a local authority. The reality is that this was probably not just your call. But our reality as parents, is that you are taking us to court. Don't detract from your professional responsibility; you are the lead social workers on the case and you had a part in this. You need to 'own' it. How you do that will vary wildly, but even just being able to stand by your professional judgement is helpful.

Secondly, and this is a blindingly obvious one, it is helpful to recall the weeks and months you spent at University (or wherever you undertook your social work training), focusing on the court process. Remember the time you spent with your head buried in some god-awful textbook that smelled a bit like feet learning the Children Act 1989 and reciting the law to your (long-suffering by now) significant other/parent/children/dog. Remember the excruciating role-plays in class, where you all felt a bit stupid but had a good laugh and learned something along the way. Remember the conversations you would have with other students about how scary it would be, the first time you go to court and give evidence.

Okay.

Now remember that we, as families, have had none of that.

We don't know the law, in the main. We find it difficult to follow the legal process. We've possibly never set foot inside a court building before. We are entirely flummoxed as to why the security guard removes our bottle of anti-perspirant and swaps it with a receipt, particularly when if there ever was a need for anti-perspirant, it's now. The language being used both in court and in the period beforehand makes no sense. We don't know who is who. We don't know why we're not allowed to talk about what goes on in the courtroom to anyone who isn't a party to proceedings. And we really don't understand why we aren't allowed in pre-Hearing discussions, nor why we're shushed in court by our own lawyer. It all feels a bit cloak-and-dagger and that hardly breeds trust and confidence.

In short, we have not come to this with the experience and knowledge you have. I reiterate; this may seem like a really obvious point, but it's often forgotten. We are way outside our comfort zone – and you may be too. But this concerns our children, and our future. The stakes are higher for us than ever before.

Once again, acknowledgement is key, but preparation is even more so. You as a social worker have such a vital role to play here, even if you are the one who we see as taking us to court.

Unless the legal proceedings are initiated in an emergency, you will have some idea of when you will be attending a first hearing. Here are some pointers you may want to use to help families prepare.

- Let's start with the basics. Make sure the family members know:
  a) Where the court is
  b) What time the family needs to be there for (usually a good hour before the hearing begins so they can familiarise themselves with their surroundings and also access as much legal advice as necessary)
  c) How to get there:
     - directions if the family are driving
     - public transport links if the family don't drive
     - if the family are particularly vulnerable, or in receipt of benefits, consider helping them to get there (family support worker could offer a lift, for example)
- Next, make sure the family know why you are going to court, and what you are asking the court to do. It's also imperative that family members have had sight of all of the documents that will be considered by the court. I appreciate this is the job of the legal department, but it doesn't hurt to ensure that there aren't going to be any shocks when the family arrive on the day. It goes some way to help maintain/rebuild relationships if you are transparent with the family about what you as a local authority are doing.
- Where possible, meet with the family in the days leading up to the hearing. You may not be their favourite person (sorry – you're going to have to take that one on the chin!), but if you make an effort to go and explain what is likely to happen, who will be there, where everyone sits and that there is a security system in place, it may help the family to feel reassured. I often use the analogy of going to church. There's a lot of standing up and sitting down, you can't talk (unless in a whisper to the person right next to you), and the fella at the front runs the show. There's just no Ribena and wafers and no one sings.
- During this visit, or even during a call leading up to the hearing, make sure the family knows they can have support with them on the day (but that the support might not be able to come into court). Obviously, it would be better if the support came in the form of someone they're working with professionally rather than Auntie Jean, but if Auntie Jean is going to help keep the family calm and looked after, she should be also encouraged to attend.
- Keep in the forefront of your mind the notion and toxic feeling of disempowerment. In a courtroom, where the power is directed is very clear and it can be frightening for parents. When you feel disempowered, you may get defensive, hostile, or you might just break down. These are all normal feelings when anxiety levels are high – you know this. So, if a parent does break down, or gets annoyed, take into account how you may react were it your children at stake. Too many times I hear that a parent's reaction at court is then used as evidence of mental health problems or anger issues. Yes, some of it may well be, but some of it may very well be a symptom of the power dynamic and the feelings this provokes. Food for thought.
- Acknowledge the family members when they arrive at the court building. They might ignore you (or tell you exactly which direction to go in...normally "off"). But that's okay. They're under huge stress and pressure, and they're allowed to be. Don't take it personally (and take it in context).

- Know that some parents will simply not be able to attend the court. It's just too much; too scary, too overwhelming. It doesn't necessarily mean they don't give a toss about their child. Going to court is a terrifying experience. If you find it stressful as a practitioner, I'm sure you can imagine how hard it is for a parent.
- I can't imagine attending a family court in your role as a social worker is particularly pleasant either, so I would encourage you wholeheartedly to seek as much support around this as you can. Use supervision time to talk through any worries you have – even speaking in public in a witness box is not an everyday experience, so it's natural to be anxious.
- Know your case. Back to front, inside out and in another language if needs be. Know exactly what you're worried about, know what evidence you have to demonstrate these worries to the court and know exactly what you're asking for. Know that you will be challenged, and that you might not have it right. Know that you may be criticised, and that you might have to rethink your plans. Don't write families off and don't stick with a plan because you feel foolish backtracking or changing it. These are families lives. We've all, always, got ten minutes to sit and reflect. Use your time wisely.
- Finally, don't forget that we are all human beings. You, the families, the judges and the lawyers. You can choose to carry yourself with dignity and empathy and respect. Court is a horribly adversarial environment where these things get lost. Don't lose your humanity.

Having read both the advice from Julia based on 30 years working with the law and the advice from Annie based on attending many court hearings, what are your thoughts?

What similarities or differences have you noted in the advice?

BALANCING KNOWLEDGE AND SKILLS: THE FAMILY AND YOUTH JUSTICE SYSTEM

In just the same way that not every social worker working with children and families will become part of the family court process, not every social worker will come into contact with youth justice services. Both of these areas, though, are an important part of the law for social workers.

As you put together the pieces working towards accreditation you might want to think about shadowing some social workers in other areas of practice to refresh and enhance your understanding around aspects of practice you are not heavily involved in. This can assist you in developing an understanding of wider networks and is a useful CPD activity.

PAUSE TO REFLECT

Which areas of practice would I like to learn more about?

How might I go about this in my practice?

For example, what shadowing opportunities might I arrange?

Yvonne Rusere is a social worker in Warwickshire. She worked with the youth justice service and has just started a new role in a parenting assessment team, transferring her skills from the youth justice system to the family justice system.

It is almost 4 years now since I walked into my last social work placement; highly energised, passionate and excited. At that point I had no idea that it would be here that my social work journey would begin and what a journey it has been! A year after my last placement ended at the youth justice service I was to return as not only a qualified social worker but as a new mother as well.

I have always been passionate about working with young people and for me there was no better place to do it than in the youth justice service. This is an area of social work practice that is not necessarily at the forefront of many discourses and yet the scope of work within this practice is intense and extensive. Young people who come into the service do so through 'deviant' deeds but are not necessarily born 'deviant'. A set of complex social circumstances usually propels them into the criminal justice system. Most have been impacted on by adverse childhood experiences which are a contributory factor to offences committed.

As a social worker within the service it is my job to assess young people, write pre-sentencing reports and manage court orders in the community and detention orders in custodial settings. The purpose of the orders are two-fold. Firstly to serve as punishment for crimes committed and secondly to offer intense support to young people so as to avoid re-offending and ensure better future life chances. By addressing the needs of the child further harm to victims and the wider community is reduced and/or prevented. Indeed, public protection is at the core of the work we do. There is a collaborative approach to this work, in that we work with schools, the police, children's services, CAMHS and parents/carers to support young people. Indeed, working in a multi-disciplinary environment ensures that the service delivered for young people is seamless and efficient.

It is not possible to work in youth justice/offending teams and not address the justice v welfare debate, but in my experiences there has been no dilemma; the child's needs come first, always. Through rehabilitation and the management of orders, the welfare of the child is paramount. Through processing reports and making recommendations for sentencing, again the needs of the child come first. My service has been championing the Enriched Case Management (ECM) approach to cases where young people have been significantly affected by trauma through their childhood. This approach ensures that the latter is taken into account when designing intervention plans and is addressed appropriately.

Building good relationships with young people is very important in managing their orders. I have come to realise that as you assess a young person, they are also assessing you. They are assessing whether you are reliable, honest, will do what you said you would do, that you are consistent but more importantly, that you care and listen to them not, just hear them. I worked with a young person that at the early stages of the order, the conversations took place between his door, then they moved on to me being sat on the floor while he refused to come out of bed and then lastly to them opening the front door for me, ready to have their session. In this line of work you do not take these small initiatives for granted, no, they are success stories in themselves. They highlight the journey of trust building, of realisation that it is now up to you to rehabilitate, to build up confidence and self-esteem, to empower and to believe. It is truly an amazing journey, and what makes it even better is that the results are evident. They are evident in the change of behaviour, change of body language, of mind-set and of lifestyle.

Then come the lows; when every effort is met with resistance and no matter how creative you are you can simply not get through. For me these are the cases that haunt me as I reflect on my practice, tracing every step and wondering what could have gone wrong and what I could have done better. I vividly remember the first time I witnessed a young person being sent to custody. I was shadowing court in my early days and when the sentence was read out, I put my head down and sobbed in court. I have now witnessed this happen on many an occasion and the rawness of this does not go away. I now do not cry when this happens, but it is truly a sobering event and for me personally that tells me that prison is no place for young people, but that is a debate for another day.

I also vividly remember my first custodial case. This was a young prolific offender who had been in custody a few times and had had several orders in the community before that. I remember feeling confident the first time I saw him and believing that I was the person who was going to support him turn around his life. However, as I completed his assessment it became clear that this was a young person who had been institutionalised, and what I had hoped for and envisioned was not being corroborated by my assessment. These are truly humbling moments when you realise you do not have super-powers. I still did not give up; the young person was to come out of custody a few months later and return back within weeks of coming out. I will never give up on hope! I truly believe hope is the driving force behind social work practice and the second we lose this we lose the value of our working relationships.

As I move on to new ventures from the youth justice service, I have nothing but admiration for the complex work that these teams do. 20 years from now, my wish is that at least one young person I worked with will look back on my time with them and possibly remember the work we did, vaguely remember my name, hardly remember my face, but most importantly remember the compassion I treated them with, the care I put into my work with them, the commitment I put into advocating for them and the hope I had for them, that a journey through the criminal justice system would not define their future and dreams!

PAUSE TO REFLECT

Yvonne has recently moved posts, but she will be able to transfer her skills from the youth justice system to the family justice system. In what ways might you need to think about the transfer of your own skills as you work towards accreditation?

Have things changed since I grew up in the system? I guess so. The introduction of the Children Act 1989 saw to that. It laid down legislation and pathways to protect vulnerable children. Back in the day, it was seen as 'all singing, all dancing' by most, but for me it represents a moment in time when the need to protect children and their wellbeing was at least being addressed. Like everything, time, practice, theories and understanding change and therefore updates need to be done so that it becomes relevant for today's children.

On reflection I get that my time in care was difficult, I can't help but feel that any laws, legal powers or safeguarding regimes that may have existed were never applied to me. I'd go as far to ask, did they exist?

My overriding feeling is the belief that anything could happen to me and no one would care, mind or be there to support me. No one seemed to want to take ownership or responsibility for me and the children I grew up with.

The impact had a far reaching effect for many, resulting in poor life choices, persistent criminality (or as I see it, the need to belong having never broken the 'pull' of institutionalism), dependency and reliance on substances as a way of coping with life, inability to build lasting relationships and then the usual rafters of homelessness, unemployment, poor health etc... and again I ask is it relevant today? Do we use the 'law' and allow it to become the process we work in, or do we use the law to challenge and hold the child in the forefront of our minds so that it supports and delivers the outcomes it was designed for?

During the time I have fostered, I often hear the phrase when referring to children (sometimes I'm talking about quite young children) "they're unadoptable!". Actually, what I hear is 'you haven't looked hard enough for the right family'. No child merits a lifetime in care or the prospect of care that tells them "move along, you're 18 now"... Permanence mustn't mean 18. That's what it represented for me, permanence held no real relevance, all I knew and understood was that permanence would be 'when I'm on my own.'

As a fostering family I see and hear children being split up because younger children are deemed more adoptable, the belief being that a child of 8, 9, 10 wouldn't want a family to call their own. The impact can be devastating for all concerned and perhaps more so for the one(s) left behind as that confirms to them, they're not wanted. Where's the protection in that?

To be written off is known, understood and most importantly 'felt' by the child. All children want is to belong, it's as basic as that.

When I was aged 35, I was told by one person that they had wanted to adopt me as a child but didn't want to upset their friend who I was fostered periodically out to: I told them that even at this age (35), I would want them to adopt me and give me my own family so that I could belong!

Children are aware that things are going on. They don't always 'get' that they are unable to influence things and sometimes react or behave in a way they believe will bring them a step closer to being returned to their family. I think it's best summed up from an extract I wrote, 'Can I speak Big People', where I try to articulate this particular point:

> **"It would help a lot, if you would make the decisions that you need to make, and stick to them...This is really important to me. Some days I think my mind is going to explode, because I know something is going on in my life but I can't tell what it is.....and later I'll learn that there was a court hearing that day, and everybody in my life was upset and it was adjourned... whatever that means, except, mostly, that nothing is getting decided upon, and I still don't have a family or somewhere I can belong to.. I don't get to make the decisions... you do, so have courage to make them so I can get on with my life".**

Again, it highlights the need for good communication and relationships as the danger or inevitable outcome is a child or young person believing everything is their fault, that they are to blame!

What is it I actually want? Do you know?

If you think I want to be cared for then it's only part of the answer. What I actually want, and need, is to be loved, 1st, 2nd and 3rd. I need to know that everyone around me wants the best for me and is loving me unconditionally, and unfortunately this isn't the experience for most children in care.

The need to go the extra step, as my world doesn't end at 5pm on a Friday, I still have to get through to Monday. I'm not saying give up your life, but permanence and my wellbeing can't be constrained to timelines and office hours.

I need to know that someone is there, and I matter.

Consistency, another voiced request. Think about it, most children get the 'consistency' of parents, family, home, area, culture. When in care, all of this has the potential to be thrown out of the window. Children are given uncertainty and with that comes insecurity, lower self-esteem, little sense of value or belief. Sounds negative, I know and yet there are incidences that offer the complete opposite, where social workers, fostering families and other professional services, step up and in effect 'collectively' parent with continuity and consistency. Children receiving this level of love and support are more likely to succeed and not support the negative statistics.

UNDERSTANDING WIDER LEGAL ISSUES

The KSS standards make reference to wider legal issues which children and their families might face, specifically detailing immigration, housing, welfare benefits, mental health and learning disability assessment, education and support for children with learning difficulties. The law creates a complex web around some of these areas and it is constantly changing, with the law in relation to immigration and welfare benefits perhaps changing more often than any other area. It is vital therefore that you know where to get advice and that you recognise any issue where the law may need to be used or at least clarified.

Some organisations have specific teams to cover particular areas and the social workers there will therefore have a more detailed knowledge about the law in their area of practice. Sometimes the context of your work will mean that your legal knowledge is nuanced in a particular way. So, for example, a social worker working with children with disabilities is much more likely to understand aspects of the law around education and legal rights to specific support than a social worker on a safeguarding team. The most important thing in relation to issues that you do not come across often, is to recognise what you 'don't know' and how to find out.

PAUSE TO REFLECT

Think about a situation where you needed to support a child or a family in relation to wider law. How did you get advice on the law?

The All4One Youth Group meets in Manchester.

In Greater Manchester young people seeking asylum meet as the All4One youth group at Greater Manchester Immigration Aid Unit (GMIAU). The group has been running for 11 years, meets monthly and is attended by up to 45 young people. The group has developed a document called 'Six Things' based on their own experiences of how social workers support young people in care affected by immigration control. They say: 'We are experienced and brave. We have big dreams for our futures. We want to make positive change so that young people in our situation have the best care possible'

This is what they want you to know:

1. ***Remember, we are still young people***
   We understand it might be hard to imagine where we're from, but we're just young people and we're on our own. We still need a real chance at teenage life in the UK, and we need your help.

2. ***Make time to support our futures***
   We know you have lots of young people to support, but we don't know anyone here. Our lives are complex, we face different problems to our British friends in care.

3. ***Listen to our questions***
   We ask questions because we don't understand. We don't want to feel like a burden.

4. ***Keep your promises***
   Whether it's big or small, if you don't know, don't promise. Take the time to have difficult conversations with us.

5. ***Treat us equally***
   We want to be treated the same as each other. It sometimes feels like others are a priority because they are louder about their problems or that we only get noticed if we behave badly.

6. ***Be present when you're with us***
   We need you to hear us, help us and believe us. We like it when you put down your notepad and just be with us. 'The best social worker I had said 'let's go for a 5 minute walk and talk'."

Every year around 2,500 children claim asylum on their own in the UK. Fleeing war, persecution and hardship children often arrive in the UK as teenagers and have to deal with the uncertainties of growing up alone while seeking safety in a new country. Most young asylum seekers live with foster carers or in supported lodgings, with their local authority as their corporate parent. This is why the All4One group want you to understand how important their relationship with a social worker is, and what a difference good social work practice can make to them. To find out more about the All4One group and the work behind 'Six Things' contact GMIAU on 0161 740 7722 or info@gmiau.org.

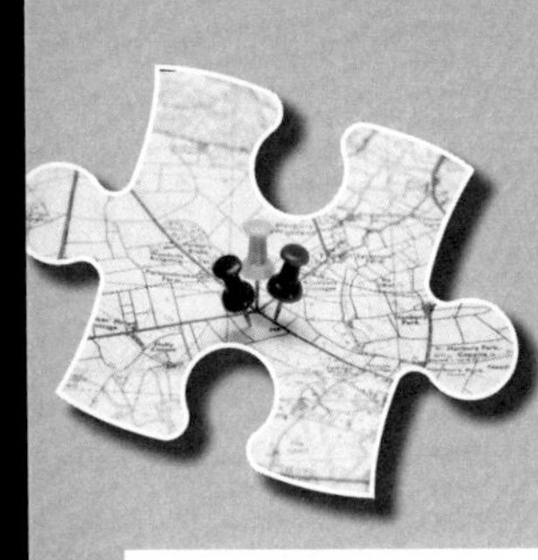

WHERE AM I NOW?

Revisit the start of the chapter. Look again at the KSS standard. Then consider the following questions:

What has surprised me in working through this chapter?

What three things would I highlight as key learning?

What do I still need to do in working towards being fully confident with this KSS statement?

What single next step should I take in working towards an improvement in my practice?

Chapter 9

THE ROLE OF SUPERVISION

This chapter will help you to explore the role of supervision in your practice. Working through the chapter will help you to think about:

- The role of supervision in social work
- Your own professional limitations
- How and when to seek advice
- Using supervision and advice to support decision making
- Finding the space you need to reflect on the emotional context of your practice
- Professional resilience

The idea of the golden thread of supervision (Wilkins, Lynch and Antonpoulou 2018) appears regularly throughout this chapter. In turn this chapter connects the what? why? how? framework as the golden thread of this resource.

THE KSS REQUIRES PRACTITIONERS TO:

Recognise one's own professional limitations and how and when to seek advice from a range of sources, including practice supervisors, senior practice leaders and other clinical practitioners from a range of disciplines such as psychiatry, paediatrics and psychology. Discuss, debate, reflect upon and test hypotheses about what is happening within families, and with children.

Explore the potential for bias in decision-making and resolve tensions emerging from, for example, ethical dilemmas, conflicting information or differing professional positions. Identify which methods will be of help for a specific child or family and the limitations of different approaches. Make use of the best evidence from research to inform the complex judgments and decisions needed to support families and protect children.

Reflect on the emotional experience of working relationships with parents, carers and children, and consciously identify where personal triggers are affecting the quality of analysis or help. Identify strategies to build professional resilience and management of self.

Take a look at the standard above in detail. Highlight key phrases and anything that jumps out at you. Then take some time to reflect on the statement.

- *What are your immediate thoughts?*
- *What might you want to discuss and clarify?*
- *How will you clarify meanings?*
- *Who will you discuss it with?*

GETTING FEEDBACK ON PRACTICE

Who can give me feedback on my practice in this area?	*How will I get the feedback?*

Make sure to keep a record of any feedback you receive.

INITIAL SELF-ASSESSMENT

What do I already do well?

How do I know? (What's my evidence?)

What do I need to work on?

How will I work on this?

SUPERVISION IN SOCIAL WORK: UNDERSTANDING THE BACKDROP

The word supervision is derived from two Latin words:

Super – which means over

Videre – which means to watch or to see

Literally taken then, the word supervision means 'overseeing'. The roots of contemporary social work supervision lie in the growth of charitable social organisations in Europe and North America which were made up of volunteer 'visitors' who were 'overseen' by a nominated 'overseer'. In the very early part of the 20th Century as casework practice became more common the beginnings of more developed approaches to supervision took root. The first books on supervision began to appear more than a hundred years ago - for example, 'Supervision and Education in Charity' by Jeffrey Bracket was published in 1904. Until the early part of this century the form and structure of supervision remained fairly constant from these early beginnings in the nineteenth century (Munson 2002).

MODELS OF SUPERVISION

There is no universally accepted model of supervision in children's social work in England, although supervision tends to be provided on a one to one basis by line managers, who are often responsible for the supervision of a small group of workers (often around six to eight). Separate reflective supervision is sometimes provided to workers undertaking specific qualifications or at particular points in their career.

Wilkins, Forrester and Grant (2016) analysed a number of recordings of supervision in one inner London Local Authority. They found significant similarities between the sessions, which started with a 'checking in.' They specifically comment that, "*No formal model of supervision is used, although there is a clear structure – beginning with a 'verbal deluge' by the social worker, followed by the identification of 'the problem' and the provision of a solution by the manager*" (Wilkins, Forrester and Grant 2016:6). They concluded that there were limited references to risk in the sessions and that there was little conversation about emotions (other than frustration at perceived resistance from parents). Comments from a wide range of social workers in a wide range of settings indicates that this is a common experience of social workers. In delivering supervision training across 14 local authorities in England and Wales over the last three years I have found limited references to the use of formal models of supervision, although very often supervision policies explore the functions and practice of supervision.

This section considers two models of supervision – one which has been around for some years and has been influential in the development of supervision policy and practice across England, and one which is newly developed and being implemented in Northern Ireland at present. Both demonstrate a sustained focus on the importance of reflection in supervision.

FUNCTIONS OF SUPERVISION

Although different writers use different terminology, there is widespread agreement that there are four main functions to supervision in social work. Morrison (2005) outlined four objectives to social work supervision:

1. Ensuring competent accountable practice
2. Encouraging continuing professional development
3. Offering personal support to practitioners
4. Engaging the individual practitioner with the organisation

Morrison referred to these four objectives being met through the four key functions of supervision. I have summarised this in the following table.

Morrison's writing and work on the integrated model suggested that each supervision session should cover all four functions of supervision, but in practice many social workers feel that the majority of the supervision sessions they experienced focused on the managerial function, with a few key questions thrown in which are designed to cover the other functions.

The functions of supervision are not met by simply throwing in a question or two to the session

Objective of supervision	Associated function	The social worker should experience
Ensuring competent accountable practice.	**Managerial function** Also referred to as the accountability, administrative or normative function.	Space to discuss their work and reach decisions with guidance, creating a level of shared decision making and clearly agreed accountability.
Encouraging continuing professional development.	**Developmental function** This is also referred to as the educative or formative function.	Opportunity for reflective discussion about practice to enable learning and development. Space to discuss learning objectives and career development.
Offering personal support to practitioners.	**Supportive function** This is also referred to as the restorative or pastoral function.	Personalised support in the challenges of the role. Space for discussion about the emotional context of practice. However, it is important to remember that supervision is not a counselling session and the balance needs to be well managed with professional boundaries upheld.
Engaging the individual practitioner with the organisation.	**Mediation function** This is also referred to as the negotiation function.	Understanding of professional role and clarity about responsibilities in the organisational setting.

4X4X4 MODEL

In 2005 Tony Morrison developed an integrated model of supervision which identified four objectives of supervision met through four functions of supervision. Morrison's model brought these functions and objectives together with the four stages of experiential learning, whilst also referring to 4 key stakeholders:

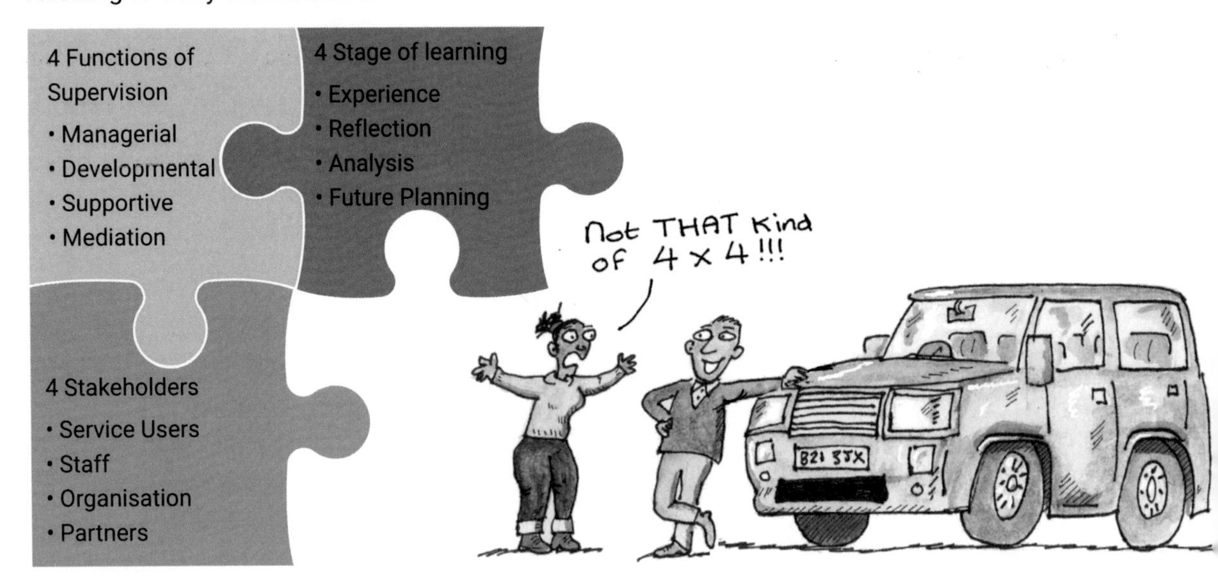

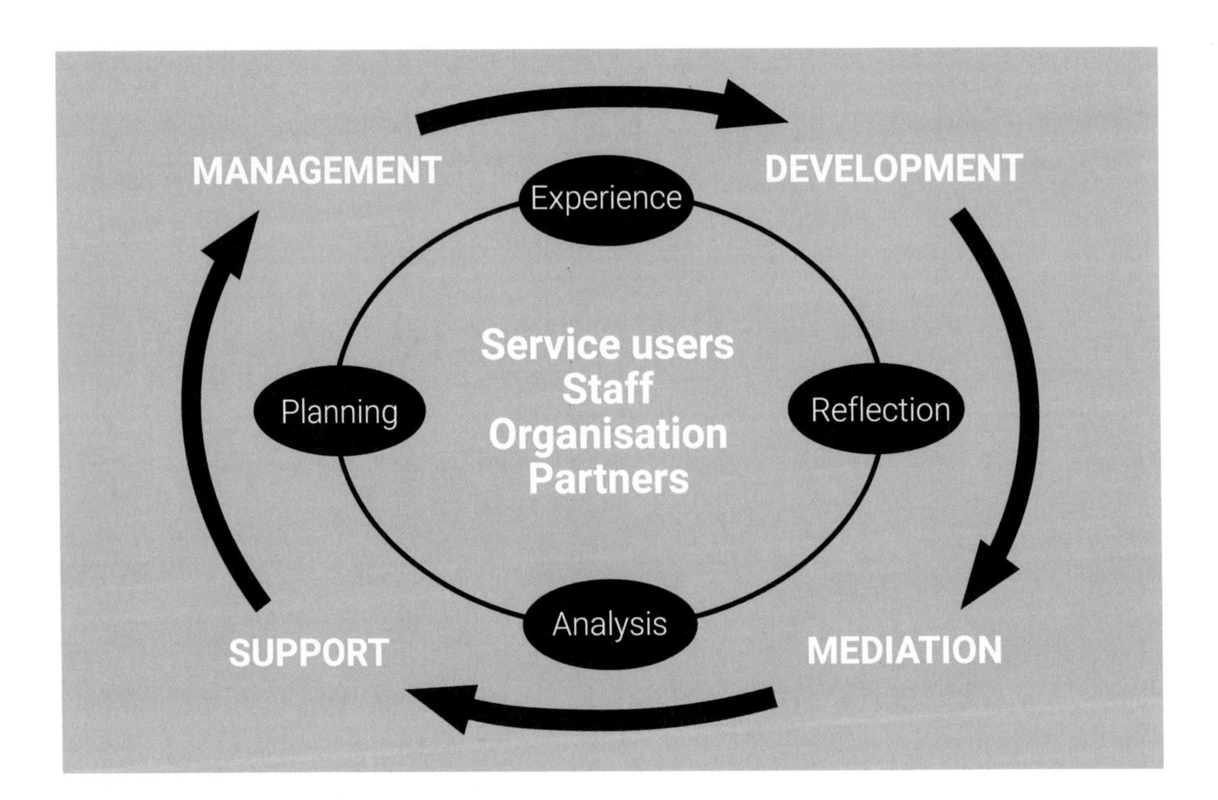

This integrated model, often referred to as the 4x4x4 model became very popular in social work and its influence can still be seen in many organisation's supervision policies.

5X5 MODEL

The Northern Ireland Social Care Council worked with social work practitioners and academics led by Stan Houston to develop a model of supervision built around five domains and five dimensions (Houston 2015). The domains are issues to be considered in reflective supervision discussion:

1. Psychobiography – addressing issues of narrative, identity, emotions and life-course
2. Relationship – covering attachment, family and recognition.
3. Culture – covering core ideas, difference and inequality.
4. Organisation – covering bureaucracy and management issues.
5. Politics/Economy – covering Neo-liberalism and Globalisation.

Whilst the dimensions provide a model to enable reflection, through:

1. Reflecting on self.
2. Reflecting on the enabling process.
3. Reflecting on the service user's experience.
4. Reflecting on social work practiced.
5. Final reflection – bringing it all together.

The idea of the model bringing together both domains and dimensions is to enable a social worker to develop a deeper reflection and understanding of themselves, their role and the needs of the service user. The dimensions do not need to be sequential and the domains do not all need to be considered in each supervision session.

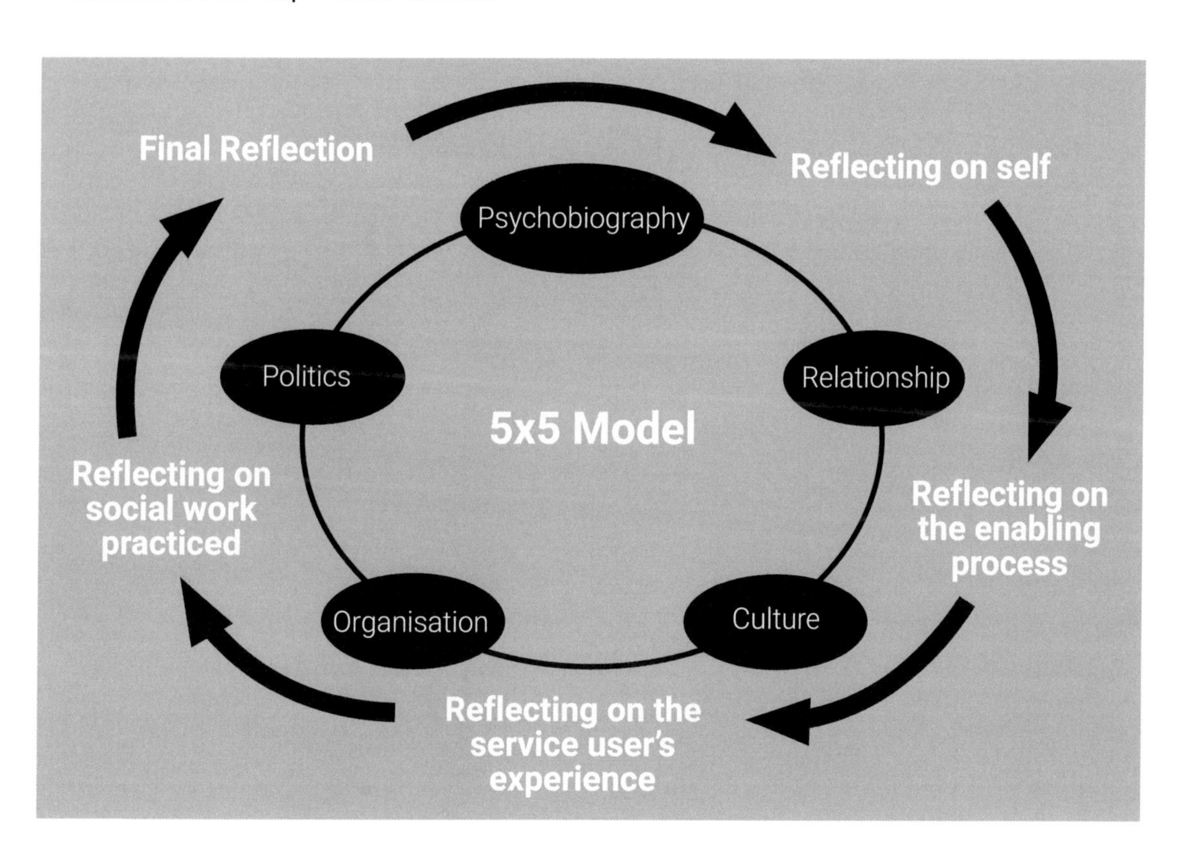

FORMS OF SUPERVISION

There are a range of different types or forms of supervision and often a variety of these are used in social work and child care settings.

Direct or Indirect: Supervision can be described as direct or indirect. Originally, direct supervision referred to supervision 'on the job' – basically discussion, advice and guidance whilst a social worker is actually undertaking a task. Indirect supervision is supervision which takes place away from the actual 'tasks' at hand. Direct supervision is rare in social work where most supervision takes place away from children and families in an office setting. Increasingly, social workers and supervisors see the indirect/direct element of supervision being about whether they are actually together during the supervision. So, for example they may view direct supervision as supervision where they sit together in a private space in the office environment. On the other hand, they may view indirect supervision as being the 'virtual' supervision that can take place via technology.

Formal or Informal: Informal supervision is unplanned. Basically, any discussion or consultation providing advice, guidance and answers to a supervisee's questions is informal supervision. Formal supervision on the other hand is planned and structured, has a formal agenda and should take place in a private environment with no interruptions. Social workers must receive formal supervision but all practitioners, however experienced, will also need opportunities for informal supervision as and when the need arises.

Named Supervisor/Other professional: This is sometimes referred to as managerial or clinical. Social workers must have supervision with their named supervisor (often their line manager) but supervision can also take place with other professionals. There may be someone on the team who has experience in a particular area who is best placed to offer advice and supervision on a specified piece of work. Alternatively, it may be appropriate for a social worker to have advice, support and supervision in relation to particular pieces of work or specific themes relating to practice. For example, a social worker might seek advice from a psychologist or psychiatrist in terms of working with a parent who has a mental health condition.

Group or Individual: Supervision is probably most often carried out on a one to one basis. However, it can also take place in groups. Group supervision is not simply a team meeting but allows space and time for the four functions of supervision to be addressed. Group supervision is being used much more widely in UK contemporary social work. Intervision is a specific example of group supervision.

Every supervision session can be described in four ways – with most supervision sessions traditionally being:

Individual, indirect, formal, with a named supervisor.

However, a variety of forms of supervision can be useful in social work and practitioners should draw on all available supervision opportunities in their practice.

INTERVISION

If supervision is about 'watching over' then intervision is 'watching between' (Romeo 2017). Intervision groups have a long history in continental Europe (van der Haar 2007) and are becoming increasingly popular in the UK context (Fairtlough 2017). In the UK intervision still remains more popular in other professions such as medicine and therapy (Klimek and Atkinson 2016), but there is a growing recognition of the value of intervision in social work and there have been some trials of the use of intervision in social work education and practice learning (Staempfli and Fairtlough 2018).

Intervision describes the process of a group of professionals coming together to discuss situations which they are finding emotionally challenging. The discussion groups promote peer critical reflection based around in-depth compassionate listening and exchanges which recognise the emotional context of the practice. Intervision is based around a mutually supportive exchange and challenge between professionals who are equal. There is no hierarchy, although sessions should be chaired and recorded to support learning, these roles are shared and rotated.

The United Nations Intervision Guidelines which were written for staff working with people in drug services identify the key differences between intervision and other forms of support and peer learning (Trautmann 2010:5). This categorisation, as follows, can helpful in thinking about supervision in social work.

- Team meetings generally cover the two themes of management issues (organising/creating conditions for the work of the team) and facilitating the work with service users.
- Case discussions focus on an individual case including the staff involved to reach agreement on the intervention plan or to evaluate progress.
- Intervision and supervision are both forms of work-related learning, aiming at improving the (quality of) work of professionals. Supervision and intervision have a number of shared/common characteristics. Both focus on learning and the development of staff. They aim at increasing knowledge, improving skills, increasing self-reflection and insight in personal functioning and on learning how to deal with emotions related to work situations. Whilst supervision is individual and guided by a supervisor, intervision takes place in a group of equals prompted by a chairperson.

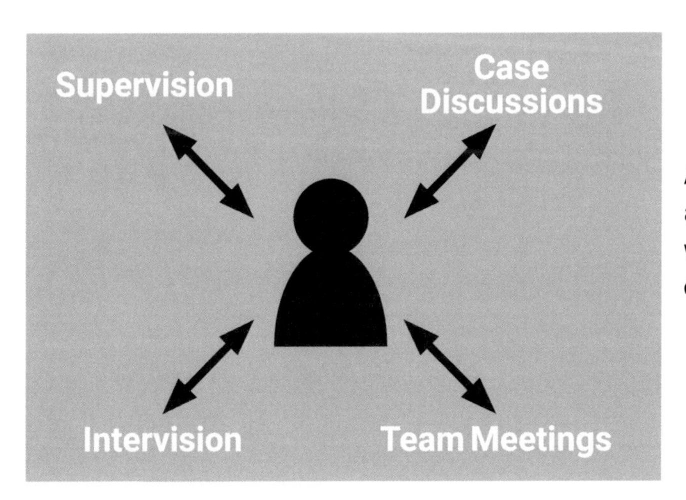

A social worker should receive support and an opportunity to reflect on their work in a range of ways, but they will only get out of it what they put into it.

PAUSE TO REFLECT
REVIEWING PERSONAL SUPERVISION EXPERIENCES

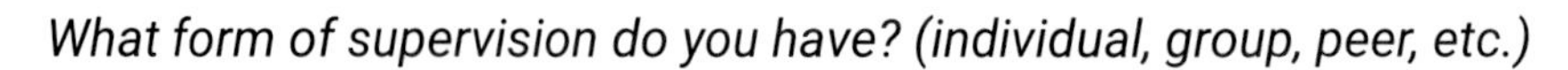

What form of supervision do you have? (individual, group, peer, etc.)

How often does your supervision occur? Is this often enough?

What do you expect from it? Does it match what your supervisor expects?
How do you know?

How is supervision recorded and how is that record used?

Does your organisation offer training on the use of supervision? In what ways could you make use of this?

How do you use supervision to develop your practice?

How might you make more of supervision?

Reflecting on these questions and connecting your responses how might you adapt your approach to supervision?

RECONSIDERING SUPERVISION FOR CONTEMPORARY PRACTICE

Some practitioners argue that the implementation of managerialist approaches in contemporary social work have led to a regression to earlier forms of simple overseeing (Manthorpe et al 2013). Kadushin and Harkness (2002) referred to the concept of 'Snoopervision' where the purpose and nature of professional supervision has been misunderstood. Supervision must be about more than simply 'overseeing' performance if it is to have any real value.

Reconsidering the very roots of the word supervision can be helpful in supporting a move away from simple 'overseeing'. Understanding the concept of vision differently can be helpful here. Vision isn't simply about 'seeing' or the physicality of sight. In organisational and leadership terms the concept of vision is about:

- Outlining an organisation's key objectives to guide future planning and decision-making processes.
- Working with foresight rather than hindsight – in business terms this is often about the ability to envisage future trends and patterns.
- The ability to think about and plan the future with imagination and insight.

Thinking of vision in this way rather than as 'seeing' or 'watching' means that supervision is about a practitioner being supported to think about the vision for their practice and developing future creative plans for their work.

- What does a good outcome look like for this child/young person/family?
- How can they be supported to get to that point?
- Working with foresight and insight rather than just hindsight.
- Imagination, curiosity and creativity.

Organisations often have mission statements and visions and professional leaders often discuss their vision for service delivery (Trowler 2016). Professionals should also have a vision for their individual practice. Supervision should provide the space for this vision to be discussed and shared – the supervisor's vision may be about organisational requirements whilst the supervisee's vision may relate more to the needs of individual children and their families. Supervision should bring together both perspectives enabling a shared vision for intervention and practice to be developed.

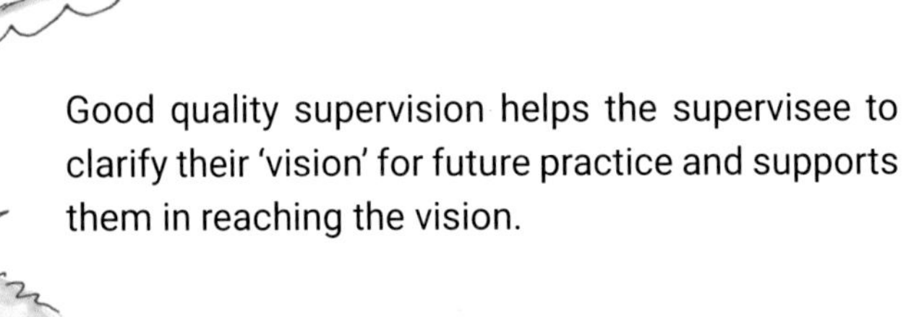

Good quality supervision helps the supervisee to clarify their 'vision' for future practice and supports them in reaching the vision.

COMBINING THE FORMS AND FUNCTIONS OF SUPERVISION TO CREATE AN INDIVIDUAL SUPERVISION PASSPORT

Supervision can be seen as providing the passport for a social worker's professional journey. It is possible to travel without a passport, but you can't go very far, and you are less likely to be able to experience other cultures and climates than if you travel with a passport. Passports are unique to each individual and this reflects the approach that you should take to supervision. Think about your own passport:

Passport photo: What is your passport photo like? Is it how you see yourself? Is it how you want others to see you? *So, how does your supervisor see you? Is it the way you would like them to see you? How do you present yourself in supervision? How does that impact on the way your supervisor sees you?*

The state of your passport: Experienced travellers tend to have passports with curled edges, the passports look well used. People who travel less often have shiny new looking passports. *What is yours like? Have you been receiving supervision for some time? How has it impacted on you, your practice and the service users you have supported?*

The origins of your passport: Some people have more than one passport – reflecting their dual nationality for example. This can reflect key aspects of identity, culture and a sense of belonging. *How are aspects of culture, identity and belonging addressed in your supervision?*

Gathering stamps on passports: In the past when people visited different countries they would often receive a stamp on their passport. Some people enjoyed collecting the range of different stamps and used them to reflect on their travels. *Your supervision passport can be stamped in a range of ways when you ask different colleagues and professionals to support you in reflecting on your practice. Have you collected a wide range of stamps? How can these help you to reflect on your own journey and the journeys of the families you have worked with?*

Additional documentation: Sometimes travellers need to have additional documents to be able to travel to certain places – for example some countries require a visa. *Are you clear about what you need for your journey? Are you arriving at supervision with all the documentation required?*

Professional identity: Passports are often used as a key form of identification. The supervision that you receive can enhance your sense of professional identity if you use it well. *How are you bringing your social work identity into supervision? How is your supervision supporting the further development of your social work identity?*

The worth of a passport: Passports cost a fair amount and have considerable worth (think about what it would cost you if you lost your passport). *Do you always recognise the value of your supervision? How might you increase its worth?*

CHENAI

Chenai is an experienced practitioner. For seven months the team she is on has not had a permanent manager. The newly qualified social workers on the team are all receiving supervision from different team mangers. Chenai had one session booked with a senior manager, but that was cancelled due to work commitments. Chenai hasn't had any formal supervision for nine months now. She is able to seek advice and consultation from a range of managers in the area but is beginning to feel that she would really benefit from formal supervision.

What should Chenai do?

ASHA

Asha feels that all of her supervision focuses on managerial issues. She feels that getting through each case and ensuring that targets and timescales are met is the only thing discussed in her supervision. Asha would like to have more space for reflection in supervision.

What should Asha do?

THE GOLDEN THREAD OF SUPERVISION

The idea of a golden thread of supervision in social work has become very popular. Wilkins, Lynch and Antonopoulou (2018: 8) describe a

> "golden thread between supervision (of a particular type), improved practice skills (measured in a certain way), and better parental engagement and goal agreement (within a specific context). The starting point for this golden thread is practice based supervision."

In their research Wilkins, Lynch and Antonopoulou (2018) listened to audio recordings of supervision. To decide whether they thought the supervision was practice-focused they considered the questions:

1. Do we know what the social worker is going to do in the next home visit or the next few home visits with the family?
2. Do we understand why the social worker is going to do these things and how?
3. Has this discussion helped the social worker think more carefully about what they are going to do, how and why?

The golden thread of supervision, then, is reliant on :

- What?
- Why?
- How?

This What? Why? How? framework has provided a 'golden thread' for this resource. Starting with page 7 where we explored the importance of the basic what? why? how? framework this resource has considered the what? why? and how? of each KSS statement. What is described by Wilkins as a golden thread in supervision is in fact one of the key connecting factors in social work.

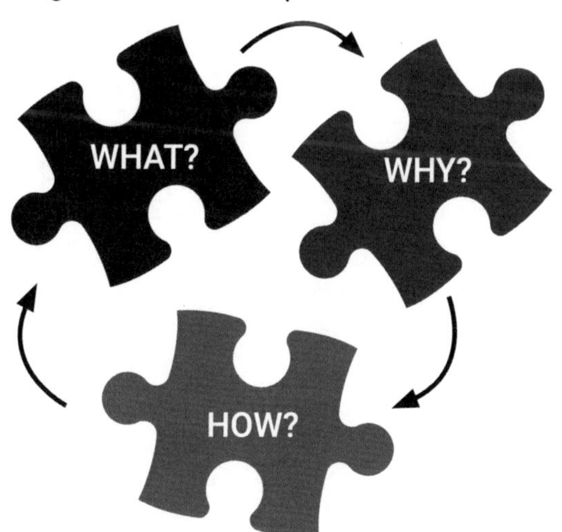

Supervision very often focusses on what the social worker is doing. It needs to focus much more on the why? and the how? connecting the answers each to these questions around a clear focus on the child - with the main concluding question being 'how will this impact on the child?'

UNDERSTANDING PROFESSIONAL LIMITATIONS

Supervision is closely related to practitioners understanding their own professional competence and limitations.

Cohen and Laufer (1999) clearly identified that social workers who are satisfied with their supervision have stronger perceptions of their own professional competence and are more prepared for autonomous practice.

Social workers need to take concerns which they feel are outside of their professional capabilities to supervision.

Knowing your own limitations is vital in terms of safe practice.

In social work professional limitations are not fixed, they can change over time and may be particularly fluid in relation to certain areas. This means it is vital to be clear about professional limitations and to reflect on these regularly. Professional limitations might relate to:

- Learning needs
- Lack of experience
- Workload demands
- Emotional pressures
- Personal blocks or bias
- How you see things
- The way that personal issues might be impacting on professional practice

Any consideration of professional limitations should always be balanced with:

- Strengths
- Professional abilities
- Networks of support

What are your own professional limitations?

How do these impact on your work?

HOW AND WHEN TO SEEK ADVICE

Social workers need to seek advice on a range of issues from a range of people. The key questions relating to advice raised in the standards are how? and when? (as the standards refer to knowing how and when to seek advice). However, drawing on the fullest range of questions, as follows, is important in reaching decisions about seeking advice and support:

What: What advice do I need? Be as specific as possible. People very often think of advice as what based questions ("What should I do?" "What happens next?" "What if.." "What form do I need to fill in?" "What does the law say?"). However, thinking about what kind of advice is required should focus on the wider range of questions ("Why do you think this is happening?" "Where might I find more information to help guide my thinking on this?") in this way advice will help you to explore others' perspectives.

Who: Who is best placed to give the advice needed?

Why: Why do I need this advice? Why is this person best placed to give the advice?

When: When questions are always about timing. So, thinking about when you need to have the advice is important. This isn't just about understanding when advice is needed but also being clear about timescales for decision making and at what stage you will need to have received the advice.

Where: Questions which start with where always relate to environments. Thinking about this in relation to seeking advice helps to consider the wider environmental issues. What advice will you get from different professionals? How will their organisational positions impact on the advice they give you?

Which: Questions starting with which always relate to asking about specifics. When asking for advice make sure that you have thought through some specific questions so that you make the most of the potential advice you can gather.

How? How should I ask for the advice (by email, by phone, in person) this will be affected by the answers to each of the questions already considered.

Sometimes advice can be transformational in the way we think about something. Think about a situation where you sought advice which you found particularly helpful. What was it that was so helpful?

How might you be able to use your learning about seeking advice from that situation to influence you in other aspects of your practice?

Chapter 9

USING SUPERVISION AND ADVICE TO SUPPORT DECISION MAKING

Supervision should enable social workers to reflect on their work, sound out their hypotheses and reach sound evidence-based decisions. Often social workers report feeling more confident when the decision-making process is supported within the supervisory relationship. In fact, Stevenson (2005) claimed that the element of supervision which social workers value most is the concept of shared decision making. According to Stevenson, shared decision making involves six main safeguards and benefits:

1. Peer review of professional decisions.
2. Protection of civil liberties: Ensuring that no service user's liberty is affected without scrutiny of that decision.
3. Protection of service users: Service users are not left in unacceptable risks on the basis of an individual's assessment or actions.
4. Protection of staff: Ensuring that professionals are not put in positions where situations may exceed their knowledge, skills or experience or where they have to deal with very stressful situations.
5. Protection of the agency: Shared decision making ensures a fail-safe element and confirms that the agency has taken the importance of scrutiny seriously.
6. Openness: It encourages collective responsibility and creates a climate where professionals are open about their decisions and can explore the reasons behind them. A culture should be created where practitioners are prepared to jointly take responsibility for key decisions and, to achieve this, are prepared to challenge each other in the interests of the service user and, indeed, the agency.

Stevenson was writing about adult social work but what he wrote about the benefits of shared decision making is still relevant today, almost 15 years later, and it is just as applicable to children's social workers. Social work managers sometimes report feeling that social workers come to them looking for decisions, rather than bringing an analysis and recommendation for shared decision making. Social workers are gathering information and simply presenting the information to managers expecting direction to be provided. Professional social work is about much more than information gathering and social workers must be able to present an analysis and recommendation to managers to enable shared decision making.

How do I use supervision and advice to support shared decision making?
How might I improve this?

REACHING SHARED DECISIONS IN SUPERVISION

Drawing on the SHARE model (Maclean, Finch and Tedam 2018) as part of reflection on casework can be particularly helpful in reaching shared decisions in supervision discussion. The social worker maintains an open curious perspective as they work with a family, drawing on what they see, hear, do (action) and read, evaluating this, bringing their hypothesis to supervision for discussion which will culminate in a decision being reached. In this way the process becomes SHARED in supervision.

Seeing – the social worker should draw on their observations, for example of the family environment, interactions between family members, children's' behaviour, family members' responses. They also need to think about what they haven't seen and what they may have lost sight of. Developing a vision is also a key part of 'seeing' so the practitioner should reflect on what they think a good outcome for the family would look like.

Hearing – the social worker should draw on what they hear in conversation with children and their families, what they hear from other professionals and other stakeholders. They should also consider what they haven't heard, whose voice is being privileged and why. Has the child's voice remained central throughout the intervention?

Action – the practitioner needs to reflect on what they have done. What have others done? What impact has this had? Why?

Reading – has the social worker read the chronology, previous case notes, written communication from other stakeholders? Have they read any theory or research that may relate to the child's situation?

Evaluation – drawing on the first four components of the model the social worker should evaluate what they have seen, heard, done and read drawing conclusions. This enables the practitioner to develop an understanding of what is happening by drawing on the evidence gathered. The evaluation should enable the social worker to develop a hypothesis about what is happening, what needs to happen and what would be helpful in moving towards this. This hypothesis can be taken to supervision to enable a shared understanding between supervisee and supervisor, the 'D' is added when they reach a shared decision.

Decision making – whilst the supervisee should take a clear hypothesis to supervision, this should be open to discussion and debate within the supervisory process. This discussion and debate can help to address issues of individual bias in decision making (as covered in Chapter 7).

Leanne Boylan has worked in social care for more than ten years. Her contribution here is based on a blog which Leanne wrote titled 'What the supervisory relationship means to me'.

I've worked within the social care sector for over ten years. My roles have varied but the primary focus has been in the area of intensive family support. It has afforded me the opportunity to hold small caseloads and work intensively with families. This position has allowed me the time to get me to know families and understand their individual set of circumstances. This has helped me realise that it has been the relationships that I built with families which have enabled me to work 'with' the families and bring about positive change. My skills and knowledge base and being flexible in my approach have also been important factors in supporting families. For example, completing role plays with a family to bring about understanding of each other's perspectives about a particular narrative. I have also completed psychological based training over the past 12 months to understand how our thoughts, behaviours and feelings interact with each other. However my focus in my spare time is 'trauma informed' work. I think it's important to focus on the reasons 'why' people may be vulnerable and struggling because of their life experiences, and recognising that without dealing with the trauma, it's near impossible to be the person you want to be. During my time in practice it has also become increasingly clear that the context people live in has been a large determining factor in how change can be accomplished or how the move from survival mode can change to that of thriving. I believe in drawing from sociological perspectives and recognising that the culture in which a person is situated is important when working with systems that already exist in a person's life.

Since May 2018 I have been working with New Beginnings in the capacity of co facilitator. The Programme Director Jadwiga Leigh, is the driving force behind the programme and she is also my supervisor. When I met with Jad for the first time it was special. I realised we have shared values and beliefs and I was instantly enthusiastic about working with Jad and the New Beginnings programme. I still do appreciate and feel enormously privileged to have been welcomed onto the team and to work so closely with Jad and our social care colleagues in the way we do. My role on the programme is to work closely with Jad in the delivery of the trauma informed group sessions, facilitate the family activities, and provide support to the women and the families we work with. These take place for 20 weeks, at which point parents have the opportunity to move onto become peer mentors. Jad leads on the group work sessions. At points I have developed some ideas relating to our chosen topic for example 'shame catchers'. We had been utilising the work around shame and vulnerability and to finish the session we 'caught' the thoughts around shame in the net to symbolise letting them go, and attached positive thoughts and sentences to counter act this.

I am also the keyworker for a number of the women/families. However, together with Jad, we have regular conversations about our interactions with the women. An important focus of our work is to listen and learn from the women as we believe this is how they will reach their goals, which may include house move, attending appointments and providing evidence at court. I support families to disable any possible barriers of attending New Beginnings or reaching their goals and moving forwards. Following the group we set homework tasks, the women and I go through their homework to embed learning and together we reflect on the thoughts and feelings that may have derived from completing the work. In addition to this we run family activities, for example going to the allotment or bowling. We have found these fun and energetic, but also a time for the families to come together and support each other. We have found an important feature is to work alongside professionals who provide support to the family and, if necessary, represent families at meetings, working towards empowering families to lead their meetings where possible.

One of Jad's many strengths is the knowledge she brings with regards to culture, and the impact this has on our identity. For example, Jadwiga Leigh (2017) discusses how shame can get in the way of authentic and creative practice. I've come to realise how important this is in social care because it not only affects the kind of support we are able to provide each other, but also our families. Part of the 'culture' I want to talk about in this chapter is the supervisory relationship because, for me, it sets the tone for the type and the quality of practice I am enabled to do. I believe the primary reason for my own growth is 'the supervisory relationship' I have with Jad. I wanted to make reference to it being a relationship, because, as I will go onto discuss, that's exactly what it is, and I and the families I support benefit from this way of working. The relationship with my families isn't the only determinant for good practice, but my relationship with Jad is imperative in being able to see clearly and practice effectively.

SUPERVISION

Supervision in social care is an important feature, as we debate and scrutinise current models and practice all the time. It's only been through New Beginnings that I've experienced the reach and potential the supervisory relationship has to offer. David Wilkins and colleagues (2018) make reference to supervision being a 'golden thread'- a process which links supervision to practice to parental engagement and finally, goal agreement. This idea resonates with my journey in understanding what my supervisory relationship with Jad has achieved. David Wilkins et al (2018) recently discussed that evaluating the quality of supervision and what it achieves remains a challenge in the sector but that a good relationship between supervisor and supervisee is recognised as fundamental.

In my opinion, in order to develop the reach and depth in the form of supervision Wilkins and colleagues refer to, lies in the development of the relationship with your supervisor and is further complemented and enhanced through the traditional reflective supervision process. For me, the ability to check in with Jad when I feel that something has shifted, or difficulties arise means that I am able to apply the learning and advice in 'live' time. Having someone to 'talk things through' with helps me organise my thoughts about an interaction with a family or colleague. I feel that my visits and contact with my families and colleagues are more focused and present as a result. I've noted that I'm less likely to drift, feel confused or anxious. Therefore, my supervisory relationship brings a level of comfort and togetherness that provides the safety blanket many of us crave, alongside an ability for me to grow and develop for the benefit of our families. I appreciate that most workplaces are not able to provide this level of oversight from supervisors (I am lucky) but I also believe that we can't do this alone.

It's important to note that whilst I do recognise I have the privilege to co facilitate sessions with Jad it does have its challenges, co working with your manager, (a lecturer and highly skilled practitioner at that). I've found it nerve wracking and at times a little bit scary, which has thrown me off kilter at points. Our practice and interaction with our families are always openly discussed and debated, sometimes daily, but with Jad's help I've been able to make sense of what has happened and move forward. I've come to realise we are invested in the programme together; we observe what is going on around us together. Jad may see one thing and I see another – but what we do do is spend time getting to know each other and our families and we do this 'together'. This dual approach seems to work for our families because we pick up on different things. They welcome our dual approach and seem to benefit from it. This finding is supported by David Wilkins who has said that delivery, support and good 'outcomes' are improved when responsibility is shared between the supervisor and supervisee. I certainly feel safer in making changes, in thinking outside of the box, in trying something different and in holding and containing more risk and pain. The supervisory relationship gives me more strength and courage.

Responsibility for the supervisory relationship lies with both parties. It is of particular importance that I respect and value the relationship and the time we put aside for the traditional reflective supervision. I'm honest with Jad about my struggles. I make sure that something I'm worried about or can't make sense of is brought to supervision so we can discuss it. I try to respond to her comments using curiosity and absorbing the knowledge that Jad brings. What I value is that there is always more we can learn from a situation; there is no perfect interaction and I always come away having learned something about the families I work with.....and also about me.

Whilst this all sounds positive, as I have mentioned before it is not always comfortable. We all have our off days and I have had more than my fair share. When I do have an off day, Jad sees right through it. She doesn't berate me for it, instead she nurtures me. She won't let me withdraw and hide, instead she encourages me to identify my barriers and face any difficulties head on (even when sometimes I'd rather not). It's a technique that seems to work for me; it makes me pull my socks up, learn, grow and bizarrely I'm always keen to go back for more. To be better for the families I work with, to reflect on what has happened and then adapt and act. I walk away from the process feeling taller and braver. I think as a supervisee it helps to be open: open to change and challenge but be ready for growth. I find it exciting and strangely addictive.

My supervisory relationship made me realise that good supervision feels like 'good therapy 'it feels this way because I feel I can trust Jad and she supports me to explore painful and emotive experiences. Jad has also identified areas where I can improve. For example, a particular focus has been on my relationship with my colleagues and peers, which can be, for me, an area of frustration. We have a relationship that is built on honesty and it is this platform that has enabled us to explore what is working well and what is, perhaps, not going so well. As we are both practitioners, we realise how important it is to work together so that we can build empathetic and trustworthy relationships with the women we are working alongside. I've learned that sometimes we need to not only recognise their pain but feel it. In fact, one of the group's favourite mantras is 'You've got to feel it to heal it' and this I think, goes both ways. By feeling their pain, whilst maybe carrying my own, I have learned to contain the level of emotion and trauma that I may have experienced in earlier life. I've learned that we need to explore painful and difficult topics but that, as a practitioner, I want (and need) a space to explore that too, so that I can ensure that I have clear insight into my part of that relationship and what I'm bringing to the table.

Due to the close relationship that Jad holds with the families I work with, it allows the families to be heard and listened to in respect of my practice. Their views, needs and maybe wishes play an integral part of my discussions with Jad and our supervisory relationship. We have grown to realise that we don't always get it right, but the dual approach and relationships we do have with the women means we soon realise when we don't, and we will soon find out why it hasn't worked from the feedback they give us. Regular discussions about what is helpful and what is not helpful should be a topic explored openly with both our families and our peers. I have learned that seeking feedback from the families and colleagues I work with helps me to grow alongside my supervisor not apart from her.

I have to admit that sometimes when I hear the stories that the women share in the group I feel shocked, sad and also angry for them. However, I feel I have grown through this process of feeling their pain because rather than at times feeling overwhelmed by it I have learned to talk about it, understand it and then respond to it. As a worrier by nature, the concept of doing reflection in the past felt safe. It was quite straight forward to think about 'What happened? What could have gone better?' I used to find that all of this would be taken over by what I call 'rumination': the process of not being able to stop and organise my thoughts that derive from my reflections. I realise now that it wasn't helpful for my wellbeing or my relationship with the families I support I have learned that rumination is a restrictive activity and soon becomes very much like a broken record. Rumination prevented me from being able to see what I was feeling and since I've been with New Beginnings, I now feel my reflections have somewhere to go. They no longer weigh me down with 'what ifs' 'the buts' or the 'you're not good enough' fears. Jad helps me to see what I'm not seeing and gives another dimension to what the family may be communicating. However, I realise that it is important to be brave. If it doesn't feel right, I need to ask for further clarification. I am the messenger and if I don't feel comfortable it's likely the family will feel the same way. I have found that the 'timing' of the delivery is a critical factor in the success of the conversation with families and professionals.

Part of the ethos of the New Beginnings project is to encourage the women to think about their past, their present and their future. Part of that process is to curb the critical self and to exercise empathy and compassion towards themselves and, at times, others. The women have learned that to understand and navigate what they have been through, they need to not blame others but to sometimes accept responsibility for their actions without it crushing them.

I have learned that this is a process that also takes place in my supervisory relationship as I am given the space to utilise my reflections and move forward, learn and grow. Similarly to the women in our group. Jad will also set homework type tasks for me to do so that I can go away and read either articles or books which relate to the work we do. I have enjoyed this part of the role, spending time researching and reading, developing my skills and practice - it has been like a second job. It has quenched my thirst but made me hungrier as I have wanted to learn and apply different theories to my practice. It is a process that makes me feel great, like it's the right thing to do and more importantly it appears to be working for our families (well, most of the time anyway!). It has been through this unique relationship that I have been supported to filter the thought processes I have around the work I do and try to do. It is in supervision that I am allowed to be human, to not be enveloped by shame and to embrace the mistakes I make by turning them into opportunities to learn, to listen to the families we work with and finally, to adapt to meet their needs. Because of the culture we are all in, one which is therapeutic, flexible, dynamic but more importantly helpful, I now feel more confident in my practice with families. I believe that to help and be helped is the real golden thread between relationships and humanity.

Reading about Leanne's supervision and the impact she feels it has had, what are your thoughts?

FINDING THE SPACE TO REFLECT ON THE EMOTIONAL CONTEXT OF PRACTICE

The vital importance of emotions in social work practice has been recognised for many years. In his seminal text Biesteck (1961) refers to the importance of controlled emotional involvement in the development of an effective working relationship. Despite the fact that social workers are faced with emotional issues on a daily basis and the acknowledgement that social work is "emotional work of a high order" (Howe 2008), social workers report a lack of support in reflecting on the emotional context of their practice. For example, in a survey of social workers, 70% of respondents felt that the emotional issues arising from their work were not adequately addressed in supervision (BASW 2011).

The phrase 'don't let your heart rule your head', which can be traced back to ancient philosophy, illustrates the uneasy connection between emotions and decision making. This may go some way to explaining why supervisors do not address the emotional context of practice in supervision. However, in social work there should be a careful consideration of the impact of emotions on decision making and the best space for this is supervision.

Hawkins and Shohet (2000:3) explained that: "the supervisors role is not just to reassure the worker, but to allow the emotional disturbance to be felt within the safer setting of the supervisory relationship, where it can be survived, reflected and learned from".

Hennessey (2011) argued that social workers who are encouraged to explore and reflect on the emotional aspects of their work are much more able to develop "sound multi-dimensional practice." In addition, Ingram (2013) believes that decision making is enhanced and is more transparent when emotions are discussed in the context of the supervisory relationship. When practitioners have the opportunity to discuss the emotional context of their work, their reflective skills are often enhanced. It is, therefore, vitally important that practitioners feel able to discuss and explore the emotions arising from their work without fear of this being negatively viewed.

PAUSE TO REFLECT

To what extent does your supervision provide a safe space for discussing the emotional aspects of your practice?

EMOTIONAL INTELLIGENCE

Emotional intelligence was introduced as a term by Peter Salovey and John Mayer in 1990 but popularised by Dan Goleman in 1995. The importance of emotional intelligence in social work was highlighted by Howe (2008) in his book 'The Emotionally Intelligent Social Worker'. Emotional intelligence (sometimes referred to as EI or EQ) now has a whole 'industry' behind it - particularly in terms of business models and leadership consultants. As such there are a number of ways of looking at emotional intelligence. As a concept, EI includes the ability to identify, understand, manage and use emotions. It can be useful to consider emotional intelligence in terms of identifying (and understanding) emotions in self and others and managing (and using) emotions in self and others. As such the following illustration may be helpful:

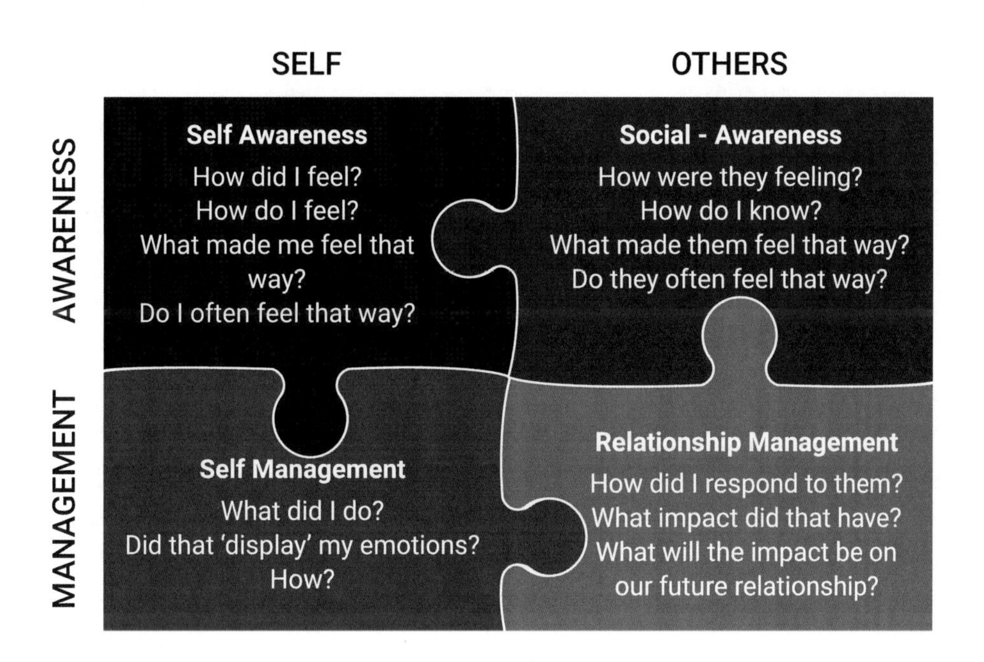

PROFESSIONAL RESILIENCE

For many years social workers have talked about the resilience of children and families, and a range of models have been developed to help explore resilience in children (see Chapter 3). In recent years there has been an increasing interest in professional resilience as a concept.

Grant and Kinman have written widely about professional resilience for social workers. They have identified that preparing effectively for supervision and making the most of supervision is important for social workers seeking to develop their resilience (2014). They have also identified that supervision which supports social workers to develop their emotional literacy and the reflective abilities is essential in developing resilience (Grant and Kinman undated online).

The whole of this resource has stressed the importance of linking internal and external factors, seeing the child and their family in the context of their environment. Therefore, it is vital when thinking about professional resilience to see the professional in the context of their employing organisation. Supervision, therefore, should be the key space for discussions about professional resilience.

SUPERVISION: RESILIENCE BUILT ON 20 RS

Supervision can certainly help practitioners to develop resilience. A number of other Rs can help to build this resilience:

Role: The KSS standard considered in this chapter is the role of supervision. Supervision is essentially about role – one person is given the role to supervise another by the organisation. The practitioner's role in working with families to bring about effective change is a central theme to supervision discussion. Supervision has a role in supporting practitioners to develop their practice and to develop their sense of self.

Relationships: Relationships are key to supervision. The relationship between the supervisor and the supervisee is fundamentally important to how effective the supervision is. A critical friendship should be created. The relationships between the supervisee and the families they support should feature regularly in supervision discussion.

Restorative: Restorative supervision recognises the complex nature of social work practice and seeks to enable the supervisee to explore the emotionally challenging aspects of their work and the potential impact on them, whilst maintaining the central focus on the service user's experience.

Reflexive: Good quality supervision goes beyond reflection to reflexivity. This means that supervision should revolve around a critical exploration of the social workers' use and sense of self, the emotional context of practice and the connections in their work which may not be immediately apparent.

Risk: Supervision should allow for a focused discussion about the risks for children and young people and the management of these risks. Professional curiosity around risk which considers uncertainty should be maintained in the supervisory relationship.

Reach: Supervision should look beyond the immediacy of crisis led decision making. The longer-term vision for practice and for individual children and young people should be clearly considered.

Resolution: The complexity of social work practice can raise a range of ethical dilemmas for practitioners. Supervision should enable discussion of the ethical issues and concerns that practitioners have such that they feel any tensions are resolved.

Responsibility: Nominated supervisors have managerial responsibility for the practitioner and their work. This will inevitably lead to a power differential in the supervisory relationship. The power dynamics need to be named and discussed to enable honest reflection and the development of the supervisory relationship.

Recognition: Supervisee and supervisor need to recognise their own strengths and limitations, ensuring that advice is sought as necessary from a wide range of professionals. Supervision needs to recognise the challenges of the role and the quality of the work being undertaken by the practitioner.

Research: Supervision discussion should include learning from the whole evidence "tree" – theory, research, evidence and expertise should be discussed as core themes in reaching decisions.

Recording: Supervision needs to be effectively recorded. Decisions reached in supervision should be clearly indicated in the case file, so that service users can understand the decision-making process when they read their file.

Reciprocity: Supervision is always a two-way process. The supervisee has a responsibility to prepare effectively, and to make the most of the supervision they receive.

Restrictions: Supervisees should be supported in exploring what restricts their practice – this may be about their own limitations, their capability, organisational or environmental barriers. When people understand the restrictions they may encounter, they are better able to deal with these.

Rigour: Supervision needs to be thorough and consider agenda items in sufficient depth to create meaningful change in practice.

Resources: social workers often raise a lack of resources as a key barrier in practice. However, they are often focussing on external resources. Supervision should enable a discussion about resource limitations and the impact of these, but it should also encourage a worker to consider inner resources – what is available within the family's support network? What can the worker bring in terms of their use of self?

Reasoning: Good supervision enables a worker to sound out their ideas and develop their own reasoning skills by testing out the evidence of their hypotheses and plans with another more experienced worker.

Reading: what is the worker reading to enhance their work and support their decision making? This should form a central focus in the supervision discussion.

Routes: Chapter 6 explored the journey that children and their families have in social work intervention. Supervision should provide a space for the worker to discuss the routes that the children and families are taking in relation to the journey. How is the practitioner supporting the journey?

Results: The outcomes of practice for children and their families must be considered in supervision. Thinking about crocheting a blanket with the golden thread explored on page 283 can be helpful here. To read a crochet pattern you need to look at the end as well as the beginning. This really exemplifies what good practice is with children and families – look to the outcomes from the start of intervention and explore these regularly in supervision.

Requirements: There should be a clarity about organisational requirements and the impact that these are having on practice in supervision.

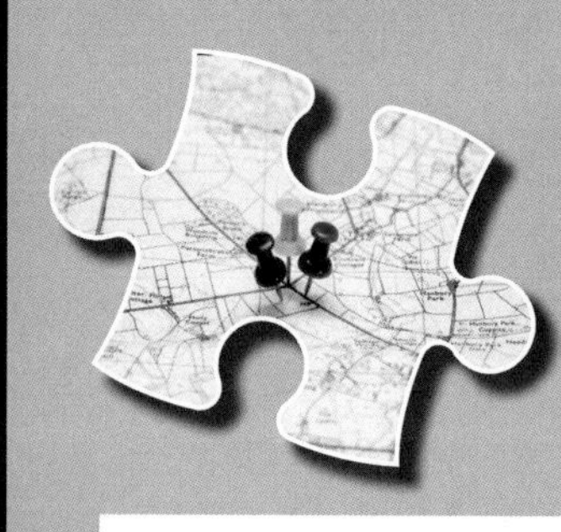

WHERE AM I NOW?

Revisit the start of the chapter. Look again at the KSS standard. Then consider the following questions:

What has surprised me in working through this chapter?

What three things would I highlight as key learning?

What do I still need to do in working towards being fully confident with this KSS statement?

What single next step should I take in working towards an improvement in my practice?

Chapter 10

ORGANISATIONAL CONTEXT

We started this resource by exploring reflexivity and the connections between internal and external factors. The I and the E is about connecting the person with their environment. Of course, it is also important to think about the social worker in the context of their environment. In this chapter you will explore the organisational context in which you operate. Ensuring that children are central to every aspect of this resource, the chapter concludes by looking at the organisation's role as corporate parent.

THE KSS REQUIRES PRACTITIONERS TO:

Operate successfully in a wide range of organisational contexts complying with the checks and balances within local and national systems which are a condition of employment. Maintain personal and professional credibility through effective working relationships with peers, managers and leaders both within the profession, throughout multi-agency partnerships and public bodies, including the family courts.

Act in ways that protect the reputation of the employer organisation and the social work profession, whilst always privileging the best interests of children. Manage the specific set of organisational tasks relating to lead responsibility for children with the support of an appropriately qualified supervisor and use of the multi-agency support network.

Contribute to the organisation's role as corporate parent to children in public care, encouraging and advocating for organisational focus, resource and support so that children and young people can thrive and enjoy their childhood and move into independence with confidence in and ambition for their futures.

Take a look at the standard above in detail. Highlight key phrases and anything that jumps out at you. Then take some time to reflect on the statement.

- *What are your immediate thoughts?*
- *What might you want to discuss and clarify?*
- *How will you clarify meanings?*
- *Who will you discuss it with?*

GETTING FEEDBACK ON PRACTICE

Who can give me feedback on my practice in this area?	*How will I get the feedback?*

Make sure to keep a record of any feedback you receive.

INITIAL SELF-ASSESSMENT

What do I already do well?

How do I know? (What's my evidence?)

What do I need to work on?

How will I work on this?

Sam Clayton is the Principal Social Worker for Lincolnshire.

When I started to work as a qualified social worker the number of systems, regulatory requirements and expectations I was expected to operate within seemed, at times, overwhelming. Having worked in children's homes for a number of years previously, I was familiar with my corporate parenting responsibilities and the importance of listening, understanding and supporting young people to be the best they could, often after years of trauma, inconsistency, reduced opportunities or lack of focus on their needs. The need to advocate for these young people in a system that often seemed inflexible was a challenge and this is what led to my decision to become qualified, my thinking being that maybe earlier input could avoid some of the issues further down the line in the child's life if dealt with effectively at the earliest opportunity.

Having qualified on 2002 and securing my first job I was struck by the number of different expectations and requirements that were now placed on me in my role as qualified social worker. Firstly, there was the regulator and the requirement for adhesion to a code of practice, the need to meet professional standards, continually develop (CPD) and the fact that the title of social work was a legally protected one and all that this brought with it. Secondly there was the fact that I was employed by the Local Authority, the organisation specifically charged with the exercise of statutory duties enshrined in legislation, including the help and protection of children and vulnerable people. As an employee of the council I was a public servant employed to uphold the seven principles of public life. These principles were set out by the Nolan committee which was established following the 'cash for questions' scandal during John Major's government. 25 years later the Nolan principles are still relevant and useful to help social workers navigate their way thought the systems of Local Authorities, Trust arrangements and the wide range of commissioned services who are exercising some statutory functions on behalf of the Local Authorities who fund them.

- Selflessness
- Integrity
- Objectivity
- Accountability
- Openness
- Honesty
- Leadership

In practice these principles should enable individual social workers to consider the culture of the organisation they work for and how this culture enables them to thrive as a social worker and provide the best service they can to those who receive it; it also describes behaviours which at the same time protect both the reputation of the employer and the social work profession and lead to the best use of public money for the provision of the best public services, delivered to the public.

Social work is often described as a 'value based' profession and has a code of ethics. Most individual social workers do the job because they believe in the importance of human relationships, social justice, integrity, competence, dignity and the worth of the individual, these values resonate with the Nolan principles and should be the foundation for the organisational culture in which social work will flourish. For social workers to be able to practice well they need a well-developed sense of their organisation including the challenges and limitations; in the current climate the funding pressures Local Authorities are subject to combined with increasing referrals makes it more necessary for the individual worker to have the support of an effective team and skilled manager to enable them to ensure they continue to have a relentless focus on doing the best for the children and families that they serve.

Social workers must have the ability to navigate multiple systems and layers, develop high functioning professional networks, internally and externally, effective partnerships with children, families and other professionals and minimise the organisational quirks if they are to survive and indeed thrive in social work in the longer term.

PAUSE TO REFLECT

The KSS standards require you to act in ways that protect the reputation of the employer organisation. Sam has suggested some ways that a social worker might do this. How do you do this in your practice?

THE SOCIAL WORK ZOO

Drawing on the use of creative reflection techniques I often ask groups to present their group discussions through the use of analogies and aspects of the creative arts. This flipchart was the result of a group of newly qualified social workers exploring what it felt like to be a new member of a social work team. It provides an interesting way to reflect on how a social work team can feel. In reading about the way in which the animals have been described, try to reflect on how you are seen in your team – which animal might you be?

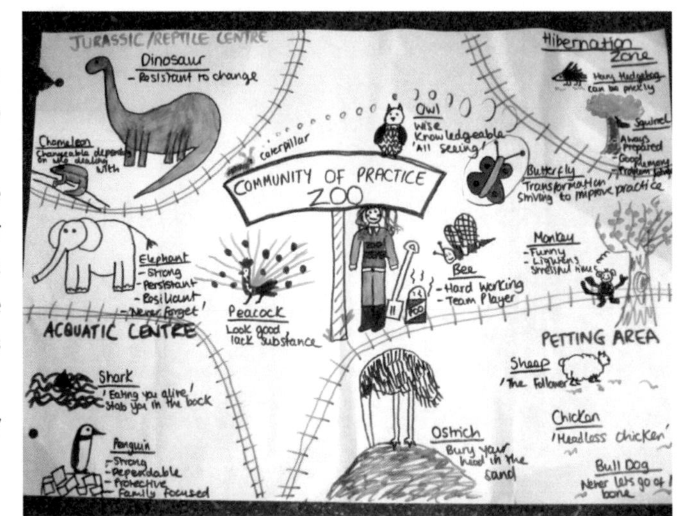

JURASSIC / REPTILE CENTRE

The dinosaurs: They have been around for years and are resistant to change.

The chameleons: They are changeable and adapt to whatever situation they are in. They sometimes appear to change what they say in line with what they think the person wants to hear.

Elephant: Strong and resilient, they never forget anything.

AQUATIC CENTRE

The shark: Is likely to eat you alive or stab you in the back.

The penguin: based on the old advertising slogan about walking like a penguin, the penguin is someone to admire. They represent the social worker who focuses on service users and who the new workers see as protective and supportive.

HIBERNATION ZONE

Consistently students and new practitioners talk about the number of staff who they are told are off sick or away for other reasons – effectively they are hibernating never to be seen!

Squirrels: These characters have lots of nuggets of information and are always prepared, but they save the information for themselves. They hide their nuts up a tree only sharing them with others when asked a direct question.

Hedgehogs: They are the workers who look friendly enough, but if you ask them a question they curl up and become prickly. They are certainly not open to challenge.

PETTING AREA

Sheep: Followers, who simply do what they are instructed to do.

Ostrich: With their head in the sand, the ostrich has no idea of what is going on around them.

Bulldog: The bulldog has a focus on a particular idea and never lets go of that bone.

Chicken: The chicken on the flipchart is headless. Every team knows what the headless chicken is like – they come in from a difficult visit flapping around everywhere. Everyone else stops their own work to step in and help, only to find that they become splattered by it all whilst the chicken goes home feeling fine.

OTHER ANIMALS

The monkey: Every team has a monkey, who lightens the mood with some humour when it's needed.

The bee: The hard working team player – often they are particularly good at cross pollination with multi-agency working

Peacock: They look very impressive but there is little substance behind the peacock.

Owl: The wise character who is able to turn their head almost full circle to oversee the team and understand what is happening from a range of angles. Students in particular have talked about their desire to have the wise owl providing supervision.

THE ZOOKEEPER

There was some debate in the group that put the flipchart together about who the zookeeper could represent. They might be the person in the team who cleans up the mess left behind by others, or they could be the 'feeder' every team has that person who brings in the cakes and the biscuits and effectively establishes feeding time at the zoo.

Finally, the newly qualified workers depicted themselves as a butterfly who through their early experiences in a social work team, can learn and develop a great deal, turning into a butterfly through the process of transformational learning. This may sound somewhat cheesy but of course they concluded by saying that they could then fly away if they didn't like the zoo environment.

Since this original flipchart was drawn a number of practitioners have added some animals they felt were missing from the zoo. For example, meercats could represent the real team players – sometimes though they like to stand together in a clique that people new to the team can find difficult to penetrate.

Looking at the social work zoo, where would you place yourself? How do you think your colleagues see you? If we are honest most of us play different parts on different days. I'd like to think that I am never a shark, but I know that there are days when people probably see me as a dinosaur (I have been qualified almost thirty years after all!) and I am often a busy bee.

PAUSE TO REFLECT

What other 'animals' do you recognise in social work teams?

WORKING WITH OTHERS

Multi-agency working is part of working with every family - which services might the family be connected with? How might you work with these organisations to undertake a thorough assessment? How might you engage with them to bring about support for change within the family? Multi-agency working can also be about the bigger picture too, so social workers may be part of a range of multi-agency partnerships, which work together to address specific issues or themes. This is really about creating a 'community of practice' which might seek to support a particular child (in a team around the child/family approach) or it may be wider 'community of practice' which shares a common goal around wider issues within communities.

So, working as part of a multi-professional or multi-agency network is vital in social work, and yet it is often fraught with difficulties and challenges. One of the themes that has run throughout this workbook is that there is always simplicity to be found in the complexity. Sometimes we need to remind ourselves of this simplicity. The following two contributions come from colleagues who work alongside children and family practitioners. What might you take from these in terms of your own multi-professional working?

Simon Bland is a caseworker for Derbyshire, Leicester, Nottinghamshire and Rutland Community Rehabilitation Company.

Part of my role is to work with Care Leavers in custody and on licence. I've found Leicestershire County council to be both receptive and proactive in this field. We have information exchange protocols in place, allowing Care Leavers to be located quickly upon their arrival in prisons, and contact details of key workers exchanged so the Personal Advisors (PAs) can get on with their jobs and (critically for prisons) share their expertise on the clients, allowing the prisons to work with them more effectively.

The first few days in prison are notoriously critical, so to have access to the PA's knowledge and understanding about a vulnerable youngster about whom we often know nothing can, quite literally, be the difference between life and death. At their invite I'm part of a regular, multi-agency panel where the most vulnerable and challenging Care Leavers are discussed, and actions developed.

However, it has been Leicestershire County Council's response to the change of regulations, entitling Care Leavers to greater support between the ages of 21 and 25 that has been the most impressive. All we, in prisons, need to do is let the manager know when an eligible Care Leaver from their area arrives into custody, or receives a community penalty, and they immediately assign them to a Personal Assistant and put us in touch. The PA can then become a key part of the ongoing work, hopefully making everyone's life a little bit easier. This may seem ridiculously simple, but it's also ridiculously effective, and I believe if it was replicated across the criminal justice system it would make a huge positive difference to so many lives.

Phil Coleman is a Social Worker and Service Development Manager at The National Association of Child Contact Centres.

Parenting Shouldn't End when Relationships Do! As a Social Worker and Service Development Manager from the National Association of Child Contact Centres (NACCC) I have noted through practice experience that, following the changes to Legal Aid in 2012, parents have found it difficult to know where or how to access support following separation. The consequence of this is that people turn to the Family Courts, often without representation.

This results in the Courts seeing more and more families that do not understand legal processes trying to navigate a system that they do not really need. The reality is, when people separate, the one thing they have in common is the love of their children.

In my experience, people generally want what is best for their children but disagree about what this is and seek the Court to reach outcomes about this. The problem is, that the Judge doesn't know the child and will Order things that have life long and possibly life changing implications for the child. Court Orders are blunt instruments that arguably do not account for a child's individuality or the changes that happen in life.

For some families there will be no alternative other than Court, particularly where risks are elevated. I believe, however, that for a good number of families this is not required and not in their best interests. An alternative plan that works could be as follows:

1. The **Family Justice Young Peoples Board (FJYPB)** provide information written by children about what children want when their parents separate. This can help parents to focus on the needs of their children.
2. **Parenting Plans** (Freely available in print or as a download) can help parents work together to consider and plan for the needs of their children.
3. **NACCC, Families Need Fathers** and **Gingerbread** have **advice lines** that can offer advice and guidance about options available to parents and grandparents when they lose contact with children (or are at risk of this).
4. **Cafcass** provide a range of information and support for parents separating.
5. **Separated Parents Information Programmes (SPIPS)** can be an opportunity to understand the needs of children and the ways that adult behaviours can impact upon them.
6. **Mediation** could be used where all other options seem out of reach. A mediator will work impartially, helping people to focus on what matters during the pain of separation.
7. **Supported Contact** can help as a short term stepping stone to support building trust where this has broken down.
8. **Supervised Contact** could be used as a step towards supported contact if the risks are too high for Supported Contact.
9. **ChildLine** provides a listening service for children and young people and could support them though difficult transitions.

Contact centres are not the most natural place for children to see parents, grandparents or other people they love and no longer live with, or regularly get to spend time with. Therefore, a NACCC accredited contact service will be keen that they are nothing more than a stepping stone with an emphasis on moving towards arrangements that are flexible, safe, appropriate and in the best interests of children.

PAUSE TO REFLECT

Draw up an ecomap, demonstrating your links with other professionals. This might relate to a specific piece of work you are doing or might be more general. Don't forget to indicate the flow of energy in the relationships.

Looking at the ecomap, what do you notice?

What barriers do you face in relation to working with other professionals?

What enables good multi-agency working?

Think about a time when you were able to work with other professionals to support a family or child. What worked well? What might you be able to take from this learning to use in other situations?

When I read the statement that this chapter relates to, I had to sit back and ask myself, what does it mean? What did it mean to me, as a child of the state? What does it mean to me now, as someone who fosters?... So I'm going to come at this from a slightly different angle with a perspective that probably makes more sense to me, and look at what organisational relationships existed and exist now, and how they work together to ensure that support is given to families and that children are protected.

I write part of this, from my point of view with regards to the childhood I experienced. Some of what I write is me being reflective and looking back to see what was happening, other aspects will relate to what does or doesn't appear to happen now.

As a child of the state growing up in institutions that were religiously controlled and funded by charitable organisations, it felt that the organisation was untouchable and unaccountable for the charges it looked after. Everyone working in the organisation appeared to have some sort of connection, whether that was faith based, relationship (marriage or otherwise) or had once been a resident.

I had already learned to be mistrustful and found to my detriment that disclosure of any kind resulted in violent retribution. I therefore withdrew and felt unable to approach or speak with any confidence in relation to what I was experiencing or what was going on.

Steps were taken by those looking after me, who schooled my responses with veiled threats, so that the social workers, clergy or visitors who called in and saw or spoke with me, would be given smiles. Believe me though when I say that 'abject fear' of retribution, lurked behind those smiles!

The question I ask myself is, 'Who was checking who'? Why did it take so long for other authorities to get involved? Shouldn't those connections have already been in place? Failure to have robust systems can mean that those who are caught in the middle become real victims of circumstances!!

No one was speaking to anyone. I, and others, were part of a process that had to be seen, no steps or discussions were being held with those in charge or involved in my life such as my school, GP etc. The paperwork appears to be 'dis-jointed' which again highlights 'missed opportunities'.

The notes in my file prior to my birth detail a picture of a frightened woman caught in a predicament, she felt unable to control. The systems in place to help her were limited. It clearly shows no aftercare or support either through the organisation I was born into or through potential signposting was available, and she was left to her own devices during and after my birth. The impact has been far reaching and despite us reconnecting in my mid-twenties, she struggles with her own feelings of guilt and the abandonment she believes she committed. She doesn't or didn't receive the support to explain why relinquishment was the best option. All she was advised was, she wouldn't have a good life if she kept me, especially as I might be noticed 'coloured'. She wrote prior to my birth and after it, about the treatment she received at the mother and baby unit, describing how a dog was looked after and treated better, "at least they are treated with a degree of compassion". The response she got, though heavily redacted does refer to “the need for her to atone for her mistake” ... hardly supportive?

As I’ve stated, my file has comments and missed opportunities that condemned me to the upbringing I endured and all due to no checks or partnership working as potentially someone may have noticed.

Interestingly some of the phrases said to me these days, from people who either lived in the area I grew up in or worked in the local vicinity are:

“We knew something wasn’t right about that place”

“We always felt sorry for you lot, none of you looked really happy”

An ex Policewoman said to me “We used to argue which of us would return any of the escapees we caught as we found it a really scary place”... My response to her “How do you think we felt then”?

All organisations need to develop strong and effective relationships, communicating in order to build and assist practice and we appreciate that most roads seem to lead to relationships, so what is it that needs to be done here.

Today the system has of course improved, yet serious case reviews still spew out the same commentary that children sadly suffer, even die because services aren’t joined up, but I do see more of a willingness and recognition from those involved to work jointly with other organisations.

Incidents of both good and poor practice exist and I’m sure I won’t be the first to say that I’ve attended meetings where rooms haven’t been booked and meetings have been cancelled, significant and relevant people involved not attending because they haven’t been informed. As a foster carer I’ve even had occasion to be the only person to arrive and then told after waiting around that the meeting has been cancelled. When this involves birth family, social workers, IROs, foster carers, nurses, doctors, therapists and educators the casualty will always be the child because it means that their life is still in limbo, nothing is being sorted and then they may have to deal with the anxiety of not understanding what is going on. Equally I’ve attended meetings where all organisations and significant people have been in attendance. The upshot is that decisions are made and progress happens and the child is able to move forward.

I’m not perfect by a long stretch, however in my role as a foster carer I aim to include everyone associated with any child we are looking after with regards to updates. I’d rather duplicate an email or phone call to confirm appointments with all those that need to be in attendance rather than risk people not turning up as I know it makes my role harder when I have to explain to a child that something didn’t take place or why decisions are still up in the air because someone hasn’t turned up.

What I have experienced is by going this extra step, others want to get on board and a movement of positivity is created, it builds and strengthens relationships. It becomes far easier achieving outcomes together. It generates trust and helps when hearing details that may be difficult.

THE ORGANISATION AS CORPORATE PARENT

The Children and Social Work Act 2017 says that when a child or young person comes into the care of the local authority, or is under 25 and was looked-after by the authority for at least 13 weeks after their 14th birthday, the authority becomes their corporate parent. This means that they should:

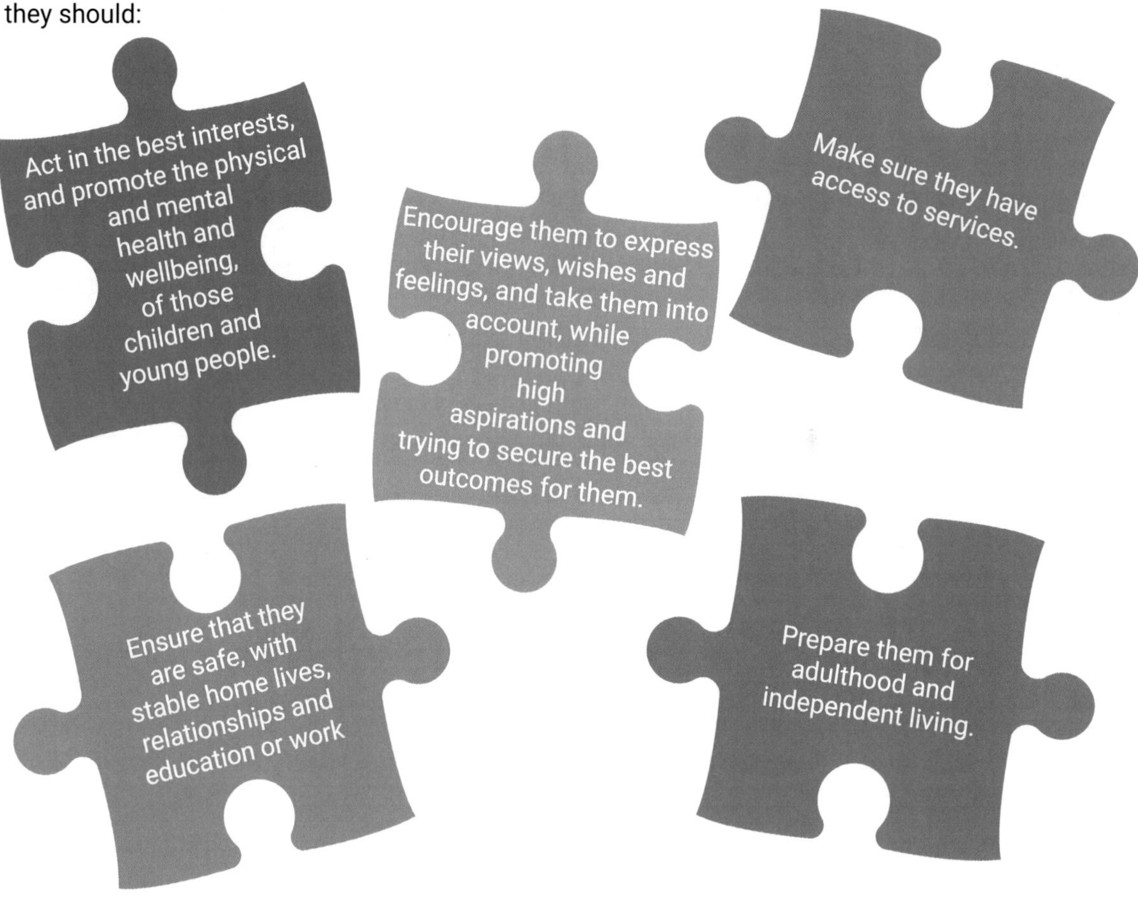

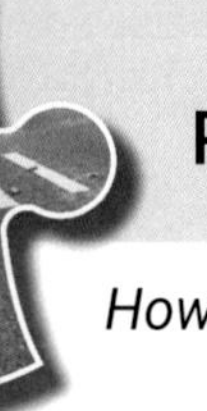

PAUSE TO REFLECT

How do you contribute to your organisation's role as a corporate parent?

How often do you stop and think: "What if this was my child? Would this be good enough for them?" And what is the answer? The standards require you to "encourage and advocate for organisational focus, resource and support so that children can thrive..." Are you able to do that? How?

I will leave the final words to Paul, who had a corporate parent, what is his view?

PAUL'S PERSPECTIVE

The idea that a child brought into the 'care' system gains a 'Corporate' parent has, for a long time, raised a smile for me. The idea feels so far removed from reality, and seems to only serve as a reference to point the finger of blame and shame. It feels impersonal, cold and unapproachable. I believe the old saying 'It takes a village to raise a child', meaning many are responsible for the wellbeing of our most vulnerable.

Perhaps reference to the 'Collective' or 'Public' parent would sit better as it refers to foster carers, adopters, social workers, Local Authority, teachers, health services, youth services and Government. Together we represent, and act to parent, our most vulnerable children and therefore share the positive and negative aspects of parenting. For it to succeed we need to act together, ensuring Communication, Consistency and Connectivity increasing positive Relationships with each other, working in a Reflective environment in order to build an improved service and Reward, which should be our overall goal. The Reward of raising and providing future generations with the skills and belief to succeed and live a good life.

PAUSE TO REFLECT

What do you see as the 'reward' of your work?

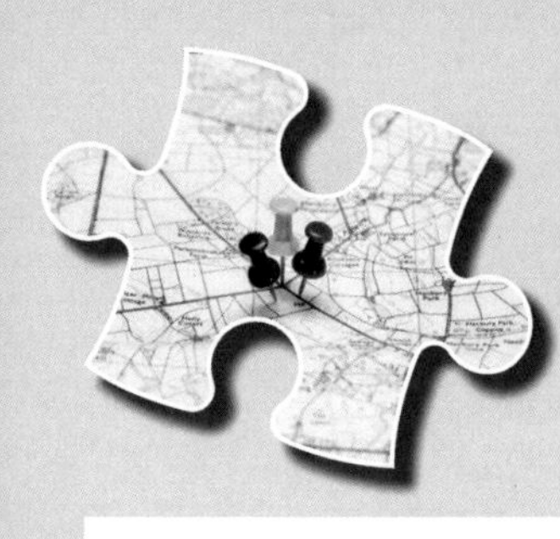

WHERE AM I NOW?

Revisit the start of the chapter. Look again at the KSS standard. Then consider the following questions:

What has surprised me in working through this chapter?

What three things would I highlight as key learning?

What do I still need to do in working towards being fully confident with this KSS statement?

What single next step should I take in working towards an improvement in my practice?

ARE YOU READY?

So, you have worked through this resource, reminding yourself about each aspect of the KSS, revisiting theory, and some of the 'basics.'

On the assessment day you will experience four elements of the NAAS:

KNOWLEDGE ASSESSMENT

There will be 30 multiple choice questions. Some have one correct answer and others have a number of correct answers. The questions will tell you how many correct answers there are. Take your time with this. It's not a race! Make sure to read the question carefully.

SIMULATED PRACTICE ASSESSMENT

This is pretty much a role play, with actors. You will have some preparation time.

REFLECTIVE ASSESSMENT

After the simulated practice assessment, you will receive a couple of questions. You will have time to think about them to prepare your responses. Then you will 'speak' your answers to the assessor. In many ways it is like a reflective monologue, reflect on the points you have been asked to. There isn't much 'discussion' because this is all about you – but think of it as pretty much a one-person discussion.

WRITTEN ASSESSMENT

There will be a short computer-based exercise. You will be asked to write a short piece – maybe a care plan, or analysis. This is really looking at your recording skills.

The most important thing is DO NOT GET NERVOUS! You will not do justice to your practice.

You will be apprehensive certainly, but anxiety will impede you on the day. The purpose of the day is to enable you to demonstrate that you meet the requirements of the KSS in your daily practice. The purpose of the day is not to catch you out or give you a difficult time. Everyone I know who has experienced the day said the assessor put them at their ease and that the day was "nowhere near as bad" as they thought. Many have actually enjoyed the opportunity to have their work valued.

You have prepared well.

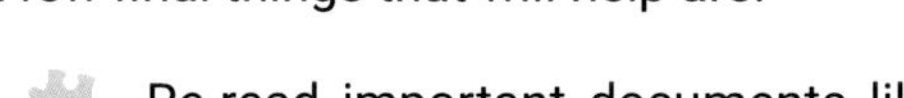

A few final things that will help are:

- Re-read important documents like Working Together and the Assessment Framework. Some people find it helps them to write a few notes to aid memory.
- Think about the approach you like to take to your practice, and as part of that think about a couple of theories, models and methods you like to use. This will help you feel more comfortable in preparing for the reflective assessment (Chapter 7 will help you with this if you want to take a look again).
- Spend a bit of time thinking about how you like to reflect on your practice – find a model of reflection or a framework that helps you to be more reflective. This resource has provided a range of ways of thinking about your work, encouraging you to pause and reflect on your practice. Read through your responses again, this might help you to think more reflexively.
- Your employer will be able to offer further support, and possibly opportunities to practice the assessment day.

Janine Connor qualified in 2010 and has worked as a social worker in a long term locality team, an assessment duty team and a MASH team. She has been employed as the NAAS Coordinator for Oldham Children's Social Care since May 2018. Janine undertook NAAS in 2018.

I very much see the NAAS as a development opportunity. Personally, for me courses and qualifications I've done since qualifying didn't really help my practice as much as I'd have liked and actually, they felt quite removed from the work I was actually doing. I am more of a 'hands on' and practical person. In my experience, NAAS does make you look at your own practice. When I qualified, we didn't do the Assessed and Supported Year in Employment (ASYE) but now, people benefit from that support. I work with the Knowledge and Skills Statements (KSS) with the NQSWs and I think they are good at recognising what we do day to day.

To be honest, if I had not been in this post, I would have done the assessment anyway. It is important to think about our own career progression and development and I wanted us to lead by example. It's been helpful in my current role that I have undertaken NAAS, because I can talk people through the process and remind them that it is the work that we do every day.

Don't get me wrong, it was nerve-wracking! I kept thinking, 'please let me get a met' but this is only normal. I really think that if I had got a 'not met' outcome, I would have carried on redoing it until I got accredited as I do see NAAS as a development tool.

Despite what I had initially thought, our social workers were not worried about the knowledge assessment. I had given them some general information about the Knowledge and Skills Statements (KSS) because, in Oldham, our more experienced staff were not familiar with them and were more familiar with the Professional Capabilities Framework (PCF). What I found in the assessment was that the knowledge questions were quite varied. Even if we had put on a million workshops, they would not have covered some of the questions that came up! People did however ask for some workshops on the law but we do this quite often anyway in Oldham so it was easy to organise with the help of our legal team.

In the busy world of social work, you don't often get observed by your managers/seniors, except if a case is in pre-proceedings or in the court arena, so being observed as part of NAAS and having it aligned to the KSS is positive. I do believe you should be observed in your practice and that managers should go out on visits more but they have restrictions on their time. That is where NAAS is useful. For me personally, I hadn't worried about being assessed but I didn't really like the idea of being video recorded. However, in reality the actors were really good, and I was quite surprised that I forgot I was being filmed and in an assessment.

A lot of my role is about reassuring people. Yes, it's important to prepare workers for the fact it is quite an intense day and there might be parts of the assessment day and feedback that you don't like. If people have 'not met', I would encourage social workers to feedback their experience to their NAAS coordinator and re-take the assessment again, with appropriate support being provided for their 'not met' areas. My advice to any social workers considering NAAS would be, don't stress about it and make it a bigger deal than it is. It's what you're doing in your day to day practice and NAAS is not intended to trick you. It's easy to get hung up on what you should say but try and be as natural as you can be and use the reflective discussion of the NAAS to talk about any areas you feel you did not cover in the practice simulations. And finally, use those breaks!

REFERENCES

ACMD. (2011) Hidden Harm: Full Report. Available online at: https://assets.publishing.service.gov.uk/government/uploads/system/uploads/attachment_data/file/120620/hidden-harm-full.pdf

Association of Directors of Childrens Services. (2016) Safeguarding Pressures Phase 5. (Manchester) The Association of Directors of Children's Services.

Baldry, A.C. (2003) Bullying in Schools and Exposure to Domestic Violence. Child Abuse and Neglect, 27(7) 713-732.

Bandura, A. (1977) Social Learning Theory. (Englewood Cliffs, New Hersey) Prentice Hall.

BASW (2011) BASW/CoSW England Research on supervision in social work, with particular reference to supervision practice in multi-disciplinary teams. (Birmingham) BASW.

BASW (2018) 80-20 Campaign: How much 'direct' time do social workers spend with children and families? Available online at: www.basw.co.uk/resources/80-20-campaign-final-report-2018 Accessed 28.01.19.

Baynes, P. and Holland, S. (2012) Social work with violent men: a child protection file study in an English local authority. Child Abuse Review, 21 53-65.

Beddoe, L. and Davys A. (2016) Challenges in Professional Supervision. (London) Jessica Kingsley Publishers.

Bengtsson, E., Chamberlain, C., Crimmens, D. and Stanley, J. (2008) Introducing social pedagogy into residential child care in England: An evaluation of a project commissioned by the Social Education Trust (SET). (London) NCB/NCERCC.

Benner, P. (2004) Using the Dreyfus Model of Skill Acquisition to Describe and Interpret Skill Acquisition and Clinical Judgment in Nursing Practice and Education. Bulletin of Science, Technology and Society. doi.org/10.1177/0270467604265061.

Bercow, J. (2008) The Bercow Report: A review of services for children and young people (0-19) with speech, language and communication needs. (Nottingham) DCSF.

Best Beginnings. (2019) Disabled Parents. Available online at: https://www.bestbeginnings.org.uk/parents-with-disabilities Accessed 02.06.19.

Biestek, F. (1961) The Casework Relationship. (London) George Allen and Unwin.

Borton, T. (1970) Reach, Teach and Touch. (London) McGraw Hill.

Broadhurst, K., Mason, C., Bedston, S., Alrouh, B., Morriss, L., McQuarrie, T., Palmer, M., Shaw, M., Harwin, J. and Kershaw, S. (2017) Vulnerable Birth Mothers and Recurrent Care Proceedings. Nuffield Foundation. Available online at: http://www.nuffieldfoundation.org/sites/default/files/files/rc-final-summary-report-v1_6.pdf Accessed 02.06.19.

Broadhurst, K., Wastell, D., White, S., Hall, C., Peckover, C., Thompson, K., Pithouse, A. and Davey, D. (2010) Performing 'Initial Assessment': Identifying the Latent Conditions for Error at the Front- Door of Local Authority Children's Services. British Journal of Social Work, 40(2) 352-370.

Bronfenbrenner, U. (1994) Ecological Models of Human Development. Available online at: http://www.psy.cmu.edu/~siegler/35bronfebrenner94.pdf Accessed 22.12.10.

Brown, H., Sawyer, R.D. and Norris, J. (Eds) (2016) Forms of Practitioner Reflexivity. Critical Conversational and Arts Based Approaches. (New York) Palgrave Macmillan.

Brown, L., Moore, S. and Turney, D. (2012) Analysis and Critical Thinking in Assessment. Resource Pack – Core Publication. (Dartington) Research in Practice.

Brown, S., Brady, G., Franklin, A. and Crookes, R. (2017) The use of tools and checklists to assess risk of child sexual exploitation. An exploratory study. Coventry University. Available online at: www.csacentre.org.uk/research-publications/cse-risk-tools/exploratory-study-on-the-use-of-tools-and-checklists-to-assess-risk-of-child-sexual-exploitation/ Accessed 01.06.19.

Burnham, J. (2012) Developments in Social GRRRAAACCEEESSS: visible-invisible and voiced-unvoiced. In Krause, I.B. (Ed) Culture and Reflexivity in Systemic Psychotherapy Mutual Perspectives. (Oxon) Routledge.

Bywaters, P., Brady, G., Bunting, L., Daniel, B., Featherstone, B., Jones, C., Morris, K., Scourfield, J., Sparks, T. and Webb, C. (2017) Inequalities in English child protection practice under austerity: A universal challenge? Child and Family Social Work. https://doi.org/10.1111/cfs.12383

Carvalho, S. and White, H. (1997). Combining the quantitative and qualitative approaches to poverty measurement and analysis: The practice and the potential. World Bank Technical Paper 366. (Washington, D.C.) World Bank.

Chowdry, H. (2018) Estimating the Prevalence of the 'toxic trio'. Evidence form the Adult Psychiatric Morbidity Survey. Children's Commissioner. Available online at: https://www.childrenscommissioner.gov.uk/wp-content/uploads/2018/07/Vulnerability-Technical-Report-2-Estimating-the-prevalence-of-the-toxic-trio.pdf Accessed 18.01.19.

Clapton, G. (2017) 'Good practice with fathers in children and family services' Institute for Research and Innovation in Social Services (IRISS), 38 1-16.

Cleaver, H., Unell, I., and Aldgate, J. (2011) Children's Needs – Parenting Capacity. Child abuse: Parental mental illness, learning disability, substance misuse and domestic violence. (2nd edition) Department for Education. (London) HMSO.

Cohen, B. Z and Laufer, H. (1999) The Influence of Supervision on Social Workers' Perceptions of Their Professional Competence. The Clinical Supervisor, 18(2) 39-50.

Corcoran, M and McNulty, M. (2018) Examining the role of attachment in the relationship between childhood adversity, psychological distress and subjective wellbeing. Child Abuse and Neglect, 76(1) 297–309.

Cronholm, P. F., Forke, C. M., Wade, R., Bair-Merritt, M.H., Davis, M., Harkins-Schwarz, M., Fein, J. A. (2015) Adverse Childhood Experiences: Expanding the Concept of Adversity. American Journal of Preventive Medicine, 49(3), 354-361. [4343]. https://doi.org/10.1016/j.amepre.2015.02.001.

D'Cruz, H., Gillingham, P. and Melendez, S. (2007) Reflexivity: A Concept and its Meanings for Practitioners Working with Children and Families. Critical Social Work, 8(1) 1-18.

de Haan, E. and Stewart, S. (translator) (2008) Relational Coaching; Journeys towards mastering one to one learning. (London) John Wiley.

Department for Education and Department of Health and Social Care. (2017) Joint statement on the relationship between the Professional Capabilities Framework (PCF) for Social Work and the Knowledge and Skills Statements for Children and Families and Adults. Available online at: www.basw.co.uk/sites/default/files/basw-pcf-and-kss-joint-statement.pdf Accessed 01.03.19.

Department of Health and Social Care. (2018) Post-qualifying standards for social work supervisors in adult social care. Available online at: www.gov.uk/government/publications/adult-social-work-post-qualifying-standards-knowledge-and-skills-statement Accessed 03.03.19.

Dreyfus, H.L. and Dreyfus, S.E. (1986) Mind over Machine: the power of human intuition and expertise in the era of the computer. (Oxford) Basil Blackwell.

Dyke, C. (2018) Why a chronology should be the first thing you do in an assessment. Available online at: https://www.communitycare.co.uk/2018/08/15/chronology-first-thing-assessment/ Accessed 02.05.19.

Egan, G. (2002) The skilled helper. (Pacific Grove, CA) Brooks/Cole.

Elliott, N. (2017) Psychosocial and Relationship-based Practice. Journal of Social Work Practice, DOI: 10.1080/02650533.2017.1373083.

Erikson, E. (1950) Childhood and Society. (New York) Norton.

Ewart-Boyle, S., Manktelow, R. and McColgan, M. (2015) Social work and the shadow father: lessons for engaging fathers in Northern Ireland. Child and Family Social Work, 20 470-479.

Fairtlough, A. (2017) Professional Leadership for Social Work Practitioners and Educators. (Oxon) Routledge.

Fantuzzo, J.W. and Mohr, W. K. (1999) Prevalence and Effects of Child Exposure to Domestic Violence The Future of Children. Domestic Violence and Children, 9(3) 21-32.

Featherston, R.J., Shlonsky, A., Lewis, C., Luong, M., Downie, L.E., Vogel, A.P., Granger, C., Hamilton, B. and Galvin, K. (2018) Interventions to Mitigate Bias in Social Work Decision-Making: A Systemic Review. Research on Social Work Practice. doi.org/10.1177/1049731518819160

Ferguson, H. (2014) What social workers do in performing child protection work: Evidence from research into face-to-face practice. Child and Family Social Work, 21(3) 283-294.

Ferguson, H. (2016) How Children Become Invisible in Child Protection Work: Findings from Research into Day-to-Day Social Work Practice. British Journal of Social Work, 47(4) 1007–1023.

Festinger, L. (1957) A Theory of Cognitive Dissonance. (Stanford) Stanford University Press.

Finkelhor, D. (2017) Screening for adverse childhood experiences (ACEs): Cautions and suggestions. Child Abuse & Neglect, 85. 10.1016/j.chiabu.2017.07.016.

Firmin, C. (2017) Contextual Safeguarding: An overview of the operational, strategic and conceptual framework. Institute of Applied Research. Available online at https://contextualsafeguarding.org.uk/assets/documents/Contextual-Safeguarding-Briefing.pdf Accessed 1.3.19

Firmin, C. (2019) Contextual Safeguarding: a new way of identifying need and risk. Available online at https://www.communitycare.co.uk/2019/03/25/contextual-safeguarding-new-way-identifying-need-risk/ Accessed 2.5.19

Fook, J., Ryan, M. and Hawkins, L. (2000) Professional Expertise: Practice, theory and education for working in uncertainty. (London) Whiting and Birch.

Forrester, D. (2019) What Skills Make a Difference? Available online at: https://sites.cardiff.ac.uk/cascade/2019/03/04/what-skills-make-a-difference/ Accessed 02.06.19.

Forrester, D., Kershaw, S., Moss, H. and Hughes, L. (2007) Communication skills in child protection: how do social workers talk to parents? Child and Family Social Work, 13(1), 41-51.

Ginsburg, K.R. (2011) Building Resilience in Children and Teens: Giving Kids Roots and Wings. (2nd ed) (Elk Grove) American Academy of Paediatrics.

Goldsmith, L. (1999) Recording with Care: Inspection of Case Recording in Social Services Departments. (London) SSI and DoH.

Graham, P. (2009) Susan Issacs: A Life Freeing the Minds of Children. (London) Karmac Books.

Grant, L. and Kinman, G. (2014) Developing Resilience for Social Work Practice. (London) Palgrave.

Grant, L. and Kinman, G. (undated) Guide to Developing Emotional Resilience. Community Care Inform. Available online at: file:///C:/Users/Siobh/AppData/Local/Packages/Microsoft.MicrosoftEdge_8wekyb3d8bbwe/TempState/Downloads/Guide-to-emotional-resilience-download%20(1).pdf

Gresell, A. (1954) The First Five Years of Life. (London) Methuen.

Hardy, R. (2018) The toxic trio: what social workers need to know. Working with domestic abuse, substance use and mental ill health. Community Care. Available online at: https://www.communitycare.co.uk/2018/03/05/toxic-trio-social-workers-need-know/ Accessed 01.06.19.

Harold, G., Acquah, D., Sellers, R., and Chowdry, H. (2016). What Works to Enhance Inter-Parental Relationships and Improve Outcomes for Children. DWP ad hoc research report no. 32. Early Intervention Foundation.

Harold, G.T. and Sellers, R. (2018) Annual Research Review: Interparental conflict and youth psychopathology: an evidence review and practice focused update. Journal of Child Psychology and Psychiatry. https://doi.org/10.1111/jcpp.12893

Hawkins, P. and Shohet, R. (2006) Supervision in the Helping Professions. (3rd edition) (Berkshire) Open University Press.

Hedges, S. and Kenny, C. (2018). Parental Alcohol Misuse and Children. (London) Parliamentary Office of Science and Technology.

Hennessey, R. (2011) Relationship Skills in Social Work. (London) Sage.

Her Majesty's Inspectorate of Constabulary (2015) Increasingly everyone's business: A progress report on the police response to domestic abuse. Available online at: www.justiceinspectorates.gov.uk/hmicfrs/publications/increasingly-everyones-business-a-progress-report-on-the-police-response-to-domestic-abuse/ Accessed 03.12.18.

Hiatt, J.M. (2006) ADKAR A Model for Change in business, Government and our Community. (Colorado) Prosci Research.

Hood, R. (2018) Complexity in Social Work. (London) Sage.

Hood, R., Gillespie, J. and Davies, J. (2016) A conceptual review of interprofessional expertise in child safeguarding. Journal of Interprofessional Care, 30 493-498.

Houston, S. (2015) Reflective Practice: A Model for Supervision and Practice in Social Work. (Belfast) Northern Ireland Social Care Council.

Howe, D. (2008) The Emotionally Intelligent Social Worker. (Basingstoke) Palgrave Macmillan.

IFSW, ICSW, IASSW (2012) The Global Agenda for Social Work. (Berne) IFSW.

Ingram, R. (2013) Emotions, Social Work Practice and Supervision: An Uneasy Alliance. Journal of Social Work Practice, 27(1) 5-19.

Issacs, S. (1929) The Nursery Years. (London) Routledge Kegan Paul.

Kadushin, A. and Harkness, D. (2002) Supervision in Social Work. (4th edition) (New York) Columbia Press.

Kanfer, R., Chen, G. and Pritchard, R. D. (eds) (2008) Work Motivation: Past, Present, and Future. (New York) Taylor & Francis Group.

Klimek, A. and Atkisson, A. (2016) Parachuting Cats into Borneo and other Lessons from the Change Café. A Toolkit of Proven Strategies and Practices for Building Capacity and Creating Transformation. (Vermont) Chelsea Green Publishing.

Kranstuber Horstman, H., Hays, A. and Maliski, R. (2016) Parent-Child Interaction. In Nussbaum, J. (Ed) Oxford Research Encyclopaedia of Communication. (Oxford) Oxford University Press.

Laming, L. (2003) The Victoria Climbie Inquiry. HMSO, London. Available online at: www.gov.uk/government/uploads/system/uploads/attachment_data/file/273183/5730.pdf Accessed 09.08.17.

Lefevre, Michelle (2015) Becoming effective communicators with children: developing practitioner capability through social work education. British Journal of Social Work, 45(1) 204-224.

Leigh, J. (2017) Blame, Culture and Child Protection. (Basingstoke) Palgrave Macmillan.

Lewing, B., Doubell, L., Beevers, T. and Acquah, D. (2018) Building Trusted Relationships for Vulnerable Children and Young People with Public Services. Available online at:

www.eif.org.uk/report/building-trusted-relationships-for-vulnerable-children-and-young-people-with-public-services/ Accessed 16.01.19.

Lindon, J. and Brodie, K. (2016) Understanding Child Development 0-8 Years. (London) Hodder Education.

Lloyd, A. (2016) A restorative approach to working with adolescents. Presentation at Association of Directors of Children's Services Conference. Relationships, Risk and Restorative Approaches: Doing Things Differently for Young People.

Lynch, A., Newlands, F. and Forrester, D. (2018) What does empathy sound like in social work communication? A mixed methods study of empathy in child protection social work practice Child and Family Social Work. Child and Family Social Work, 24 (1)139-147.

Maclean, S. (2016) Journeys through Change: Keep calm and keep on travelling. Keynote at Scottish Organisation of Practice Teaching Conference. Glasgow. November 2016.

Maclean, S., Finch, J. and Tedam, P. (2018) *SHARE*: A New Model for Social Work. (Lichfield) Kirwin Maclean Associates.

Mager, D. (2017) How to have difficult conversations. Psychology Today. Available online at: https://www.psychologytoday.com/blog/some-assembly-required/201703/how-have-difficultconversations Accessed 20.8.17

Manthorpe, J., Moriarty, J., Hussein, S., Stevens, M. and Sharpe, E. (2013) Content and Purpose of Supervision in Social Work Practice in England: Views of Newly Qualified Social Workers, Managers and Directors. British Journal of Social Work, 45(1) 52-68.

Marcia, J. E. (1966). Development and validation of ego-identity status. Journal of Personality and Social Psychology, 3(5), 551-558.

Masten, A. S. (2014). Ordinary magic: Resilience in development. (New York, NY, US) Guilford Press.

McIntyre, N. and Pegg, D. (2018) Councils use 377,000 people's data in efforts to predict child abuse. The Guardian online. https://www.theguardian.com/society/2018/sep/16/councils-use-377000-peoples-data-in-efforts-to-predict-child-abuse Accessed 01.01.19.

McLeod, A. (2008) Listening to Children: A Practitioner's Guide. (London) Jessica Kingsley.

McManus, S., Bebbington, P., Jenkins, R. and Brugha, T. (eds) (2016) Mental health and wellbeing in England: Adult Psychiatric Morbidity survey 2014. (Leeds) The National Health Service.

Megele, C. (2015) Psychosocial and Relationship Based Practice. (London) Critical Publishing.

Megele, C. (2017) Safeguarding Children and Young People Online. (Bristol) Policy Press.

Milner, J. and O'Byrne, P. (2009) Assessment in Social Work. (3rd edition) (Basingstoke) Palgrave MacMillan.

MIND (2019) Mental Health Facts and Statistics. Available online at: https://www.mind.org.uk/information-support/types-of-mental-health-problems/statistics-and-facts-about-mental-health/how-common-are-mental-health-problems/#.XQ-6_I97laQ Accessed 01.06.19

Moran, H. J. (2010) Clinical observations of the differences between children in the autism spectrum and those with attachment problems: The Coventry Grid. Good Autism Practice. 11(2) 46-59.

Morris, K. (2017) Child Welfare Inequalities. Keynote Presentation. Resilience in Times of Austerity. Joint PSW Conference. 21 July 2017, Kings College London.

Morrison, F. (2016) Social workers' communication with children and young people in practice. IRISS Insight 34. Available online at: https://www.iriss.org.uk/resources/insights/social-workers-communication-children-and-young-people-practice Accessed 02.01.19.

Morrison, T. (2005) Staff Supervision in Social Care: Making a Real Difference for Staff and Service Users. (Brighton) Pavilion.

Munro, E. (2010) The Munro Review of child protection – Part one: A systems analysis. (London) Department for Education.

Munro, E. (2011) Munro Review of child protection: Final report – A child-centred system. (London) Department for Education.

Munson, C.E. (2002) Handbook of Clinical Social Work Supervision. (3rd edition) (Binghampton)Haworth Social Work Press.

NASW. (2017) Standards and Indicators for Cultural Competence in Social Work Practice. Available online at: www.socialworkers.org/LinkClick.aspx?fileticket=7dVckZAYUmk%3D&portalid=0 Accessed 01.11.17.

NSPCC (2014) How safe are our children? Available online at: https://lfstest.nspxyz.net/globalassets/documents/research-reports/how-safe-children-2014-report.pdf Accessed 02.02.19.

NSPCC (2018) How safe are our children? The most comprehensive overview of child protection in the UK. Available online at: https://learning.nspcc.org.uk/media/1067/how-safe-are-our-children-2018.pdf Accessed 03.04.19.

Osborn, M. (2014) Working with fathers to safeguard children. Child Abuse and Neglect, 38 993-1001.

Oxford Dictionary (109) Hypothesis. Available online at: https://www.lexico.com/en/definition/hypothesis Accessed 27.12.18.

Page, J. Whitting, G. and Mclean, C. (2008) A review of how fathers can be better recognised and supported through DCSF policy. (London) DCSF.

Patterson, K., Grenny, J., McMillan, R., Switzler, A. (2102) Crucial Conversations: Tools for talking when stakes are high. (London) McGraw Hill.

Pellico, L.H., Friedlaender, L. and Fennie, K.P, (2005) Looking is not Seeing: Using Art to Improve Observational Skills. Journal of Nurse Education, 8(11) 648-653.

Pelco, L. E. and Ball, C. (2018). Identity status, service-learning, and plans for the future. Journal of Higher Education Outreach and Education, *22*(2) 103-125.

Petrie, N. (2014) Vertical Leadership Development – Part 1. Developing Leaders for A Complex World. (Brussels) Center for Creative Leadership.

Piaget, J. (1928) Judgement and Reasoning in the Child. (London) Routledge and Kegan Paul.

Pritchard, J, and Leslie, S. (2011) Recording Skills in Safeguarding Adults: Best Practice and Evidential Requirements. (London) Jessica Kingsley Publishers.

Prochaska, J. and DiClemente, C. (1983) Stages and processes of self change of smoking: Toward an integrative model of change. Journal of Consulting and Clinical Psychology, 51 390-395.

Public Health England. (2016) The Public Health Burden of Alcohol and the Effectiveness and Cost-Effectiveness of Alcohol Control Policies. (London) Public Health England.

Radford, L., Aitken, R., Miller, P., Ellis, J., Roberts, J. and Firkic, A. (2011) Meeting the needs of children living with domestic violence in London. Research report. (London) NSPCC and Refuge.

Romeo, L. (2017) Think you know supervision? It's about to become a different animal... Blog available at: https://lynromeo.blog.gov.uk/2017/01/11/think-you-know-supervision-its-about-tobecome-a-different-animal/ Accessed 03.09.17.

Roskill, C. (2011) Research in three children's services authorities. In Ashley, C. (ed) Working with risky fathers: research findings on working with domestically abusive fathers and their involvement with children's social care services. (London) Family Rights Group.

Rothlisberger, F. J. and Dickson, W. J. (1939) Management and the Worker. (Cambridge) Harvard University Press.

Royal College of Psychiatrists (2019) Domestic Violence and Abuse – the impact on children and adolescents. Available online at: https://www.rcpsych.ac.uk/mental-health/parents-and-young-people/information-for-parents-and-carers/domestic-violence-and-abuse-effects-on-children Accessed 31.05.19.

Ruch, G. (2014) Helping children is a human process: Researching the challenges social workers face in communicating with children. British Journal of Social Work, 44(8) 2145–62.

Ruch, G. (2015) Regarding the use of practice observation methods as part of the assessment of social work practice: Evidence Scope. (Totnes) Research in Practice.

Sandstrom, H., Gearing, M., Peters, H.E., Heller, C., Healy, O. and Pratt, E. (2015) Approaches to Father Engagement and Fathers' Experiences in Home Visiting Programs (Washington DC) US Department of Health and Human Services.

Seabury, B., Seabury, B. and Garvin, C.D. (2011) Foundations of Interpersonal Practice in Social Work: Promoting Competence in Generalist Practice. (London) Sage.

Sercombe, H. and Paus, T. (2013) What Does the 'Teen Brain' Research say, and What Does it Mean for Practitioners? In Curran, S., Harrison, R. and Mackinnon, D. (Eds) Working with Young People. (London) Sage.

Sinek, S. (2009) Start with Why: How Great Leaders Inspire Everyone to Take Action. (London) Penguin.

Skinner, B.F. (1971) Beyond Freedom and Dignity. (Indianapolis) Hackett Publishing Company.

Social Care Institute for Excellence. (2017) Effective supervision in a variety of settings: SCIE Guide 50. Available online at: ww.scie.org.uk/publications/guides/guide50/ Accessed 21.09.18.

Spivak G. C. (1985) The Rani of Sirmur: an essay in reading the archives. History and Theory, 24(3) 247-272.

Staempli, A. and Fairtlough, A. (2018) Intervision and Professional Development: An Exploration of a Peer-Group Reflection Method in Social Work Education. The British Journal of Social Work. doi.org/10.1093/bjsw/bcy096.

Stevenson, J. (2005) Professional Supervision in Social Work. Unison. Accessed online at: www.unisonedinburgh.org.uk/socialwork/supervision.html. Accessed 15.10.11.

Strega, S., Fleet, C., Brown, L., Dominelli, L., Callahan, M. and Walmsley, C. (2008) Connecting father absence and mother blame in child welfare policies and practice.

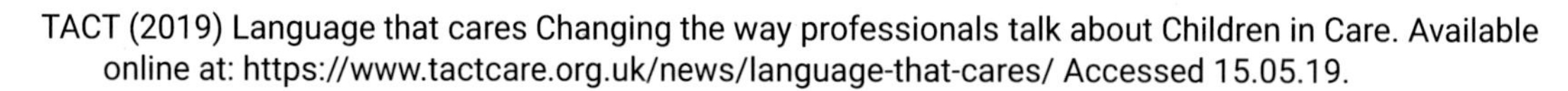

TACT (2019) Language that cares Changing the way professionals talk about Children in Care. Available online at: https://www.tactcare.org.uk/news/language-that-cares/ Accessed 15.05.19.

Taylor, B. and Devine, D. (1993) Assessing Needs and Planning Care in Social Work. (London) Arena Press.

The Carers Trust (2019) Young Carers: Care for me too. Available online at: https://carers.org/young-carers-awareness-day-2019-england Accessed 02.03.19.

Trautmann, F. (2010) Intervision Guidelines. (United Nations Office on Drugs and Crime). Available online at: https://www.unodc.org/documents/balticstates/Library/PharmacologicalTreatment/IntervisionGuidelines/IntervisionGuidelines.pdf Accessed 21.02.19.

Turner, A. (2019) Good intentions but the right approach? The case of ACEs. Available online at: http://publichealthy.co.uk/good-intentions-but-the-right-approach-the-case-of-aces/ Accessed 07.04.19.

UK Research councils (undated) Joint Statement of the Seven Research Councils. Available online at: https://www.ukri.org/skills/policy-and-frameworks/ Accessed 01.02.18.

UNICEF (2006) Behind Closed Doors: The Impact of Domestic Violence on Children. Available online at: https://www.unicef.org/protection/files/BehindClosedDoors.pdf Accessed 27.12.18.

Van der Haar, M. (2007) Ma(r)king Differences in Dutch Social Work: Professional Discourse and ways of Relating to Clients in Context. (Amsterdam) Dutch University Press.

Wachtel, T. (2016) Defining Restorative. International Institute for Restorative Practices. Available online at: https://www.iirp.edu/images/pdf/Defining-Restorative_Nov-2016.pdf Accessed 19.08.17.

Walsh, G. (2019) Adverse Childhood Experiences: a social justice perspective. Available online at: https://blogs.ed.ac.uk/CRFRresilience/2019/05/15/aces-a-social-justice-perspective/ Accessed 03.04.19.

Welbourne, P. (2012) Social Work with Children and Families: Developing advanced practice. (Oxon) Routledge.

Whincup, H. (2015) Direct work and home supervision requirements: A qualitative study exploring experiences of direct work from the perspectives of children, young people, and social workers. Doctoral Thesis, University of Stirling.

Wilkins, D. and Boahen, G. (2013) Critical Analysis Skills for Social Workers. (Maidenhead) OU Press.

Wilkins, D., Forrester, D. and Grant, L. (2016) What happens in child and family social work supervision? Child and Family Social Work. Available online at: https://doi.org/10.1111/cfs.12314

Wilkins, D., Lynch, A. and Antonopoulou, V. (2018) A golden thread? The relationship between supervision, practice, and family engagement in child and family social work. Child and Family Social Work. doi.org/10.1111/cfs.12442.

Winter, K. (2015) Supporting positive relationships for children and young people who have experience of care. Insight 28. Available online at:

www.iriss.org.uk/resources/insights/supporting-positive-relationships-children-young-people-experience-care Accessed 02.01.19

Winter, K., Cree, V., Hallett, S., Hadfield, M., Ruch, G., Morrison, F. and Holland, S. (2017) Exploring communication between social workers, children and young people. British Journal of Social Work, 47 (5) 1427-1444.

Women's Aid. (2018) Survival and Beyond: The Domestic Abuse Report 2017. (Bristol) Women's Aid.

Zariski, A. (2014) Legal Literacy: An Introduction to Legal Studies. (Canada) AU Press.